Test Bank to Accompany Myers

Social Psychology

Fifth Edition

Martin Bolt

Calvin College

The McGraw-Hill Companies, Inc.

New York   St. Louis   San Francisco   Auckland   Bogotá
Caracas   Lisbon   London   Madrid   Mexico City   Milan   Montreal
New Delhi   San Juan   Singapore   Sydney   Tokyo   Toronto

This book is printed on recycled, acid-free paper containing a minimum of 50% recycled de-inked fiber.

Test Bank to Accompany Myers
SOCIAL PSYCHOLOGY
Fifth Edition

ISBN 0-07-044379-3

2 3 4 5 6 7 8 9 0 BKM BKM 9 0 9 8 7 6

CONTENTS

GUIDE TO USING THE TEST BANK
TO ACCOMPANY *SOCIAL PSYCHOLOGY, FIFTH EDITION*

For each chapter in David G. Myers' *Social Psychology, Fifth Edition*, this Test Bank provides the instructor with 100 multiple-choice items to use in composing tests. In each case, the last 15 items also appear in the Study Guide which accompanies the text.

The test items appear in the order of their corresponding page references. The following information is supplied with each item:

Answer: The correct answer for the item.

Type: The type of understanding the item tests for:

> DEF = Definition items require recognition of the key terms and basic concepts of the discipline.

> FAC = Factual items require knowledge of information that is explicitly presented in the textbook. They test knowledge of research findings, methods, and important people and events.

> CON = Conceptual items require analysis, synthesis, or application of information presented in the textbook. Designed to promote critical thinking, these items often require deduction from key principles or application to everyday life.

Reference: The page number of the text reference to the material that answers the item is provided; if more than one page in the text provides answering information, the first such page is listed here.

Test Composition

There are usually several different ways to test knowledge of a particular concept. In this Test Bank you will occasionally find that several items address the same or similar knowledge. In such cases it is best to select only one of the items for inclusion in a test. Further, with 100 multiple-choice items to choose from per chapter, you may find that the wording of some items provides clues for answering other items. Be sensitive to this possibility so you do not inadvertently choose items that, in combination with others, render certain questions useless or redundant

To encourage student use of the accompanying Study Guide and thus their mastery of the text material, you may want to announce that a limited number of test items will come directly from it. Items 86 to 100 in each chapter of this test bank are specifically drawn from the *Study Guide to Accompany Myers' Social Psychology, Fifth Edition*.

This test bank has benefitted from the feedback and comments of classroom teachers who have used earlier editions. Please continue to share your suggestions for making our testing package more effective.

Martin Bolt
Department of Psychology
Calvin College
Grand Rapids, Michigan 49546

CHAPTER ONE: INTRODUCING SOCIAL PSYCHOLOGY

<u>Multiple Choice</u>

(1)   Answer D, Type FAC, Reference 2
Which of the following questions is <u>not</u> likely to be addressed by social psychologists?
A.   Are our social beliefs self-fulfilling?
B.   In what ways do other people influence our attitudes and actions?
C.   What situations trigger people to be helpful or greedy?
D.   Is human development a continuous process or does it proceed through a series of stages?

(2)   Answer A, Type FAC, Reference 3
The examples cited in your text as phenomena of particular interest to social psychology are similar to each other because they all
A.   deal with how people view and affect one another.
B.   show the influence of personality on behavior.
C.   represent various forms of groups and organizations.
D.   show the power of internal influences on human action.

(3)   Answer A, Type DEF, Reference 3
Social psychology is the scientific study of
A.   how people think about, influence, and relate to one another.
B.   how people perceive, think about, and communicate with one another.
C.   how people observe, predict, and control one another.
D.   social groups, organizations, and institutions.

(4)   Answer B, Type FAC, Reference 3
The history of social psychology indicates that
A.   the first book on social psychology was published in the late nineteenth century.
B.   social psychology did not assume its current form until the 1930s.
C.   the first social psychology experiments were reported during World War I.
D.   the first correlational studies in social psychology were reported in the 1950s.

(5)   Answer B, Type FAC, Reference 4
Contemporary social psychology emphasizes the importance of
A.   emotion.
B.   cognition.

C. development.
D. language.

(6)   Answer D, Type FAC, Reference 4
Contemporary social psychology emphasizes the
A.   power of the situation.
B.   power of the person.
C.   importance of cognition.
D   All of the above.

(7)   Answer C, Type DEF, Reference 4
Sociologists study the structure and function of
A.   relationships.
B.   societies.
C.   groups.
D.   cultures.

(8)   Answer B, Type DEF, Reference 4
The social psychologist is usually interested in studying the
A.   group.
B.   individual.
C.   institution.
D.   community.

(9)   Answer C, Type CON, Reference 4
Social psychology is to _____ as sociology is to _____.
A.   cognition; influence
B.   manipulation; control
C.   individuals; groups
D.   social theory; social problems

(10)   Answer A, Type CON, Reference 4
In studying racial attitudes, a social psychologist would be most interested in understanding
A.   how individuals develop racial attitudes.
B.   how the attitudes of one class are different from those of another.
C.   age differences in racial prejudice.
D.   the history of racial prejudice.

(11)   Answer C, Type CON, Reference 4
Which of the following examples is a question a social psychologist would be

most likely to study?
A.   How have divorce rates changed over time?
B.   What accounts for racial differences in intelligence?
C.   In deciding how they will vote in an election, are people more influenced by one persuasive medium than by another?
D.   In what ways do children learn differently than do adults?

(12)   Answer A, Type CON, Reference 5
Of the following studies, which is most likely being conducted by a social psychologist?
A.   An experimenter watches to see whether hungry game players use a more aggressive strategy than players who are not hungry.
B.   An interviewer does a case study of a physically disabled veteran.
C.   An archival researcher examines records of divorce rates across cultures.
D.   A test administrator measures the skills of an adolescent whose class performance has been poor.

(13)   Answer B, Type FAC, Reference 5
Social psychologists rely more heavily than sociologists on studies in which they
A.   conduct naturalistic observations of real-world events.
B.   manipulate a factor to see what effect it has on behavior.
C.   consult records of past events and statistics to identify important trends in the data.
D.   focus their efforts on analyzing and sometimes solving social problems.

(14)   Answer A, Type FAC, Reference 5
The factors that sociologists study, such as economic class, are typically
A.   difficult or unethical to manipulate.
B.   easy to translate into experimental research.
C.   better understood with the research methods preferred by social psychologists.
D.   identical to those examined by social psychologists.

(15)   Answer B, Type FAC, Reference 5
Personality psychologists are more interested in _____, while social psychologists more likely focus on _____.
A.   normal personality; disordered or abnormal behavior
B.   individual differences; our common humanity
C.   situational influences; internal motivations
D.   cognition; emotion

(16)   Answer D, Type FAC, Reference 5
Most of the heroes of social psychology are
A.   well known even to laypersons.
B.   people who worked in the late nineteenth and early twentieth centuries.
C.   best known for having developed grand theories of human behavior.
D.   alive today and making smaller-scale contributions to theory.

(17)   Answer A, Type FAC, Reference 5
Compared to personality psychology, social psychology
A.   has a shorter history.
B.   is more likely to focus on the individual.
C.   is more likely to use the case study in research.
D.   places greater emphasis on the value of correlational research.

(18)   Answer A, Type FAC, Reference 6
The various disciplines that study human beings
A.   often offer different levels of explanation that are all valuable.
B.   typically offer conflicting perspectives that have to be sorted out.
C.   are usually free of value judgments.
D.   can be useful only to the extent that they employ the scientific method.

(19)   Answer D, Type FAC, Reference 6
Which of the following statements best summarizes the relationship among different "levels of explanation"?
A.   They compete with each other.
B.   They discredit each other.
C.   Higher-level explanations replace lower-level ones.
D.   They complement each other.

(20)   Answer B, Type FAC, Reference 6
Sociologist Andrew Greeley notes that the perspective of psychology is limited because it cannot explain
A.   differences in individuals' motives.
B.   the purpose of human existence.
C.   the external forces influencing behavior.
D.   the biochemistry of consciousness.

(21)   Answer D, Type FAC, Reference 8
The influence of values on social psychology is demonstrated by the fact that _____ appears to be a popular topic of research in the 1990s.
A.   persuasion

4

B.   decision making
C.   conformity
D.   multicultural diversity

(22)   Answer D, Type FAC, Reference 8
How do values enter the picture in social psychology?
A.   Values influence researchers' choice of topics.
B.   Values affect the types of people attracted to various disciplines.
C.   Values are frequently the object of social psychological analysis.
D.   All of the above.

(23)   Answer B, Type FAC, Reference 8
Which of the following statements about values and social psychology is true?
A.   Research trends are usually out of step with the social concerns of their times.
B.   The fact that human thinking always involves interpretation is precisely why we need scientific analysis.
C.   Research into how values form, change, and influence one another helps us identify which of them are right.
D.   All of the above are true.

(24)   Answer B, Type FAC, Reference 8
Contrary to popular opinion, scientists investigate nature
A.   from a position of pure objectivity, with no personal motives or social agenda.
B.   by interpreting it according to their own mental categories.
C.   for its aesthetic value with little or no regard for the artificial value of objectivity.
D.   with a keen and shared awareness that there is no objective reality out there.

(25)   Answer C, Type FAC, Reference 9
During the 1980s, feminists and Marxists played an important role in
A.   helping social psychology become value-free.
B.   encouraging social psychology to place greater emphasis on laboratory experimentation.
C.   exposing some of social psychology's unexamined assumptions.
D.   alerting social psychologists to the hindsight bias.

(26)   Answer C, Type FAC, Reference 9
In the 1950s, Hastorf and Cantril asked rival students at Princeton and Dartmouth

to evaluate a film of a recent football game between their schools' teams. Which of the following summarizes their judgments?
A.   The Princeton students saw twice as many Princeton violations as the Dartmouth students saw.
B.   The Dartmouth students saw the Princeton players as "victims" of unfair infractions and fighting.
C.   Each school's students agreed that the opposing team was responsible for the rough play.
D.   When asked to be objective, each school's students seemed able to put aside their biases.

(27)   Answer A, Type DEF, Reference 9
We tend to take for granted the shared beliefs that European social psychologists call our _____, our most important but least debated convictions.
A.   social representations
B.   symbolic interactions
C.   hindsights
D.   naturalistic truths

(28)   Answer D, Type FAC, Reference 10
Which of the following psychological terms illustrates a disguised value judgment?
A.   well-adjusted
B.   mentally ill
C.   self-actualized
D.   All of the above.

(29)   Answer D, Type CON, Reference 10
Which of the following labels implies a judgment based on subjective values rather than one based on objective description?
A.   freedom fighter
B.   brainwashing
C.   adultery
D.   All of the above.

(30)   Answer C, Type DEF, Reference 10
"The way things <u>are</u> is the way they <u>ought</u> to be." This statement reflects the
A.   hindsight bias.
B.   social representation bias.
C.   naturalistic fallacy.
D.   correlation-causality bias.

6

(31) Answer A, Type CON, Reference 11
A cross-cultural researcher finds that across the world most legislators are male. He concludes that political office in his own country should be closed to women. The researcher is most clearly guilty of
A.   the naturalistic fallacy.
B.   the hindsight bias.
C.   illusory correlation.
D.   false consensus effect.

(32) Answer C, Type FAC, Reference 12
According to Fathali Moghaddam, which of the following countries compose psychology's first world?
A.   United States and Great Britain
B.   Great Britain and Germany
C.   United States and Canada
D.   United States and Russia

(33) Answer D, Type FAC, Reference 12
In comparison to social psychologists elsewhere, those in third-world countries are
A.   more likely to use questionnaires in their research.
B.   less likely to explore issues related to poverty and conflict.
C.   more likely to give attention to the personal and interpersonal levels of explanation.
D.   less likely to explore the basics of human nature.

(34) Answer B, Type FAC, Reference 12
European social psychologists question the emphasis that social psychologists in the United States place on
A.   social issues.
B.   individualism.
C.   the natural observation of behavior.
D.   the intergroup level of explanation.

(35) Answer C, Type FAC, Reference 14
The hindsight bias contributes to the idea that
A.   psychological experiments lack mundane realism.
B.   social psychology is potentially dangerous.
C.   the results of psychological experiments are mere common sense.
D.   psychological experiments lack experimental realism.

(36)   Answer B, Type FAC, Reference 15
The day after Ronald Reagan defeated Jimmy Carter in the 1980 presidential election, survey respondents claimed that just before the election they would have predicted
A.   a slim Reagan victory.
B.   a landslide Reagan victory.
C.   a slim Carter victory.
D.   a landslide Carter victory.

(37)   Answer A, Type FAC, Reference 15
One week after Clarence Thomas was confirmed as a new Supreme Court justice in 1991, students were _____ likely to guess that just before the confirmation they would have predicted he would be _____.
A.   more; confirmed
B.   less; confirmed
C.   more; rejected
D.   None of the above.

(38)   Answer B, Type FAC, Reference 17
The hindsight bias affects the way we view decision makers, making us more likely to
A.   see their decisions as surprisingly insightful and correct.
B.   blame them for making obviously bad choices.
C.   forgive them for making understandable mistakes in crises.
D.   admire them for handling well those choices we ourselves cannot make.

(39)   Answer C, Type CON, Reference 17
A closely watched tournament game between the Wolverines and the Eagles goes into overtime, and ultimately the Eagles win by just one point. According to research on the hindsight bias, fans of _____ will probably say _____.
A.   the Wolverines; the Eagles victory was a surprise
B.   the Eagles; they thought the Wolverines would win
C.   both teams; they thought the Eagles would win
D.   both teams; they thought the Wolverines would win

(40)   Answer B, Type FAC, Reference 18
Professional social psychologists have an advantage over the amateur in that they
A.   do not permit personal bias to influence their observations of behavior.
B.   study behavior in ways that pin down cause and effect.
C.   develop theories about why people act as they do.

8

D.   have a greater knowledge of literature and philosophy.

(41)   Answer B, Type FAC, Reference 19
Most social psychological research takes place in either
A.   the laboratory or the classroom.
B.   the laboratory or the field.
C.   the field or the classroom.
D.   the classroom or the office.

(42)   Answer D, Type CON, Reference 19
Of the following, _____ would be an example of a setting for a field experiment.
A.   a classroom
B.   a busy shopping mall
C.   a popular state park
D.   All of the above.

(43)   Answer C, Type FAC, Reference 19
Smith and Bennett used grave markers to study the relationship between
A.   age and prejudice.
B.   gender and social status.
C.   social status and longevity.
D.   gender and longevity.

(44)   Answer A, Type CON, Reference 19
A researcher is interested in learning whether young people whose fathers are absent from the home are more likely to engage in delinquent behavior. She compares the arrest rates of boys whose fathers are absent with those of boys whose fathers are present in the home. This is an example of a
A.   correlational study.
B.   laboratory experiment.
C.   field experiment.
D.   self-report study.

(45)   Answer A, Type DEF, Reference 19
A naturally occurring association among variables is known as
A.   a correlation.
B.   a coefficient.
C.   an attribution.
D.   a causal link.

(46)   Answer D, Type FAC, Reference 20

Variable X is correlated with Variable Y. Which of the following would explain this correlation?
A.   X causes Y.
B.   Y causes X.
C.   A third variable causes or influences both X and Y.
D.   All of the above.

(47)   Answer D, Type CON, Reference 20
A researcher finds that the more psychology courses students take, the higher they score on tests of mental health. What could be the explanation for this finding?
A.   Taking psychology courses improves one's mental health.
B.   Mentally healthy people are more likely to take psychology courses.
C.   Other factors--like having well-adjusted families--may contribute both to being mentally healthy and taking psychology courses.
D.   All of the above.

(48)   Answer C, Type FAC, Reference 21
In a study of Minnesota students, Maruyama and colleagues concluded that self-esteem and achievement are positively correlated because
A.   higher self-esteem boosts achievement.
B.   achievement produces higher self-esteem.
C.   both self-esteem and achievement are linked to underlying intelligence and family social status.
D.   both self-esteem and achievement are linked to healthy physical and psychological adjustment.

(49)   Answer D, Type FAC, Reference 21
From a study of over 1600 teenagers, McCarthy and Hoge concluded that a correlation between low self-esteem and delinquency is explained by the fact that
A.   low self-esteem leads directly to delinquent "acting out."
B.   father absence causes both low self-esteem and delinquency.
C.   lower social status causes both low self-esteem and delinquency.
D.   delinquent acts lead to a lowered sense of self-esteem.

(50)   Answer B, Type FAC, Reference 21
The great strength of correlational survey research is that it
A.   so easily brings important factors into the laboratory.
B.   studies factors in real-world settings that cannot be manipulated in the laboratory.
C.   establishes clear cause-and-effect connections among variables.

10

D.   maintains high mundane realism and thus increases generalizability.

(51)   Answer A, Type FAC, Reference 21
Which of the following statements about correlational research is true?
A.   It enables prediction of one variable given knowledge of the other.
B.   It specifies the cause-and-effect relationship among variables.
C.   It can only be carried out in controlled laboratory settings.
D.   All of the above.

(52)   Answer C, Type FAC, Reference 21
In selecting a random sample from a population, a researcher must
A.   allow chance to determine the size of the sample.
B.   sacrifice control by disregarding information about the population.
C.   make sure every member of the population has an equal chance of being chosen for the sample.
D.   select most sample members from the middle of any ordered listing.

(53)   Answer A, Type DEF, Reference 21
The best way to guarantee the fair representation of population subgroups in a group one wishes to survey is the method of
A.   random sampling.
B.   random assignment.
C.   naturalistic observation.
D.   subjective itemization.

(54)   Answer B, Type FAC, Reference 21
Surveying about _____ will enable a survey researcher to be 95 percent confident of describing the entire population, with only a 3 percent margin of error.
A.   12,000 randomly assigned participants
B.   1200 randomly selected participants
C.   one-third of the total population
D.   one-twelfth of the total population

(55)   Answer B, Type CON, Reference 21
A news reporter wants to survey voters about their candidate preferences in an upcoming national election. In order to be 95 percent confident of her results, and have only a 3 percent margin of error, she should make sure the sample has at least _____ individuals.
A.   200
B.   1200
C.   15,000

D.   55,000

(56)   Answer A, Type FAC, Reference 22
Which of the following best expresses the meaning of the results of opinion polls and surveys?
A.   They describe public opinion at the moment they are taken.
B.   They predict respondents' behavior in the near future.
C.   They predict respondents' long-range behavior.
D.   They are so biased and erroneous that they are meaningless.

(57)   Answer B, Type FAC, Reference 22
Ann Landers' 1984 survey of women readers' opinions about romantic affection and sex was probably
A.   not valid because it did not include men.
B.   flawed because it was not representative of the population.
C.   worthless because the sample size was too small.
D.   as valid and informative as other, more "scientific" surveys.

(58)   Answer D, Type FAC, Reference 23
The answers respondents give to surveys may be influenced by biases from which of the following sources?
A.   the order in which questions are asked
B.   the wording of the questions themselves
C.   the response options
D.   All of the above.

(59)   Answer A, Type CON, Reference 24
A surveyor wants to assess popular support for a new law to reduce car engine noise. Which of the following wordings is likely to get the highest percentage of agreement?
A.   "The government should not allow people to drive vehicles that are not properly muffled."
B.   "The government should prohibit people from driving vehicles that are not properly muffled."
C.   "The government should forbid people to drive vehicles that are not properly muffled."
D.   "The government should punish the driver of a vehicle that is not properly muffled."

(60)   Answer B, Type FAC, Reference 25
Social psychologists conduct experiments by constructing social situations that

12

A. confront subjects with unique choices.
B. simulate important features of everyday life.
C. are more complex than everyday life experiences.
D. have unpredictable effects on human behavior.

(61) Answer A, Type DEF, Reference 25
The experimental factor that a researcher manipulates in an experiment is the
A. independent variable.
B. dependent variable.
C. control group.
D. hypothesis.

(62) Answer B, Type CON, Reference 25
In an experimental study of the effects of fear on the desire to affiliate, fear would be the _____ variable.
A. experimental
B. independent
C. control
D. dependent

(63) Answer C, Type FAC, Reference 25
The essence of experimental control is to manipulate
A. all variables in the experimental situation.
B. all variables in the laboratory environment.
C. one variable while holding others constant.
D. all variables other than the one you are holding constant.

(64) Answer D, Type FAC, Reference 25
The research laboratory has provided the setting for about _____ of all experiments in social psychology.
A. one-fourth
B. one-half
C. two-thirds
D. three-fourths

(65) Answer A, Type FAC, Reference 26
Snyder and Haugen found that when men were asked to evaluate a woman whom they presumed was obese, she
A. spoke less warmly and happily.
B. spoke with more humor and laughter.
C. tried to compensate with more intelligent conversation.

D.   showed greater interest in politics and sports.

(66)   Answer C, Type DEF,. Reference 27
In a psychological experiment, the factor being measured is called the _____ variable.
A.   independent
B.   experimental
C.   dependent
D.   controlled

(67)   Answer B, Type CON, Reference 27
In an experimental study of the effects of alcohol consumption on aggression, aggression would be the _____ variable.
A.   controlled
B.   dependent
C.   experimental
D.   independent

(68)   Answer C, Type FAC, Reference 27
The two essential ingredients of a social psychological experiment are
A.   random assignment and correlation.
B.   control and random sampling.
C.   control and random assignment.
D.   random sampling and random assignment.

(69)   Answer B, Type CON, Reference 27
An experimenter studying competition wants to compare the behavior of students performing a difficult task with that of students doing an easy task. She designates participants for each task, making sure that each student has an equal chance of being in either the hard or the easy condition. This procedure is known as
A.   random sampling.
B.   random assignment.
C.   conditional selection.
D.   selective designation.

(70)   Answer C, Type FAC, Reference 27
The random assignment of people to either a condition that receives the experimental treatment or a control condition that does not can
A.   guarantee that every member of the population has an equal chance of being included in the sample.

14

B. guarantee that the study will not be contaminated by the researcher's values.
C. give the researcher confidence that any later difference is somehow caused by the treatment rather than by other factors.
D. guarantee experimental realism.

(71) Answer A, Type DEF, Reference 28
When the laboratory situation strongly resembles conditions in the real world, we say the experiment is high in
A. mundane realism.
B. experimental realism.
C. field quality.
D. situational validity.

(72) Answer B, Type DEF, Reference 28
Experiments that absorb and involve participants have
A. field quality.
B. experimental realism.
C. situational validity.
D. mundane realism.

(73) Answer A, Type FAC, Reference 28
For an experiment to be useful and conclusive, it must have
A. experimental realism.
B. demand characteristics.
C. low generalizability.
D. low control.

(74) Answer C, Type FAC, Reference 29
Deception of participants is employed when necessary to maintain
A. experimenter authority.
B. situational validity.
C. experimental realism.
D. demand characteristics.

(75) Answer C, Type FAC, Reference 29
About _____ of all social psychological studies actually involve some form of deception.
A. one-tenth
B. one-quarter
C. one-third

D.   one-half

(76)   Answer B, Type DEF, Reference 29
Experimenters try to hide their experimental predictions from subjects to prevent them from seeking cues about how to be "good subjects" and provide expected behaviors. Such cues are called
A.   hidden values.
B.   demand characteristics.
C.   naturalistic fallacies.
D.   coefficients.

(77)   Answer C, Type FAC, Reference 29
American Psychological Association ethical principles dictate that potential research participants should be told enough about the experiment to
A.   make inaccurate guesses about its true purpose.
B.   accurately perceive demand characteristics.
C.   be able to give their informed consent.
D.   detect the researcher's hidden values.

(78)   Answer C, Type DEF, Reference 30
A theory may best be described as
A.   a test.
B.   a fact.
C.   an explanation.
D.   a proof.

(79)   Answer D, Type FAC, Reference 30
A good theory will make clear predictions that
A.   confirm or modify the theory.
B.   generate new exploration.
C.   suggest practical application.
D.   All of the above.

(80)   Answer A, Type DEF, Reference 30
A research hypothesis is a
A.   testable prediction.
B.   theory.
C.   collection of empirical observations.
D.   technique for analyzing data.

(81)   Answer B, Type FAC, Reference 30

Hypotheses are useful because predictions give research
A.   constructive criticism.
B.   direction.
C.   a generous margin of error.
D.   freedom from limits.

(82)   Answer A, Type FAC, Reference 30
One of the purposes of theoretical prediction is summed up by Kurt Lewin, who asserted, "There is nothing so _____ as a good theory."
A.   practical
B.   abstract
C.   observable
D.   immutable

(83)   Answer B, Type FAC, Reference 30
Social psychologist Kurt Lewin has aptly commented, "There is nothing so practical as a good _____."
A.   experiment
B.   theory
C.   laboratory
D.   guess

(84)   Answer B, Type FAC, Reference 31
When theories are discarded, it is usually because they
A.   have been falsified.
B.   have displaced by newer, better theories.
C.   attempted to summarize too large a body of data.
D.   generated too many testable hypotheses.

(85)   Answer A, Type FAC, Reference 31
Which of the following statements about generalizing from laboratory research is true?
A.   Research yields information about a simplified, controlled reality, so it should be interpreted cautiously.
B.   Almost any subject population will reveal the same content in social thinking, although the thinking processes may vary.
C.   People of different cultures tend to hold the same opinions although they form those opinions in different ways.
D.   All of the above.

THE FOLLOWING ITEMS ALSO APPEAR IN THE STUDY GUIDE:

(86)   Answer C, Type FAC, Reference 3
Social psychology began to emerge as the vibrant field it is today during
A.   the Depression of the early 1930s when researchers examined the effects of deprivation on aggression and altruism.
B.   World War I, when psychologists conducted studies of social conflict and cooperation.
C.   World War II, when researchers performed studies of persuasion and soldier morale.
D.   the Korean War, when psychologists examined the effects of brainwashing on prisoners of war.

(87)   Answer B, Type FAC, Reference 4
In comparison to the sociologist, the social psychologist
A.   is more likely to study the social causes of behavior.
B.   is more likely to study individuals than groups.
C.   gives less attention to our internal functioning.
D.   relies more heavily on correlational research.

(88)   Answer C, Type FAC, Reference 6
The text states that as a scientific discipline, social psychology
A.   is superior to those disciplines which assume a more subjective approach to the study of human nature.
B.   can assist in explaining the meaning of life.
C.   is one perspective from which we can view and better understand human nature.
D.   offers explanations for human nature that often contradict the claims of other disciplines.

(89)   Answer C, Type FAC, Reference 25
Which of the following distinguishes the correlational method from experimentation?
A.   The correlational method uses a smaller group of subjects.
B.   The correlational method enables researchers to study social attitudes.
C.   No attempt is made to systematically manipulate one or more factors with the correlational method.
D.   The findings from the correlational method are more likely to be contaminated by the experimenter's values.

(90)   Answer C, Type FAC, Reference 25
To determine whether changing one variable (like education) will produce

changes in another (like income), we need to conduct _____ research.
  A. survey
  B. correlational
  C. experimental
  D. statistical

(91)   Answer D, Type FAC, Reference 15
According to the text, _____ tends to make people overconfident about the validity of their judgments and predictions.
  A. the fundamental attribution error
  B. illusory correlation
  C. the naturalistic fallacy
  D. the hindsight bias

(92)   Answer B, Type FAC, Reference 12
In comparison to North American social psychologists, European social psychologists tend to give more attention to the _____ levels of explanation.
  A. intrapersonal and interpersonal
  B. intergroup and societal
  C. interpersonal and intergroup
  D. intrapersonal and societal

(93)   Answer D, Type CON, Reference 4
Who among the following would be most likely to study how the political attitudes of middle-class people differ from those of lower-class people?
  A. a personality psychologist
  B. a social psychologist
  C. a social biologist
  D. a sociologist

(94)   Answer C, Type CON, Reference 19
You would like to know the relationship between the number of psychology courses people take and their interpersonal sensitivity. You survey college students to determine how much psychology they have taken and then have them complete a test of social sensitivity. Finally you plot the relationship. This is an example of
  A. a laboratory experiment.
  B. a field experiment.
  C. a correlational study.
  D. participant observation.

(95)   Answer A, Type CON, Reference 27
A research psychologist manipulates the level of fear in human subjects in the laboratory and then examines what effect the different levels of fear have on the subjects' reaction times. In this study, reaction time is the _____ variable.
A.   dependent
B.   correlational
C.   independent
D.   experimental

(96)   Answer D, Type CON, Reference 29
In conducting a study of conformity, the experimenters decide to tape-record the instructions that are to be presented to all subjects. Their decision is most likely an attempt to minimize the effect of
A.   hindsight bias.
B.   mundane realism.
C.   naturalistic fallacy.
D.   demand characteristics.

(97)   Answer D, Type CON, Reference 11
A researcher finds that Americans bathe on the average of once a day. He concludes that an educational program is necessary to encourage more frequent bathing by those who bathe less often than once a day. The researcher is probably guilty of
A.   hindsight bias.
B.   the "I knew it all along" phenomenon.
C.   illusory correlation.
D.   the naturalistic fallacy.

(98)   Answer A, Type CON, Reference 25
Which of the following research methods would be most effective in demonstrating that the presence of others improves our performance of a task?
A.   an experiment
B.   a correlational study
C.   a survey
D.   a field study

(99)   Answer C, Type CON, Reference 19
Which of the following techniques would be the most effective way of investigating the relationship between the political preferences and the age of American citizens?

A. an experiment
B. a case study
C. a correlational study
D. participant observation

(100) Answer B, Type CON, Reference 27
In a research study investigating the effects of stress on the desire to affiliate, half the participants complete an easy test of mental ability and half complete a difficult test. What technique should the investigators use to ensure that any posttest differences in the group's desire to affiliate actually result from the differences in test difficulty?
A. random sampling
B. random assignment
C. replication
D. correlational measurement

CHAPTER TWO: THE SELF IN A SOCIAL WORLD

<u>Multiple Choice</u>

(1)   Answer A, Type FAC, Reference 38
The most researched topic in psychology today is
A.   the self.
B.   attitudes.
C.   cultural influence.
D.   problem solving.

(2) Answer D, Type DEF, Reference 39
The beliefs about self that organize and guide the processing of self-relevant
information are called
A.   self-references.
B.   possible selves.
C.   social comparisons.
D.   self-schemas.

(3)   Answer B, Type CON, Reference 39
John's perceptions of himself as studious, impatient, and reserved constitute his
A.   egocentric cognitions.
B.   self-schemas.
C.   self-categorizations.
D.   self-references.

(4)   Answer D, Type DEF, Reference 39
The tendency to process efficiently and remember well information related to
oneself is called the _____ effect.
A.   self-aggrandizement
B.   self-actualization
C.   false uniqueness
D.   self-reference

(5)   Answer A, Type FAC, Reference 39
The self-reference effect illustrates how
A.   our sense of self is at the center of our world.
B.   self-efficacy promotes achievement.
C.   individualism leads to social isolation.
D.   most of us suffer from a negative self-image.

(6)   Answer D, Type DEF, Reference 39
The images of what we dream of or dread becoming in the future constitute our
_____ selves.
A.   unlikely
B.   imaginary
C.   future
D.   possible

(7)   Answer B, Type CON, Reference 39
Psychologists would consider both Rena's dream of becoming a professional
violinist and her persistent fear that she will die prematurely to be part of her
A.   anticipatory self.
B.   possible self.
C.   future self-monitoring.
D.   unlikely self.

(8)   Answer D, Type DEF, Reference 39
A person's overall self-evaluation or sense of self worth constitutes his or her
A.   self-efficacy.
B.   self-awareness.
C.   possible self.
D.   self-esteem.

(9)   Answer C, Type FAC, Reference 39
When students were told that having "integrative ability" was very important,
those with high self-esteem were more likely to
A.   report they did not care whether they had it or not.
B.   want to be assessed to see whether they had it.
C.   report that they had it.
D.   wonder what the trait actually consisted of.

(10)   Answer C, Type FAC, Reference 40
Petty found that when low self-esteem people were put in a negative mood they
often retrieved _____ memories, and when high self-esteem people were put
in a negative mood they often recalled _____ memories.
A.   positive; positive
B.   positive; negative
C.   negative; positive
D.   negative; negative

(11)   Answer C, Type FAC, Reference 41

24

Nisbett and Schacter gave students a series of increasingly intense electric shocks. Some were given a fake pill and told it would produce symptoms similar to those of experiencing shock. Results indicated that, compared to students who did not receive the pill, those students who took the pill
A.   were not able to withstand as much shock.
B.   were able to withstand about the same amount of shock but firmly believed that their tolerance for shock had increased.
C.   withstood more shock but denied the pill had any influence.
D.   withstood more shock and maintained that the pill had helped them.

(12)   Answer A, Type FAC, Reference 41
Nisbett and Wilson had students rate a film while a noisy power saw was operated nearby. Results indicated that most felt the noise
A.   affected their ratings, but it didn't.
B.   affected their ratings, as it had.
C.   had not affected their ratings, though it had.
D.   had not affected their ratings, and they were correct.

(13)   Answer A, Type FAC, Reference 42
When Schrauger had college students predict the likelihood of their experiencing different events, such as becoming romantically involved during the ensuing two months, the results indicated that
A.   students' self-predictions were hardly more accurate than predictions based on the average person's experience.
B.   students were accurate in predicting controllable but not uncontrollable events.
C.   students were accurate in predicting positive not negative events.
D.   females were more accurate than males in predicting their future.

(14)   Answer C, Type FAC, Reference 42
The best advice for predicting your own behavior is to
A.   ask an expert.
B.   analyze your current mood.
C.   consider your past behavior in similar situations.
D.   ask your closest friend.

(15)   Answer A, Type FAC, Reference 43
According to social psychologist Timothy Wilson, the mental processes that control our social behavior are
A.   distinct from those we use to explain our behavior.
B.   the same as those we use to explain our behavior.

C.   well known to ourselves but not apparent to others.
D.   well known to ourselves as well as to those closest to us.

(16)   Answer B, Type FAC, Reference 43
Wilson and his colleagues found that people's expressed attitudes predicted their later behavior
A.   especially if people analyzed their feelings before indicating their attitudes.
B.   unless people analyzed their feelings before indicating their attitudes.
C.   only if their attitudes were clearly related to their central values.
D.   only if their attitudes were assessed shortly before they acted.

(17)   Answer D, Type FAC, Reference 43
People who had been asked to choose one of two art posters to take home with them later showed less satisfaction with their choice if
A.   before making their choice they had been told about other people's preferences regarding the posters.
B.   in making their choice they had simply gone with their gut feelings.
C.   they had been asked to make a charitable contribution before making their choice.
D.   before making their choice they had been asked to identify their reasons for making it.

(18)   Answer B, Type FAC, Reference 43
 Research suggests that drawing people's attention to _____ diminishes the usefulness of attitude reports in predicting behaviors driven by _____.
A.   values underlying their behavior; self-esteem
B.   reasons for their behavior; feelings
C.   feelings underlying their behavior; physical safety
D.   reasons for their behavior; cognitions

(19)   Answer A, Type FAC, Reference 44
If you are planning to conduct research, the literature on human thinking suggests that you should be particularly cautious in using which of the following methods?
A.   subjects' self-reports
B.   naturalistic observation
C.   laboratory experiments
D.   field experiments

(20)   Answer D, Type FAC, Reference 44
Which of the following is a practical implication of findings discussed in the chapter on the self?

A. The sincerity with which people report their experience is one useful indicator of their testimony's accuracy.
B. Self-reports are less erroneous and more trustworthy than the reports of external observers.
C. The persuasiveness of personal testimonies is highly predictive of their accuracy.
D. Introspective self-reports are often untrustworthy.

(21) Answer C, Type CON, Reference 44
Western cultures are to _____ as Asian cultures are to _____.
A. the actual self; the possible self
B. self-forgetfulness; self-esteem
C. the independent self; the interdependent self
D. self-denial; self-acceptance

(22) Answer B, Type FAC, Reference 44
Japanese are more likely than Americans to complete the sentence "I am ..." with their
A. personal traits.
B. group identities.
C. negative rather than their positive characteristics.
D. physical rather than their psychological characteristics.

(23) Answer D, Type FAC, Reference 45
What motto best represents societies that nurture an interdependent self?
A. "To thine own self be true."
B. "Opposites attract."
C. "Familiarity breeds contempt."
D. "No one is an island."

(24) Answer D, Type FAC, Reference 45
Societies that nurture an independent self are most likely to disapprove of _____ while societies that nurture an interdependent self are most likely to disapprove of _____.
A. conflict; jealousy
B. materialism; spirituality
C. self-love; security
D. conformity; egotism

(25) Answer C, Type FAC, Reference 47
Research on locus of control and learned helplessness provides evidence

confirming the benefits of
A.   collectivism.
B.   realism.
C.   self-efficacy.
D.   attributional bias.

(26)   Answer B, Type DEF, Reference 47
The sense that one is competent and effective constitutes one's
A.   self-esteem.
B.   independent self.
C.   learned helpfulness.
D.   self-efficacy.

(27)   Answer A, Type FAC, Reference 47
People with strong feelings of self-efficacy are likely to be more
A.   academically successful.
B.   prone to stress.
C.   socially sensitive.
D.   anxious.

(28)   Answer D, Type DEF, Reference 47
The extent to which people perceive their lives as internally controllable by their own efforts and actions or as externally controlled by chance or outside forces constitutes their
A.   interdependent-independent self.
B.   intrinsic-extrinsic motivation.
C.   controllability quotient.
D.   locus of control.

(29)   Answer C, Type FAC, Reference 47
"Receiving a raise in pay or getting credit for my good work is just a matter of being lucky." This statement reflects
A.   self-efficacy.
B.   the fundamental attribution error.
C.   external locus of control.
D.   unrealistic optimism.

(30)   Answer D, Type FAC, Reference 47
If you believe your fate is determined by _____, you probably have an _____ locus of control.
A.   your own abilities; external

B.   personal motivation; external
C.   fate or luck; internal
D.   None of the above.

(31)   Answer B, Type CON, Reference 47
Sally believes that she will be highly successful in medical school if she works hard and carefully manages her time. Her belief most clearly illustrates
A.   integrative ability.
B.   an internal locus of control.
C.   an interdependent self.
D.   the self-reference effect.

(32)   Answer A, Type FAC, Reference 47
The person who believes that the world is run by the few people in power and there is not much the little guy can do about it reflects
A.   an external locus of control.
B.   an internal locus of control.
C.   reaction formation.
D.   the self-reference effect.

(33)   Answer D, Type FAC, Reference 47
Compared to those with an external locus of control, people who possess an internal locus of control are more likely to
A.   be pessimistic in explaining setbacks.
B.   be introverted personalities.
C.   conform to social pressure.
D.   delay instant gratification to achieve long-term goals.

(34)   Answer D, Type FAC, Reference 47
Compared to those with an external locus of control, people who possess an internal locus of control are more likely to
A.   wear seat belts.
B.   practice birth control.
C.   make lots of money.
D.   All of the above.

(35)   Answer A, Type CON, Reference 48
Bandura is to _____ as Seligman is to _____ .
A.   self-efficacy; learned helplessness
B.   internal locus of control; external locus of control
C.   self-esteem; self-concept

D.   the self-reference effect; depression

(36)   Answer A, Type FAC, Reference 48
Martin Seligman notes a basic similarity between learned helplessness in dogs and
_____ in people.
A.   conformity
B.   collective efficacy
C.   schizophrenia
D.   depression

(37)   Answer C, Type FAC, Reference 48
Researchers have found that the experience of repeated uncontrollable bad events
contributes to
A.   an internal locus of control.
B.   an interdependent self.
C.   learned helplessness.
D.   self-efficacy.

(38)   Answer A, Type CON, Reference 48
After moving into a nursing home and experiencing little control over his daily
schedule, Mr. Roark became apathetic, stopped eating, and even seemed to lose
the will to live. Mr. Roark's reaction most clearly illustrates
A.   learned helplessness.
B.   the interdependent self.
C.   reaction formation.
D.   internal locus of control.

(39)   Answer B, Type FAC, Reference 48
Hospital patients trained to believe in their ability to control stress tend to
A.   require more pain relievers and sedatives.
B.   require fewer pain relievers and sedatives.
C.   seem more anxious to nurses attending them.
D.   seem more depressed to nurses attending them.

(40)   Answer D, Type FAC, Reference 48
Langer and Rodin found that nursing home residents improved in alertness,
activity, and happiness if they were
A.   cared for by professionals who met all their needs.
B.   cared for by affectionate, sympathetic volunteers.
C.   periodically transported to visit close friends and relatives.
D.   asked to make personal choices and given opportunities to influence

nursing home policies.

(41) Answer B, Type FAC, Reference 49
Prisoners given some control over their environments--being able to move chairs, control TV sets, and switch the lights--
A.   become more manipulative of prison officials over time.
B.   commit less vandalism.
C.   experience greater stress and more health problems.
D.   experience stronger guilt feelings over past misconduct.

(42) Answer C, Type FAC, Reference 50
According to the text, groups that take an active role in working for social reforms are moved by a sense of
A.   anger and hopelessness.
B.   reaction formation.
C.   collective efficacy.
D.   interdependent helplessness.

(43) Answer C, Type FAC, Reference 51
Bandura believes that self-efficacy grows primarily by
A.   self-persuasion.
B.   the support and encouragement of family and close friends.
C.   undertaking and succeeding at challenging tasks.
D.   being exposed to models of competence and success.

(44) Answer D, Type FAC, Reference 52
Research in social psychology calls into question the
A.   idea that self-reports are often untrustworthy.
B.   idea that a person with an interdependent self has a greater sense of belonging.
C.   the power of positive thinking.
D.   the idea that most of us suffer from low self-esteem.

(45) Answer B, Type DEF, Reference 52
The tendency to perceive ourselves favorably is known as
A.   the self-reference effect.
B.   self-serving bias.
C.   self-efficacy.
D.   internal locus of control.

(46) Answer A, Type CON, Reference 53

31

Which of the following is <u>least</u> representative of a self-serving bias?
A. "I won the tennis match because of bad referee calls."
B. "I won the tennis match because of my athletic skill."
C. "I won the tennis match because I trained hard during the last month."
D. "I lost the tennis match because of the opposing player's super effort."

(47) Answer B, Type FAC, Reference 53
In their study of young married Canadians, Ross and Sicoly reported a tendency for them to
A. believe that their spouse contributed the most household work.
B. believe that they themselves contributed the most household work.
C. feel guilty about not carrying their fair share of work.
D. feel confident that their household was run fairly and efficiently.

(48) Answer A, Type FAC, Reference 54
Stephan, Arkin, Davis, and others have found that, after receiving an examination grade, students who do well
A. tend to accept personal credit.
B. usually admit that the exam may have been too easy.
C. admit that they were lucky to have studied the right material.
D. feel grateful to their instructors for lenient grading.

(49) Answer C, Type CON, Reference 54
Jenny failed her last chemistry test. Which of the following conclusions would be <u>most</u> representative of a self-serving bias on Jenny's part?
A. "I really didn't have the motivation to study for the test."
B. "I lack competence in chemistry."
C. "I think the test questions were ambiguous and confusing."
D. "I didn't concentrate very hard during the test."

(50) Answer C, Type FAC, Reference 54
For qualities that are both subjective and socially desirable, most people consider themselves to be
A. worse than average.
B. about average.
C. better than average.
D. too different from others to permit a fair comparison.

(51) Answer D, Type FAC, Reference 54
Which of the following is true?
A. Ninety percent of business managers rate their performance as superior to

their average peer.

B.   Most drivers who have been hospitalized for accidents believe themselves to be more skilled than the average driver.

C.   Most people perceive themselves as better looking than their average peer.

D.   All of the above are true.

(52)   Answer D, Type FAC, Reference 55

In predicting their life expectancy, most college students believe that they will

A.   live as long as their grandparents did.

B.   die prematurely of some uncontrollable disease.

C.   have about an average life span.

D.   outlive their actuarially predicted age of death by about 10 years.

(53)   Answer A, Type FAC, Reference 55

People would be least likely to rate themselves as better than average in

A.   being punctual.

B.   being disciplined.

C.   being ethical.

D.   their ability to get along with others.

(54)   Answer D, Type FAC, Reference 55

In a College Entrance Examination Board Survey of more than 800,000 high school seniors, _____ percent rated themselves below average "in ability to get along with others."

A.   50

B.   30

C.   10

D.   0

(55)   Answer C, Type FAC, Reference 56

According to researcher Neil Weinstein, many people have an "unrealistic _____ about future life events."

A.   anxiety

B.   pessimism

C.   optimism

D.   helplessness

(56)   Answer B, Type FAC, Reference 56

In Scotland most late adolescents think they are much less likely than their peers to become infected by the AID virus. This best illustrates

A.   the false consensus bias.

B. unrealistic optimism.
C. the self-reference effect.
D. external locus of control.

(57) Answer D, Type FAC, Reference 57
Knowing that half of U.S. marriages end in divorce, most young Americans
A. admit they are less likely to marry at all.
B. lower their own expectations for marital success.
C. assume they will end up in the half that get divorced.
D. persist in believing that theirs will not.

(58) Answer D, Type FAC, Reference 57
Which of the following is particularly likely to increase our vulnerability to misfortune?
A. a self-monitoring tendency
B. self-analysis
C. an interdependent self
D. unrealistic optimism

(59) Answer D, Type DEF, Reference 57
Our tendency to overestimate the extent to which others think and act as we do is known as the
A. self-reference effect.
B. self-handicapping syndrome.
C. false uniqueness effect.
D. false consensus effect.

(60) Answer D, Type CON, Reference 57
Marla objects when her boyfriend Tim asks her to help write his social psychology term paper. "Come on," Tim whines, "we wouldn't be the only ones, you know. Everyone's working together on it! The teacher doesn't really expect us to work alone." Tim's argument most clearly illustrates the
A. self-reference effect
B. fundamental attribution error.
C. false uniqueness effect.
D. false consensus effect.

(61) Answer A, Type CON, Reference 58
Brian watches smugly as the car ahead of his is pulled over for speeding. Although he has just slowed his own vehicle to 55 miles per hour, he considers himself "the only one on the road" who is obeying the speed limit. Brian's

thinking most clearly reflects
A.   the false uniqueness effect.
B.   the false consensus effect.
C.   external locus of control
D.   the self-handicapping effect.

(62)   Answer C, Type CON, Reference 58
Which of the following is more likely to trigger a false uniqueness effect than a false consensus effect in your thinking?
A.   cheating on a test by glancing at a classmate's paper
B.   refusing to give a handout to a homeless person
C.   resisting the temptation to shoplift a small item
D.   tossing litter on the ground instead of into a wastebasket

(63)   Answer C, Type CON, Reference 58
Those who drink heavily but use seat belts will _____ the number of other heavy drinkers and _____ the number of seat belt users.
A.   overestimate; overestimate
B.   underestimate; overestimate
C.   overestimate; underestimate
D.   underestimate; underestimate

(64)   Answer B, Type FAC, Reference 59
Research on self-perception indicates that
A.   we judge that attractive people have personalities different from our own.
B.   if a test flatters us, we evaluate positively both the test and any evidence suggesting the test is valid.
C.   most university students believe that the Scholastic Aptitude Test is an accurate indicator of their ability.
D.   if you find yourself linked to some reprehensible person--such as finding out you have the same birthday--you will form an even harsher view of that person.

(65)   Answer A, Type FAC, Reference 60
The more physiologically aroused people are after a failure, the more
A.   likely they are to excuse the failure with self-protective attributions.
B.   likely they are to accept personal blame for their failure.
C.   effort they will exert in achieving success at their next task.
D.   distracted they will be from giving any account of the failure.

(66)   Answer A, Type FAC, Reference 60

When facing failure, high self-esteem people sustain their self-worth by
A.   perceiving other people as failing, too, and by exaggerating their superiority over others.
B.   perceiving themselves as interdependent and thus as only part of a larger group effort.
C.   engaging in altruistic acts.
D.   refusing to think about the failure and by practicing self-forgetfulness.

(67)   Answer D, Type FAC, Reference 60
According to research by Abraham Tesser, who among the following is likely to have the strongest motive for self-esteem maintenance?
A.   an adult whose spouse depends on him or her for support
B.   an adult whose opposite-sex sibling has been fired from his or her job
C.   a child whose parents have moderate hopes for him or her
D.   an older child whose younger sibling is very talented

(68)   Answer C, Type CON, Reference 60
Emily and her two sisters are all musicians. According to research by Abraham Tesser, Emily will be most motivated to act in ways that maintain her own self-esteem if
A.   she is the best musician of the three.
B.   her older sister is a better musician than she is.
C.   her younger sister is a better musician than she is.
D.   of the three, she is the least interested in a music career.

(69)   Answer A, Type FAC, Reference 61
In experiments, people whose self-esteem is temporarily bruised--say, by being told that they did miserably on an intelligence test--are more likely to
A.   disparage others.
B.   act altruistically.
C.   seek to develop an interdependent self.
D.   retreat into social isolation.

(70)   Answer D, Type FAC, Reference 62
Research indicates that people with high self-esteem tend to
A.   be very modest when explaining their successes.
B.   note that there are as many weaknesses as there are strengths in their own group.
C.   see others' strengths as more important than their own.
D.   None of the above.

(71)   Answer B, Type FAC, Reference 62
Mildly depressed people tend to
A.   be more prone to self-serving bias than are nondepressed people.
B.   see themselves as others see them.
C.   see themselves more negatively than others see them.
D.   see themselves as better than average and yet are unrealistically pessimistic.

(72)   Answer A, Type FAC, Reference 63
Subjects who worked in groups were given false feedback that they had done either well or poorly. Results indicated that, in comparison to the members of unsuccessful groups,
A.   members of successful groups claimed more responsibility for their group's performance.
B.   members of successful groups claimed less responsibility for their group's performance.
C.   males but not females of successful groups claimed more responsibility for their group's performance.
D.   females but not males of successful groups claimed more responsibility for their group's performance.

(73)   Answer C, Type CON, Reference 63
Research suggests that individual group members expect _____ rewards when their organization does well and _____ blame when it does not.
A.   greater-than-average; greater-than-average
B.   less-than-average; less-than-average
C.   greater-than-average; less-than-average
D.   less-than-average; greater-than-average

(74)   Answer B, Type FAC, Reference 64
According to the text, true humility is more like _____ than false modesty.
A.   self-contempt
B.   self-forgetfulness
C.   self-handicapping
D.   self-denial

(75)   Answer D, Type FAC, Reference 65
According to the text, self-serving bias
A.   can protect us from depression.
B.   contributes to group conflict.
C.   can motivate us to greater achievement.
D.   does all of the above.

(76)   Answer B, Type FAC, Reference 66
According to the text, the common practice of publicly exalting one's opponents before a big game likely serves a _____ function.
A.   self-destructive
B.   self-protective
C.   knowledge
D.   self-forgetful

(77)   Answer D, Type FAC, Reference 66
Students who were asked to write anonymously about "an important success experience"
A.   acknowledged as many personal weaknesses as strengths.
B.   seemed to write with an attitude of self-forgetfulness.
C.   recognized the contributions close friends or relatives made to their success.
D.   described themselves as achieving their successes on their own.

(78)   Answer C, Type FAC, Reference 67
People are most likely to resort to self-handicapping when
A.   the quality of their performance on a task is not particularly important.
B.   their success or failure at a task will not become public.
C.   they fear failure.
D.   they are certain of success.

(79)   Answer B, Type FAC, Reference 67
Experimental subjects guessed answers to very difficult aptitude questions and were told they had done well. While they still felt lucky, they were given a choice of drugs to take before answering the remaining questions. Most chose to take the drug they believed would
A.   improve their intellectual functioning.
B.   disrupt their thinking.
C.   reduce anxiety.
D.   keep them awake and alert.

(80)   Answer D, Type FAC, Reference 67
Which of the following represents a way in which people self-handicap?
A.   They report feeling depressed.
B.   They give their opponent an advantage.
C.   They reduce their preparation for an important individual athletic event.
D.   All of the above.

(81)   Answer C, Type CON, Reference 67
David has an important tennis match in one week against the highest-rated player in the state. Instead of practicing daily, David has actually reduced his playing time since knowing he would play such a formidable opponent. From material presented in the text, which of the following may best describe David's behavior?
A.   David has fallen victim to the false uniqueness bias.
B.   David is making the fundamental attribution error.
C.   David is engaging in self-handicapping.
D.   David is demonstrating the self-reference effect.

(82)   Answer D, Type DEF, Reference 68
The act of expressing oneself and behaving in ways designed to create a favorable impression or an impression that corresponds to one's ideals is referred to as
A.   self-justification.
B.   self-presentation.
C.   self-perception.
D.   self-management.

(83)   Answer B, Type DEF, Reference 68
People who score high on a scale of _____ tend to act like social chameleons: they adjust their behavior in response to external situations.
A.   social absorption
B.   self-monitoring
C.   affective sensitivity
D.   self-perception

(84)   Answer B, Type FAC, Reference 69
The tendency to self-present modesty is especially great in cultures that value
A.   aggression.
B.   self-restraint.
C.   self-aggrandizement.
D.   individuality.

(85)   Answer A, Type FAC, Reference 69
In Japan, children learn to _____ credit for success and _____ responsibility for failures.
A.   share; accept
B.   accept; deny
C.   share; share
D.   accept; share

(86)   Answer C, Type FAC, Reference 39
Our perceiving ourselves as athletic, overweight, smart, or shy constitute our
A.   egocentric beliefs.
B.   interdependent self.
C.   self-schemas.
D.   self-references.

(87)   Answer A, Type FAC, Reference 41
When people are asked whether they would comply with demands to deliver cruel
shocks or would be hesitant to help a victim if several other people were present,
A.   they overwhelmingly deny their vulnerability to such influences.
B.   they admit they might be influenced but in their actual behavior are not.
C.   males deny they would be influenced, but females admit they would be.
D.   they accurately predict their future behavior on such significant matters.

(88)   Answer D, Type FAC, Reference 41
According to the text, research on self-knowledge suggests that
A.   people tend to underestimate their own abilities.
B.   people who have an interdependent self show less self-insight than those
with an independent self.
C.   people are highly accurate in predicting their own future behavior.
D.   people's self-reports are often untrustworthy.

(89)   Answer D, Type FAC, Reference 48
Dogs who learn a sense of helplessness by being taught they cannot escape shocks
A.   tend to band together and as a group demonstrate collective efficacy.
B.   tend to become highly aggressive in other situations.
C.   more readily take the initiative to escape punishment when that becomes
possible.
D.   later fail to take the initiative in another situation when they can escape
punishment.

(90)   Answer A, Type FAC, Reference 52
Research on attribution theory challenges the notion that
A.   most people suffer from unrealistically low self-esteem.
B.   we tend to blame others for their own misfortune.
C.   we strive to protect and enhance our self-esteem.
D.   true humility consists of self-forgetfulness.

(91)   Answer A, Type FAC, Reference 56
College students perceive themselves as far more likely than their classmates to
_____ and as far less likely to _____.
A.   draw a good salary; develop a drinking problem
B.   obtain a divorce; own a home
C.   travel to Europe; be happy in their work
D.   become a mental patient; have close friendships

(92)   Answer A, Type FAC, Reference 57
We tend to _____ the commonality of our unsuccessful behaviors
and _____ the commonality of our successful behaviors.
A.   overestimate; underestimate
B.   underestimate; overestimate
C.   underestimate; underestimate
D.   overestimate; overestimate

(93)   Answer D, Type FAC, Reference 60
Research on self-perception indicates that if we find ourselves linked to some
reprehensible person, say born on the same day,
A.   we show a temporary loss of self-esteem.
B.   we form a more independent self.
C.   we form a harsher view of the person.
D.   we soften our view of the person.

(94)   Answer D, Type FAC, Reference 69
Self-presentation, self-handicapping, and self-monitoring all reflect human efforts
at
A.   self-efficacy.
B.   self-understanding.
C.   collective efficacy.
D.   impression management.

(95)   Answer B, Type CON, Reference 44
In completing the statement, "I am ..." Michelle responds by stating that she is the
youngest in her family, belongs to a sorority, and is a member of the community
orchestra. Michelle's statements most clearly reflect
A.   her possible selves.
B.   an interdependent self.
C.   a self-serving bias.
D.   a strong self-monitoring tendency.

(96) Answer C, Type CON, Reference 48

Because she gets poor grades no matter how hard she studies, Milly has decided not to study at all. Milly's behavior most clearly demonstrates

A. self-serving bias.
B. unrealistic optimism.
C. learned helplessness.
D. a self-monitoring tendency.

(97) Answer C, Type CON, Reference 54

Judging from the discussion of self-image in the text, people are least likely to see themselves as above average in

A. leadership ability.
B. tolerance.
C. weight.
D. helpfulness.

(98) Answer B, Type CON, Reference 57

Although Jeff frequently exceeds the speed limit by at least 10 miles per hour, he justifies his behavior by erroneously thinking that most other drivers do the same. His mistaken belief best illustrates

A. learned helplessness.
B. false consensus.
C. self-monitoring.
D. an interdependent self.

(99) Answer C, Type CON, Reference 58

Those who evade paying income tax but who give generously to charity will probably _____ the number of others who evade taxes and _____ the number of others who give generously to charity.

A. overestimate; overestimate
B. underestimate; overestimate
C. overestimate; underestimate
D. underestimate; underestimate

(100) Answer C, Type CON, Reference 67

Tomorrow morning Harry Smith has an interview that will determine whether he will be accepted into medical school. Rather than getting a good night's sleep, he is going to an all-night party with his friends. From the material presented in the text, which of the following may best describe Harry's behavior?

A. Harry unconsciously hopes he is not accepted into medical school.

B.   Harry is making the fundamental attribution error.
C.   Harry is engaging in self-handicapping.
D.   Harry shares with his friends a sense of collective efficacy.

CHAPTER THREE: SOCIAL BELIEFS AND JUDGMENTS

Multiple Choice

(1)   Answer A, Type FAC, Reference 74
We are especially likely to analyze and discuss why things happen as they do when the event in question is
A.   negative or unexpected.
B.   positive or altruistic.
C.   normal or public.
D.   infrequent or private.

(2)   Answer C, Type FAC, Reference 74
According to research on the attributions of married people, a partner is most likely to wonder "why?" if the other person
A.   is smiling for no reason.
B.   suddenly gives him or her a warm hug.
C.   acts cold and hostile.
D.   shows friendliness to a stranger.

(3)   Answer B, Type FAC, Reference 75
In her research, Antonia Abbey has repeatedly found that men are more likely than women to attribute a woman's friendliness to
A.   moodiness.
B.   sexual interest.
C.   loneliness.
D.   manipulativeness.

(4)   Answer B, Type DEF, Reference 76
The theory of how people explain others' behavior is known as _____ theory.
A.   dissonance
B.   attribution
C.   incentive
D.   accountability

(5)   Answer A, Type DEF, Reference 76
Attribution theory analyzes how we
A.   explain people's behavior.
B.   make decisions and solve problems.
C.   make impressions on others.
D.   form attitudes about issues.

(6)   Answer D, Type FAC, Reference 76
Fritz Heider's "_____ psychology" analyzes the way people explain everyday events.
A.   depth
B.   structural
C.   nonobvious
D.   commonsense

(7)   Answer D, Type DEF, Reference 76
According to Fritz Heider, we tend to attribute people's behavior to either _____ or _____ causes.
A.   conscious; unconscious
B.   selfish; altruistic
C.   rational; irrational
D.   internal; external

(8)   Answer B, Type CON, Reference 76
Glenda has turned in an assignment late, so her instructor concludes Glenda is lazy and unmotivated. The instructor's assumption is an example of a(n) _____ attribution.
A.   situational
B.   dispositional
C.   external
D.   self-handicapping

(9)   Answer A, Type FAC, Reference 76
Sedikides and Anderson found that American students explained Americans' defections to the Soviet Union in terms of _____ causes, and Soviets' defections to the United States in terms of _____ causes.
A.   dispositional; situational
B.   situational; dispositional
C.   dispositional; dispositional
D.   situational; situational

(10)   Answer C, Type FAC, Reference 77
Jones and Davis's theory of correspondent inferences specifies the conditions under which you are most likely to
A.   explain others' behavior in terms of your own motives.
B.   explain others' behavior in terms of conscious or unconscious motives.
C.   infer people's dispositions from how they act.

D.   find actors and observers making corresponding attributions.

(11)   Answer D, Type FAC, Reference 77
If asked to remember the statement, "The librarian carries the old woman's groceries across the street," subjects later have better recall if given the cue word
A.   accident
B.   bags
C.   books
D.   helpful

(12)   Answer A, Type DEF, Reference 78
According to theorist Harold Kelley, in making commonsense attributions to explain others' behavior, people use information about
A.   consistency, distinctiveness, and consensus.
B.   cognition, emotion, and motivation.
C.   arousal, attention, and animation.
D.   complementarity, commonality, and closure.

(13)   Answer B, Type FAC, Reference 78
When explaining why Edgar is having trouble with his new computer, which of the following questions deals with consistency rather than with distinctiveness or consensus?
A.   Does Edgar have trouble with other computers, or only this one?
B.   Does Edgar usually have trouble with his computer?
C.   Do other people have similar problems with this computer?
D.   All of the above.

(14)   Answer D, Type FAC, Reference 78
According to research by Norman Anderson, when integrating information about someone in forming an impression, you will probably give more weight to
A.   first impressions than later ones.
B.   traits that are important to you than traits that are not.
C.   negative information than positive.
D.   All of the above.

(15)   Answer D, Type FAC, Reference 79
According to the text, research psychologists study biases in social thinking for the same reason other psychologists study
A.   gender differences.
B.   social development.
C.   social conflict.

D.   visual illusions.

(16)   Answer A, Type FAC, Reference 79
Which of the following statements about the biases that penetrate our thinking is true?
A.   We are mostly unaware of them.
B.   We are usually aware of them but deny that they play a significant role in our judgments.
C.   We are aware of them and usually use them to our advantage.
D.   Very few--if any--biases affect our thinking powerfully enough to harm ourselves or others.

(17)   Answer B, Type FAC, Reference 80
According to the text, the major reason for learning about social thinking and examining our errors and biases is to
A.   develop more realistic self-esteem.
B.   develop our capacity for critical thinking.
C.   become more effective in influencing others.
D.   develop more positive interpersonal relationships.

(18)   Answer C, Type FAC, Reference 80
Social psychology's most important lesson concerns how much we are affected by our
A.   childhood experiences.
B.   personal values and standards.
C.   social environments.
D.   unconscious motives.

(19)   Answer A, Type DEF, Reference 80
The discounting of situational effects in explaining people's behavior is known as the
A.   fundamental attribution error.
B.   self-serving bias.
C.   naturalistic fallacy.
D.   representativeness heuristic.

(20)   Answer C, Type DEF, Reference 80
In explaining people's behavior, the discounting of the part played by _____ is dubbed the fundamental attribution error.
A.   internal causes
B.   unconscious motives

C.   the situation
D.   personal values

(21)   Answer A, Type CON, Reference 80
You notice that Devon, a classmate, has failed a quiz. You may be committing
the fundamental attribution error if you conclude
A.   that Devon is a lazy student who probably did not study.
B.   that the quiz was unusually difficult for all who took it.
C.   that Devon probably had to work late the night before the quiz.
D.   that you would probably have failed if you had taken it.

(22)   Answer C, Type FAC, Reference 80
Jones and Harris had students read debaters' speeches either supporting or
attacking Cuban leader Fidel Castro. When the students were later told that the
debater's position had been assigned, they
A.   assumed the debater's position merely reflected the demands of the
assignment.
B.   described the speaker's position as poorly developed.
C.   concluded that to some extent the speech reflected the speaker's true
beliefs.
D.   concluded that the debate coach was an effective persuader.

(23)   Answer B, Type FAC, Reference 81
We commit the fundamental attribution error most often when we are explaining
_____ behavior.
A.   our own
B.   other people's
C.   friendly
D.   aggressive

(24)   Answer A, Type FAC, Reference 81
Students who were told that a clinical psychology graduate student had been
instructed to act in a friendly manner for purposes of the experiment concluded
that her behavior
A.   reflected her traits.
B.   illustrated role-playing.
C.   was situationally determined.
D.   demonstrated the illusion of control.

(25)   Answer C, Type FAC, Reference 81
When viewing an actor on stage or screen or a dummy operated by a

ventriloquist, we tend to believe that the programmed behavior reflects
A. powerful environmental forces.
B. a carefully prepared social script.
C. inner dispositions.
D. audience pressures.

(26) Answer A, Type FAC, Reference 82
Ross, Amabile, and Steinmetz randomly assigned subjects to play the part of either a quiz game contestant or the questioner, while other subjects merely observed the game. Results indicated that
A. both contestants and observers thought the questioners were more knowledgeable than the contestants.
B. both contestants and observers thought the contestants were more knowledgeable than the questioners.
C. observers thought the questioners were more knowledgeable, but contestants attributed the outcomes to the situation.
D. questioners thought themselves more knowledgeable, but contestants attributed the outcomes to the situation.

(27) Answer B, Type FAC, Reference 83
In real life, those with social power usually _____, which may lead observers to _____ their knowledge and intelligence.
A. manipulate others'; overestimate
B. initiate and control conversation; overestimate
C. give credit to those who have helped and served them; underestimate
D. deny their skill in order to seem modest; underestimate

(28) Answer D, Type FAC, Reference 83
The fundamental attribution error is corrected when
A. more than one observer accounts for the actor's behavior.
B. the observer does not know the personal identity of the actor.
C. the actor's behavior is not personally relevant to the observer.
D. the actor and observer switch perspectives with each other.

(29) Answer C, Type FAC, Reference 83
One explanation for the fundamental attribution error involves
A. the representativeness heuristic.
B. belief perseverance.
C. attentional focus.
D. the illusion of control.

(30)   Answer C, Type FAC, Reference 84
Recognizing our tendency to focus on the "figure" in the figure-ground
relationship may help us to understand why we
A.   engage in counterfactual thinking.
B.   construct memories.
C.   make the fundamental attribution error.
D.   fall victim to the overconfidence phenomenon.

(31)   Answer C, Type FAC, Reference 84
The day after George Bush beat Michael Dukakis in the 1988 presidential
election, most voters polled by Burger and Pavelich attributed the outcome to the
candidates' traits and positions. Asked to explain that outcome one year later,
A.   voters still blamed personalities and positions.
B.   voters blamed the media for distorting the campaign.
C.   more voters now credited circumstances like the state of the economy and
the country's mood.
D.   nearly one-third of voters claimed that the candidates were merely victims
of fate.

(32)   Answer B, Type FAC, Reference 84
According to Wicklund, Duval, and their collaborators, _____ makes
people more sensitive to their own attitudes and dispositions.
A.   self-concern
B.   self-awareness
C.   self-forgetfulness
D.   self-denial

(33)   Answer A, Type FAC, Reference 84
According to research on self-awareness, when our attention focuses on
ourselves,
A.   we attribute more responsibility to ourselves.
B.   we are unable to concentrate on making attributions.
C.   we are likely to blame others for our own mistakes.
D.   we are likely to attribute our outcomes to fate or chance.

(34)   Answer C, Type FAC, Reference 85
Research indicates that we tend to see ourselves as more _____ than we
see other people.
A.   consistent
B.   extroverted
C.   variable

D.   self-centered

(35)   Answer D, Type FAC, Reference 85
People's impressions of someone they have often heard about from a friend are
typically more _____ than their friend's firsthand impressions.
A.   positive
B.   variable
C.   negative
D.   extreme

(36)   Answer A, Type FAC, Reference 85
Our Western worldview predisposes us to assume that _____ cause events.
A.   people
B.   fate or chance
C.   situations
D.   unconscious motivation

(37)   Answer B, Type FAC, Reference 87
The fundamental attribution error is <u>fundamental</u> because it
A.   has been found to occur universally.
B.   colors our explanations in basic, important ways.
C.   underlies all other biases in social thinking.
D.   can only be remedied through therapeutic intervention.

(38)   Answer B, Type FAC, Reference 90
Cases of blindsight illustrate how
A.   our preconceptions control our interpretations.
B.   we sometimes know more than we think we know.
C.   memories are often constructive.
D.   easily we fall victim to the fundamental attribution error.

(39)   Answer C, Type FAC, Reference 90
Although prosopagnosia patients can <u>see</u> familiar people, they do not <u>recognize</u>
them as their relatives or friends. When shown pictures of such people, the
patients
A.   become confused and anxious.
B.   show irritation.
C.   demonstrate an increased heart rate.
D.   show no measurable response.

(40)   Answer A, Type FAC, Reference 91

In testifying at a congressional hearing investigating why the *USS Vincennes* misperceived an Iranian airliner and shot it down, social psychologist Richard Nisbett blamed
A.   the expectations of the crew of the *Vincennes*.
B.   the anti-Iranian prejudice of the U.S. government.
C.   risky camouflage and deception by the Iranians.
D.   conflict between the crew members of the *Vincennes*.

(41)   Answer D, Type FAC, Reference 92
Ross, Lepper, and Lord showed mixed research results on the deterrence effect of the death penalty to students who either favored or opposed the death penalty. Showing the two sides this identical body of mixed evidence
A.   had no effect on their preexisting opinions.
B.   narrowed the disagreement between the two sides.
C.   changed the views of the pro students but not the anti.
D.   increased the amount of disagreement between them.

(42)   Answer C, Type FAC, Reference 93
In the United States, presidential TV debates have mostly
A.   changed opinions to favor the incumbent.
B.   changed opinions to favor the challenger.
C.   reinforced people's predebate opinions.
D.   confused people and weakened their existing opinions.

(43)   Answer C, Type CON, Reference 93
Suppose a group of people who oppose gun control is presented with research evidence that is ambiguous about how well gun-control legislation will deter crime. Some of the evidence suggests that such laws would reduce crime, whereas other evidence suggests it would be ineffective or even backfire. After reviewing the evidence, how will most people in the group react?
A.   They will be less opposed to gun control legislation.
B.   Their attitudes will be unchanged, but they will call for more research.
C.   They will become more strongly opposed to gun control legislation.
D.   They will be more sympathetic to the opposing point of view.

(44)   Answer D, Type FAC, Reference 94
In the Kulechov effect, an audience that has just seen a _____ judged an actor's neutral facial expression to be _____.
A.   dish of soup; thoughtful
B.   dead woman; sad
C.   girl playing; happy

D.   All of the above.

(45) Answer D, Type FAC, Reference 95
Anderson, Lepper, and Ross provided people with evidence that either risk-prone or cautious people make better firefighters. Those who wrote an explanation for the findings were particularly susceptible to
A.   the fundamental attribution error.
B.   the hindsight bias.
C.   behavioral confirmation.
D.   belief perseverance.

(46) Answer A, Type DEF, Reference 95
People tend to cling to their beliefs even in the fact of contradictory evidence. This tendency is known as the
A.   belief perseverance phenomenon.
B.   belief continuity.
C.   correspondence bias.
D.   belief disconfirmation bias.

(47) Answer D, Type FAC, Reference 96
One remedy for the belief perseverance phenomenon is to
A.   always attempt to justify one's position.
B.   carefully review the objective evidence.
C.   seek the opinions of others.
D.   explain why an opposite belief might be true.

(48) Answer A, Type FAC, Reference 96
Which of the following statements about memory is <u>false</u>?
A.   Memories are copies of past experiences that remain on deposit in a memory bank until withdrawn.
B.   We easily and unconsciously reconstruct our memories to suit our current knowledge.
C.   People often recall mildly pleasant events more favorably than they experienced them.
D.   We not only forget ideas and beliefs: we also forget our previous attitudes.

(49) Answer C, Type FAC, Reference 97
Bem and McConnell had students write essays opposing student control over university curriculum. When then asked to recall how they had felt about the same issue a week earlier, most of the students
A.   remembered having held a very different attitude.

B.   could not remember how they had felt.
C.   mistakenly "remembered" having felt the same as now.
D.   admitted they had always supported student control of curriculum but pretended to oppose it in their essays.

(50)   Answer D, Type FAC, Reference 98
When Holmberg, and Holmes interviewed several hundred married couples, they found that those whose marriages had recently soured
A.   exhibited rosy retrospection.
B.   perceived their partners as having undergone dramatic personality change.
C.   recalled that things between them had been excellent until recently.
D.   recalled that things between them had always been bad.

(51)   Answer B, Type FAC, Reference 99
Research demonstrates that people who participate in self-improvement programs show _____ and claim to experience _____.
A.   modest improvement; very little improvement
B.   modest improvement; considerable benefit
C.   no improvement; slight benefit
D.   little difficulty achieving their goals; great difficulty

(52)   Answer D, Type FAC, Reference 99
Loftus and Palmer showed students a film of a traffic accident and quizzed them on their eyewitness recall. Results showed that
A.   students who had been in traffic accidents themselves were able to recall more details than those who had not.
B.   recollection accuracy was a function of both film length and vividness of the accident.
C.   knowing they were going to be quizzed made subjects pay better attention and recall more detail.
D.   what students recalled was affected by the wording of the questions.

(53)   Answer C, Type DEF, Reference 100
To retrieve a memory, you need to activate one of the strands that leads to it, a process known as
A.   belief perseverance.
B.   reconstruction.
C.   priming.
D.   induction.

(54)   Answer C, Type DEF, Reference 100

The overconfidence phenomenon refers to the
A.   tendency to search for information that is consistent with our preconceptions.
B.   persistence of our initial conceptions, even though they have been discredited.
C.   tendency to underestimate the extent to which our beliefs and judgments are erroneous.
D.   tendency for our expectations to evoke behavior that confirms our expectations.

(55)   Answer B, Type CON, Reference 101
Investment experts' belief that their own expertise will enable them to select stocks that will outperform the market average best illustrates
A.   the misinformation effect.
B.   the overconfidence phenomenon.
C.   the availability heuristic.
D.   priming.

(56)   Answer B, Type FAC, Reference 101
Writer Chuck Ross mailed a typewritten copy of Jerzy Kosinski's previously published novel Steps to 28 publishers and agents to consider for publication. Which of the following statements is true?
A.   All but the original publisher rejected it.
B.   All rejected it, including the original publisher.
C.   The scheme was easily detected and no one was fooled.
D.   Most recipients saw value in the material and offered to publish it because Ross was a well-known writer.

(57)   Answer D, Type FAC, Reference 101
One reason people are overconfident is that they are not inclined to seek out information
A.   from experts.
B.   this is objective and factual.
C.   that involves judging estimates and comparisons.
D.   that might disprove what they believe.

(58)   Answer C, Type FAC, Reference 103
Which of the following is a remedy for overconfidence?
A.   Getting prompt feedback on the accuracy of your judgments.
B.   Thinking of reasons why your judgments might be wrong.
C.   Both A and B

56

D.   None of the above is a remedy for overconfidence.

(59) Answer B, Type DEF, Reference 103
The strategy of judging the likelihood of things by how well they match particular prototypes constitutes the _____ heuristic.
A.   availability
B.   representativeness
C.   vividness
D.   matching

(60) Answer C, Type DEF, Reference 103
_____ are simple, efficient thinking strategies, or rules of thumb.
A.   Hypotheses
B.   Hermeneutics
C.   Heuristics
D.   Theorems

(61) Answer B, Type DEF, Reference 105
Focusing on the specific individual or case being considered can push into the background useful information about the population the person came from. This is the _____ fallacy.
A.   naturalistic
B.   base-rate
C.   utilization
D.   representation

(62) Answer B, Type CON, Reference 104
The tendency to conclude that a person who likes to play chess and read poetry is more likely to be a college professor of classics than a truck driver most clearly illustrates the use of:
A.   the availability heuristic.
B.   the representativeness heuristic.
C.   belief perseverance.
D.   the illusion of control.

(63) Answer C, Type FAC, Reference 104
The danger of using the representativeness heuristic is that it may lead us to
A.   make judgments in a very inefficient, time-consuming fashion.
B.   judge event likelihood solely on the basis of event memorability.
C.   disregard probability information that is relevant to our judgments.
D.   judge objects solely in terms of their functional utility.

(64)   Answer D, Type DEF, Reference 105
Our tendency to judge the likelihood of an event on the basis of how readily we can remember instances of its occurrence is called the
A.   confirmation bias.
B.   representativeness heuristic.
C.   belief perseverance phenomenon.
D.   availability heuristic.

(65)   Answer B, Type FAC, Reference 105
The false belief that more people live in Cambodia than in Tanzania is best explained by the
A.   self-fulfilling prophecy.
B.   availability heuristic.
C.   representativeness heuristic.
D.   belief perseverance phenomenon.

(66) Answer C, Type CON, Reference 106
People's greater fear of flying than of driving may best be explained by the
A.   representativeness heuristic.
B.   confirmation bias.
C.   availability heuristic.
D.   belief perseverance phenomenon.

(67)   Answer B, Type CON, Reference 106
"If only I hadn't called Brian when I was in a bad mood," whines Jenny, "maybe we wouldn't have had that fight and broken up!" Jenny's statement most clearly reflects
A.   the self-fulfilling prophecy.
B.   counterfactual thinking.
C.   the availability heuristic.
D.   pessimistic attributional style.

(68)   Answer D, Type DEF, Reference 106
Social psychologists refer to our tendency to imagine alternative scenarios and outcomes that might have happened, but didn't as
A.   the base-rate fallacy.
B.   automatic thinking.
C.   reflective bias.
D.   counterfactual thinking.

(69)   Answer C, Type DEF, Reference 107
The perception of a relationship where none exists is called
A.   imaginary parallel.
B.   counterfactual thinking.
C.   illusory correlation.
B.   regression toward the average.

(70)   Answer C, Type FAC, Reference 107
When Ward and Jenkins showed people the hypothetical results of a cloud-seeding
experiment, people who believed such techniques are effective felt their faith was
confirmed even though the results were a mixture of success and failure. The
result illustrates
A.   the self-fulfilling prophecy.
B.   the representativeness heuristic.
C.   illusory correlation.
D.   social overconfidence.

(71)   Answer B, Type CON, Reference 107
Dottie believes that there is a correlation between washing her car and the
occurrence of rain in her area. According to research, Dottie is much more
likely now to notice when
A.   it rains and she hasn't washed her car.
B.   it rains and she has just washed her car.
C.   it doesn't rain and she has just washed her car.
D.   All of the above.

(72)   Answer B, Type FAC, Reference 108
Dice players who throw softly to get low numbers and harder to get high
numbers are demonstrating
A.   the base-rate fallacy.
B.   the illusion of control.
C.   behavioral confirmation.
D.   regression toward the average.

(73)   Answer B, Type FAC, Reference 109
The illusion of control may arise because we fail to recognize
A.   our susceptibility to base-rate fallacy.
B.   the statistical phenomenon of regression toward the average.
C.   the operation of the representativeness heuristic.
D.   our tendency to counterfactual thinking.

(74)   Answer B, Type CON, Reference 109
Although Jason once scored a 270 in bowling, he has subsequently been unable to beat that record no matter how much he practices. His experience may be partially understood in terms of
A.   illusory correlation.
B.   regression toward the average.
C.   the representativeness heuristic.
D.   counterfactual thinking.

(75)   Answer B, Type CON, Reference 109
College students who receive unusually high scores on their first biology test can reasonably expect to receive _____ scores on their second biology test.
A.   very low
B.   somewhat lower
C.   equally high
D.   even higher

(76)   Answer D, Type FAC, Reference 111
Research indicates that, compared to unhappy people, happy people
A.   are more trusting and loving.
B.   choose long-term rewards over immediate small pleasures.
C.   tolerate more frustration.
D.   show all of the above characteristics.

(77)   Answer A, Type FAC, Reference 112
Joseph Forgas and his colleagues found that subjects' judgments of their own videotaped behaviors were more positive if, while they watched the videotape, they were
A.   in a good mood.
B.   with a stranger.
C.   distracted.
D.   either depressed or anxious.

(78)   Answer A, Type DEF, Reference 114
The tendency for one's expectations to evoke behavior that confirms the expectations is called
A.   self-fulfilling prophecy.
B.   belief confirmation.
C.   self-confirming validity.
D.   behavioral perseverance.

(79) Answer B, Type FAC, Reference 115
In a now-famous study, Rosenthal and Jacobson found that randomly selected elementary school students experienced a spurt in IQ score largely as a result of
A.   increased parental involvement and support.
B.   their teachers' elevated expectations.
C.   intensified academic training.
D.   educational strategies that raised their self-esteem.

(80) Answer D, Type FAC, Reference 115
Research has indicated that _____ can be self-fulfilling.
A.   teachers' expectations of students
B.   students' expectations of teachers
C.   experimenters' expectations of subjects
D.   All of the above.

(81) Answer C, Type FAC, Reference 116
Once formed, erroneous beliefs about the social world can induce others to behave in ways that prove those beliefs true, a phenomenon called
A.   prophetic validity.
B.   expectant accuracy.
C.   behavioral confirmation.
D.   belief perseverance.

(82) Answer A, Type DEF, Reference 116
Snyder, Tanke, and Berscheid had male students speak by telephone with women they thought were either attractive or unattractive. When judges later analyzed the women's comments, they found that
A.   the women thought to be attractive spoke more warmly than the other women.
B.   the women thought to be unattractive tried harder to be likable and stimulated better conversation.
C.   the women thought to be attractive spoke in a more aloof and superior manner.
D.   women thought to be unattractive spoke more slowly and deliberately.

(83) Answer B, Type FAC, Reference 116
According to research done by Miller and his colleagues, if you want young children to litter less and put trash in wastebaskets, you should probably repeatedly
A.   tell them they should be neat and tidy.
B.   congratulate them for being neat and tidy.

C.   tell them littering is a crime.
D.   tell them that people who litter are trash.

(84) Answer C, Type FAC, Reference 117
Research confirms that people are unlikely to confirm others' expectations when those expectations
A.   involve racial or gender stereotypes.
B.   involve the performance of altruistic behavior.
C.   conflict with a clear self-concept.
D.   are held by peers rather than by authority figures.

(85) Answer A, Type FAC, Reference 117
Steven Smith found that significantly more Bloomington, Indiana residents agreed to a request to volunteer to work three hours for an American Cancer Society drive if
A.   earlier they had been asked to predict how they would react if they were to receive such a request.
B.   they had first been informed that their neighbors had refused the request to volunteer.
C.   they had first been placed in a good mood through hypnosis.
D.   they had just received a temporary boost to their self-esteem.

THE FOLLOWING ITEMS ALSO APPEAR IN THE STUDY GUIDE:

(86) Answer A, Type DEF, Reference 77
According to the theory of correspondent inferences,
A.   we tend to infer that people's intentions and dispositions correspond to their actions.
B.   we tend to infer that people's intentions and dispositions correspond to our own intentions and dispositions.
C.   we tend to infer that people share the same underlying motives and values.
D.   those who have similar values tend to make the same attributions about others.

(87) Answer A, Type CON, Reference 80
For a school debate, Sally has been asked to argue in favor of capital punishment. Research on the fundamental attribution error suggests that observers of Sally's speech will conclude that her arguments
A.   reflect her true attitude on the topic.
B.   reflect a tendency to present herself favorably.
C.   are weak because she was assigned to present a particular position on the

topic.
D.   will lead her to experience cognitive dissonance.

(88)   Answer D, Type FAC, Reference 78
Evidence of the reasonable manner in which we form judgments of one another
comes from research on
A.   informational influence.
B.   personal space.
C.   the mere-exposure effect.
D.   information integration.

(89)   Answer A, Type FAC, Reference 86
People who come from cultures that are less individualistic than that of the
United States are more likely to
A.   offer situational explanations for someone's actions.
B.   offer dispositional explanations for someone's actions.
C.   engage in self-handicapping.
D.   offer self-serving explanations for their own behavior.

(90)   Answer A, Type FAC, Reference 81
There is a tendency to attribute the causes of _____ behavior to the
situation and to attribute the causes of _____ behavior to traits.
A.   our own; others'
B.   others'; our own
C.   children's; adults'
D.   males'; females'

(91)   Answer A, Type FAC, Reference 83
According to the text, the fundamental attribution error may lead us to
A.   overestimate the brilliance of our teachers.
B.   fail to hold people responsible for their misconduct.
C.   be lenient with convicted criminals.
D.   All of the above.

(92)   Answer B, Type FAC, Reference 95
The more closely we examine our theories and explain how they might be true,
A.   the more uncertain we become of them.
B.   the more closed we become to discrediting information.
C.   the more open we are likely to become to discrediting information.
D.   the more complex our theories are likely to become.

(93)   Answer C, Type FAC, Reference 107
Research suggests that the belief that women's moods are more negative during menstruation is an example of
A.   the base-rate fallacy.
B.   a self-fulfilling belief.
C.   illusory correlation.
D.   the representativeness heuristic.

(94)   Answer D, Type FAC, Reference 117
The textbook states that a large drop in prices on the stock market sometimes illustrates
A.   the representativeness heuristic.
B.   the availability heuristic.
C.   the overconfidence phenomenon.
D.   self-fulfilling prophecy.

(95)   Answer D, Type CON, Reference 104
Linda is 31, single, and outspoken. As a college student she was deeply concerned with discrimination and other social issues. A tendency to conclude that it is more likely that Linda is a bank teller and active in the feminist movement than simply a bank teller illustrates the powerful influence of
A.   belief perseverance.
B.   the availability heuristic.
C.   regression toward the average.
D.   the representativeness heuristic.

(96)   Answer C, Type CON, Reference 95
Despite reading solid research evidence that cigarette smoking causes cancer, Philip continues to believe that smoking is harmless. Philip's thinking clearly reveals
A.   belief assimilation.
B.   belief consolidation.
C.   belief perseverance.
D.   operation of the availability heuristic.

(97)   Answer A, Type CON, Reference 92
Many people firmly believe in astrology's ability to predict the future. Assuming they are presented a history of an astrologer's past predictions which in actuality show a random mix of success and failure, they are likely to
A.   believe the astrologer is successful.
B.   question this astrologer's predictive ability but still believe in the validity

of astrology.
C.   become very defensive.
D.   give up their belief in the validity of astrology.

(98)   Answer C, Type CON, Reference 109
Bob, a baseball player, makes five hits while Joe, a member of the same team, makes none in a particular game. In the next game both obtain one hit. What term used in the text explains Bob's fewer hits and Joe's increase?
A.   overconfidence bias
B.   base-rate fallacy
C.   regression to the average
D.   schemata

(99)   Answer D, Type CON, Reference 103
What psychological term might best be used to describe the rule "I before E except after C"?
A.   base-rate fallacy
B.   hindsight bias
C.   illusion of control
D.   heuristic

(100) Answer C, Type CON, Reference 108
A person enters a casino and after inserting one silver dollar in a slot machine hits the jackpot. This person's tendency to continue putting money into the machine so that finally the amount lost exceeds the original winnings can perhaps best be explained in terms of
A.   self-fulfilling prophecy.
B.   regression toward the average.
C.   illusion of control.
D.   hindsight bias.

CHAPTER FOUR: BEHAVIOR AND ATTITUDES

<u>Multiple Choice</u>

(1) Answer C, Type FAC, Reference 124
According to the text, tobacco company executives are able to live with themselves in spite of the link between smoking and ill health by publicly
A.   acknowledging that they are simply trying to earn a living.
B.   arguing the while smoking has adverse physical effects, it has positive psychological benefits.
C.   defending the smoker's right to choose.
D.   arguing that a third variable explains the relationship between smoking and ill health.

(2) Answer B, Type DEF, Reference 124
An attitude is best defined as _____ someone or something.
A.   an informed opinion about
B.   an evaluative reaction toward
C.   personal knowledge about
D.   a set of feelings regarding

(3)   Answer D, Type FAC, Reference 125
In the ABC's of attitudes, "A" stands for
A.   avoidance.
B.   attribution.
C.   attraction.
D.   affect.

(4)   Answer D, Type DEF, Reference 125
A person's attitude will be reflected in that person's
A.   beliefs.
B.   feelings.
C.   intentions to act.
D.   All of the above.

(5)   Answer D, Type CON, Reference 125
Which of the following is a component of Peter's attitude toward classical music?
A.   Peter believes that listening to classical music raises one's IQ.
B.   Peter likes the fact that a local radio plays only classical music.
C.   Peter buys classical music recordings with any extra money he earns.
D.   All of the above are part of Peter's attitude toward classical music.

(6)　Answer B, Type FAC, Reference 125
The prevailing assumption about attitudes, which underlies most teaching, counseling, and child rearing, has been that
A.　repeated action allows certain attitudes to take root.
B.　our private beliefs and feelings determine our public behavior.
C.　both attitudes and actions are caused by a third set of influences.
D.　our attitudes have little relationship to our actions.

(7)　Answer C, Type FAC, Reference 125
In 1972, after examining the attitude-behavior relation, Robert Abelson stated that we are "very well trained and very good at
A.　distorting the evidence to fit our theories."
B.　doing what we find reasons for."
C.　finding reasons for what we do."
D.　None of the above.

(8)　Answer A, Type FAC, Reference 125
In 1969 social psychologist Allan Wicker completed a review of dozens of research studies with the conclusion that people's stated attitudes expressed _____ of the variation in their behaviors.
A.　very little
B.　about half
C.　most
D.　virtually all

(9)　Answer A, Type FAC, Reference 126
In the early 1930s, Richard LaPiere traveled the United States with a Chinese couple, and they were received with courtesy at all but one of the hotels and restaurants they visited. Six months later, when LaPiere wrote those establishments, and asked if they would serve members of the Chinese race, of those who replied,
A.　only one said yes.
B.　about 25 percent said yes.
C.　about half said yes.
D.　about 90 percent said yes.

(10)　Answer D, Type FAC, Reference 126
According to the text, which of the following has had the greatest effect on reducing traffic accident rates?
A.　television shows portraying characters obeying the law

68

B.   celebrity appeals for safe driving habits
C.   person-in-the-street appeals for safe driving habits
D.   lower speed limits and divided highways

(11)   Answer D, Type FAC, Reference 126
According to the text, which of the following statements about attempts to change behavior by changing attitudes is true?
A.   Warnings about the dangers of smoking continue to have a major impact on smokers.
B.   As a result of increasing public awareness about violence on television, Americans are watching much less media murder.
C.   Appeals for safe driving habits have proved more effective than other strategies for reducing traffic accidents.
D.   None of the above.

(12)   Answer D, Type FAC, Reference 126
Which of the following best describes the relationship between expressed attitudes and behavior?
A.   Expressed attitudes lead to behavioral intentions, which perfectly predict behaviors.
B.   Past behaviors lead to behavioral intentions, which lead to expressed attitudes.
C.   Expressed attitudes perfectly predict behaviors.
D.   They are imperfectly related because both are subject to other influences.

(13)   Answer B, Type FAC, Reference 127
Which of the following statements correctly explains the bogus pipeline strategy?
A.   Subjects' expressed attitudes are interpreted to mean the exact opposite of their true attitudes.
B.   Subjects are deceived into believing that their true attitudes are being measured directly, so they do not distort their expressed attitudes.
C.   Researchers ignore the subjects' expressed attitudes and infer true attitudes from measures of arousal and tension.
D.   Subjects' responses are evaluated by a polygraph machine that provides a measure of deception and distortion.

(14)   Answer C, Type FAC, Reference 127
The advantage of the bogus-pipeline technique is that it
A.   eliminates the need for deception in attitude research.
B.   guarantees anonymity of subjects' responses.
C.   yields an expressed attitude that is closer to the real one.

D.   guarantees that the expressed attitude will lead to action.

(15)   Answer A, Type CON, Reference 128
Alice wonders if Justin really likes her. Since his behavior toward her may be
the result of other factors besides his real attitude, the best way for her to
measure his true attitude is to
A.   observe his average treatment of her over time.
B.   see whether he invites her to a party this weekend.
C.   notice how close he sits to her in psychology class.
D.   observe his reaction to the question, "Don't you like me?"

(16)   Answer B, Type FAC, Reference 129
According to research, to change health habits through persuasion, we should
alter people's
A.   attitudes toward health in general.
B.   attitudes toward specific health practices.
C.   television viewing habits.
D.   social networks.

(17)   Answer B, Type FAC, Reference 129
Snyder and Swann asked University of Minnesota men to act as jurors in a sex
discrimination case. The men's previously recorded attitudes ended up predicting
their verdicts only if they
A.   recorded their verdicts in writing.
B.   were first instructed to recall their attitudes.
C.   were asked to decide quickly and impulsively.
D.   first discussed their opinions with the rest of the group.

(18)   Answer A, Type FAC, Reference 129
Studies of the relationship between self-consciousness and attitudes suggest that, if
you are making a decision and suddenly are induced to feel self-conscious, you
will
A.   take action that is consistent with your attitudes.
B.   take action that is inconsistent with your attitudes.
C.   momentarily forget and fail to act on your attitudes.
D.   be more vulnerable to external influences on your attitudes.

(19)   Answer A, Type FAC, Reference 129
When Diener and Wallbom had students work on an "IQ test" with a time limit,
they found that students who were seated
A.   in front of mirrors felt self-conscious and were less likely to cheat.

B.   in front of mirrors felt greater self-concern and were more likely to cheat.
C.   near someone else's reflection tried to copy that person's paper.
D.   in front of mirrors did poorly on the test because they were distracted.

(20)   Answer C, Type CON, Reference 129
Jack is tempted to shoplift an expensive camera even though he has negative
feelings about shoplifting. Jack is least likely to steal the camera if:
A.   his negative feelings about shoplifting were learned from his teachers.
B.   he notices there are few customers in the store.
C.   he carefully looks at himself in a mirror.
D.   he has recently shoplifted items from other stores.

(21)   Answer D, Type FAC, Reference 130
Researchers have found that when people rehearse their attitudes by repeatedly
stating their liking or disliking of something or someone, their attitude becomes
more
A.   complex.
B.   susceptible to social influence.
C.   variable.
D.   potent.

(22)   Answer B, Type FAC, Reference 130
A housing shortage at Cornell University forced some students to live on cots in
dormitory lounges for several weeks. Although all students tended to have
negative attitudes about Cornell's housing situation, only _____ acted on
them.
A.   males
B.   those whose attitudes came from direct experience
C.   those who might have to experience such adverse living conditions in the
future
D.   college seniors

(23)   Answer C, Type FAC, Reference 130
Compared to attitudes formed passively, those forged in the fire of experience
are more
A.   unstable.
B.   less thoughtful.
C.   more resistant to attack.
D.   more difficult to express verbally.

(24)   Answer D, Type FAC, Reference 130

Our attitudes predict our actions when
A. other influences on our actions are minimized.
B. the attitude involved is specifically about the action.
C. we are conscious of our attitudes as we act.
D. All of the above.

(25) Answer D, Type FAC, Reference 132
Which of the following refers to a set of examples or research investigations that illustrate the power of self-persuasion--of attitudes following behavior?
A. role playing
B. the foot-in-the-door principle
C. social movements and slogans
D. All of the above.

(26) Answer C, Type DEF, Reference 132
The term _____ refers to prescribed actions expected of those who occupy a particular social position.
A. constellation
B. intentions
C. role
D. status

(27) Answer B, Type FAC, Reference 133
The results of Zimbardo's Stanford prison simulation indicated that
A. prison brutality is a product of the unique traits of prisoners and guards.
B. playing the roles of prisoners and guards can harden and embitter ordinary people.
C. authoritarianism is a primary cause of prejudice and aggression.
D. crowding is a primary cause of prison violence.

(28) Answer B, Type FAC, Reference 133
In describing the effects of role playing, Jonathan Winters has remarked that a hazard for stand-up comics like himself is that "you get to
A. saying one thing and doing another."
B. believing your own stuff."
C. acting differently for every different audience."
D. the point where you no longer take your own words seriously."

(29) Answer A, Type FAC, Reference 135
Experiments confirm that people induced to speak or write in support of something they doubt will feel bad about their deceit but will nevertheless begin

to believe what they are saying, provided that
A.   they weren't bribed or coerced into doing so.
B.   they are adequately rewarded for their endorsement.
C.   they do not have to go public with their arguments.
D.   the issue has no impact on anyone else's life or choices.

(30)   Answer C, Type DEF, Reference 136
Experiments suggest that if you want people to do a big favor for you, one technique is to get them to do a small favor first; this is known as the _____ principle.
A.   insufficient justification
B.   overjustification
C.   foot-in-the-door
D.   door-in-the-face

(31)   Answer A, Type DEF, Reference 136
According to the foot-in-the-door principle, if you get someone to agree to a small request, he or she will
A.   later comply with a larger request.
B.   expect you to return the favor later.
C.   experience cognitive dissonance and refuse requests for all later favors.
D.   see himself or herself as altruistic and do similar favors for other people.

(32)   Answer C, Type FAC, Reference 136
In a study by Freedman and Fraser, Californians were found to be more willing to agree to post an ugly "Drive Carefully" sign prominently in their front yards if they
A.   were offered a small compensation for their effort.
B.   had previously scored high on a survey of attitudes favoring more stringent traffic laws.
C.   had earlier complied with a smaller request to display a safe driving window sign.
D.   had first refused to comply with a smaller request to sign a safe-driving petition.

(33)   Answer C, Type CON, Reference 136
Which of the following is an example of the foot-in-the-door principle?
A.   Ben agrees to his boss's request that he work late on a special report. When his wife objects, he tells his boss he cannot stay late.
B.   Mindy agreed to be a first-time blood donor during last semester's blood drive. This semester she refuses to co-chair the blood drive.

C.   Carol agrees to a salesperson's request to try out a free sample of a new perfume. The following week she agrees to the same salesperson's request to buy an expensive assortment of cosmetics.
D.   All of the above.

(34)   Answer B, Type FAC, Reference 137
For the foot-in-the-door principle to work, the initial compliance--signing a petition, wearing a lapel pin, stating one's intention--must be
A.   granted without much thought.
B.   voluntary.
C.   socially approved
D.   granted to a powerful authority figure.

(35)   Answer D, Type DEF, Reference 137
The low-ball technique is a strategy for
A.   improving one's self-concept.
B.   measuring a person's attitude.
C.   reducing physical aggression.
D.   getting people to agree to something.

(36)   Answer B, Type CON, Reference 137
After Gertrude reluctantly agreed to type her boyfriend's psychology term paper, he told her it might actually be 75 pages long. Gertrude appears to be a potential victim of
A.   self-monitoring.
B.   the low-ball technique.
C.   the overjustification effect.
D.   the lure technique.

(37)   Answer C, Type CON, Reference 138
A sales representative comes to your home and asks you to try a water filter system for a week, absolutely free, so you agree. He returns the next week and offers you an expensive contract to continue to rent the system and you agree.
You are most clearly a victim of
A.   self-monitoring.
B.   the overjustification effect.
C.   the foot-in-the-door phenomenon.
D.   impression management.

(38)   Answer D, Type FAC, Reference 139
Disparaging an innocent victim leads an aggressor to justify further hurtful

behavior. Research studies show that this pattern occurs especially when the aggressor

A. identifies with the victim as similar to himself or herself.
B. engages in verbal but not physical aggression.
C. is coerced into the attack by threats from superiors.
D. is coaxed but not threatened or coerced into aggression.

(39) Answer A, Type CON, Reference 139
Sally has recently started to tease and hurt her sister. If this behavior continues it is likely that Sally will

A. develop an increasing dislike for her sister.
B. experience a loss of personal control.
C. show a significant loss of self-esteem.
D. fall victim to the overjustification effect.

(40) Answer A, Type FAC, Reference 140
Which of the following statements about the effects of moral and immoral action is correct?

A. Just as immoral actions corrode the conscience of those who perform them, moral actions affect the actor in positive ways.
B. People induced to act in evil ways quickly renounce this pattern, while those coaxed to do good continue the pattern.
C. Moral acts are internalized only if they are prompted by significant rewards of threats.
D. None of the above.

(41) Answer B, Type FAC, Reference 140
Freedman asked young children not to play with an enticing robot toy by threatening some with severe punishment and others with only a mild penalty. Much later the same children had an opportunity to play with the robot again, this time with no threat of punishment. Results showed that the children

A. given the mild deterrent were first to play with the robot.
B. given the mild deterrent mostly resisted playing with it.
C. who played with the robot later feared being punished.
D. previously given the severe threat showed a great deal of anxiety when they neared the robot.

(42) Answer C, Type FAC, Reference 140
Children seem more likely to internalize their decisions to obey rules when the deterrent they are threatened with is _____ and they are given _____.

A. strong; no choice about how to behave

B.   mild; no choice about how to behave
C.   mild; a choice about how to behave
D.   strong; a reward for obeying the rules

(43) Answer B, Type FAC, Reference 140
Findings indicate that since the U.S. Supreme Court's 1954 decision to desegregate schools, the percentage of white Americans favoring integrated schools has
A.   declined slightly in those states most affected by the ruling.
B.   more than doubled and now includes nearly everyone.
C.   increased only in those states not affected by the decision.
D.   remained essentially unchanged.

(44) Answer B, Type FAC, Reference 140
Findings on racial attitudes and behavior suggest that
A.   you can't legislate morality.
B.   changes in racial attitudes have followed changes in racial behavior.
C.   interracial behavior improves only after attitudes change.
D.   desegregation has tended to make people more prejudiced.

(45) Answer D, Type FAC, Reference 141
Benjamin Franklin reported that he won the friendship of a political opponent by
A.   behaving in a consistently friendly and helpful way to him.
B.   turning the other cheek to the opponent's hostility.
C.   offering to do a favor for his opponent's friend.
D.   asking the opponent for a favor.

(46) Answer B, Type CON, Reference 141
Marty wants Lee to like him. According to the attitudes-follow-behavior principle, what should Marty do?
A.   Do Lee a favor.
B.   Get Lee to do him a favor.
C.   Become good friends before asking for any favors.
D.   Do Lee's friend a favor.

(47) Answer C, Type FAC, Reference 141
Historians suggest that, in Nazi Germany, citizens who were reluctant to support the Nazi regime experienced a profound inconsistency between their private beliefs and
A.   running a private business in Germany.
B.   enrolling their children in German schools.

C.	reciting the public greeting "Heil Hitler" as a conformist greeting.
D.	saluting the German flag but not the swastika.

(48)	Answer B, Type FAC, Reference 142
Which of the following is <u>not</u> an effective component of a brainwashing program?
A.	escalating very gradually the demands made of the prisoner
B.	offering large bribes for compliance with requests.
C.	eliciting regular participation from the prisoner rather than allowing him to be a passive recipient of propaganda
D.	having prisoners write self-criticism or utter public confessions.

(49)	Answer D, Type FAC, Reference 142
A powerful practical lesson of the chapter on attitudes and behavior is that if we want to change ourselves in some important way, it is best to
A.	wait for the insight and inspiration needed to see it through.
B.	plan carefully before undertaking any action.
C.	arm ourselves with incentives and motives beforehand.
D.	go ahead and take action even if we don't feel like it.

(50)	Answer A, Type FAC, Reference 143
Bower and Masling gave students a list of bizarre correlations to remember. They found that students recalled most if they had
A.	invented their own explanations for them.
B.	been given good explanations of them by experts.
C.	been given extra time to study them.
D.	reviewed concrete examples for each one.

(51)	Answer D, Type FAC, Reference 143
Confirming the value of self-produced lessons, philosopher-psychologist William James asserted that "the great maxim which the teacher ought never to forget" is that no student should ever be asked to <u>receive</u> information without
A.	being given time to process it.
B.	knowing how it is supposed to be applied.
C.	being instructed in its proper use.
D.	having a chance to react to it.

(52)	Answer D, Type DEF, Reference 144
_____ theory assumes that our actions are self-revealing, so we can look to them when we are uncertain about our feelings or beliefs.
A.	Self-presentation

B.   Cognitive dissonance
C.   Self-justification
D.   Self-perception

(53)   Answer D, Type CON, Reference 144
Impression management is to _____ as cognitive dissonance is to
_____.
A.   overjustification; insufficient justification
B.   Bem; Festinger
C.   self-monitoring; self-presentation
D.   self-presentation; self-justification

(54)   Answer C, Type DEF, Reference 144
According to _____ theory, people want their attitudes to appear to be consistent
with their actions, and vice versa, in others' eyes.
A.   self-perception
B.   self-justification
C.   self-presentation
D.   social orientation

(55)   Answer C, Type DEF, Reference 145
When people adjust what they say toward their listener's position in order to
please rather than offend, they are engaging in
A.   role playing.
B.   false consensus.
C.   impression management.
D.   self-justification.

(56)   Answer B, Type DEF, Reference 145
People who score high on a scale of _____ tend to act like social chameleons:
They adjust their behavior in response to external situations.
A.   social absorption
B.   self-monitoring
C.   affective sensitivity
D.   self-perception

(57)   Answer B, Type CON, Reference 145
David has a strong set of internal principles for his beliefs and behaviors and
unvaryingly says what he thinks and believes what he says. He would probably
score _____ on a measure of _____.
A.   high; self-monitoring

B.   low; self-monitoring
C.   high; cognitive dissonance
D.   low; self-perception

(58) Answer C, Type FAC, Reference 145
Cognitive dissonance theory was formulated by
A.   James Laird.
B.   William James.
C.   Leon Festinger.
D.   Daryl Bem.

(59) Answer C, Type FAC, Reference 145
Cognitive dissonance theory proposes that we experience _____ when our beliefs
are _____.
A.   security; popular
B.   self-monitoring; unpopular
C.   tension; inconsistent
D.   anxiety; rejected by others

(60) Answer A, Type DEF, Reference 145
Cognitive dissonance feels
A.   uncomfortable.
B.   stimulating.
C.   reassuring.
D.   frightening.

(61) Answer D, Type FAC, Reference 146
We experience dissonance when we have
A.   made a decision between two equally attractive alternatives.
B.   acted in ways that are not consistent with previously stated attitudes.
C.   insufficient justification for performing a costly act.
D.   All of the above.

(62) Answer B, Type FAC, Reference 146
Festinger and Carlsmith had experimental subjects perform a dull task but paid
them to lie by telling a prospective subject that the task had been enjoyable.
Results showed that the subjects who were paid _____ came to believe the task
had been _____.
A. $1; tedious and boring
B. $1; interesting and enjoyable
C. $20; interesting and enjoyable

D. $1; frightening

(63) Answer C, Type CON, Reference 146
Though she is opposed to capital punishment, Lisa is asked to give a speech in favor of it to round out a class debate. Dissonance theory predicts that her true attitude will undergo the most change if she
A.   makes a speech implying capital punishment is really wrong.
B.   agrees to give the speech but only if she tells both sides.
C.   agrees to give the speech without special incentives.
D.   agrees to give the speech for a large reward.

(64) Answer B, Type CON, Reference 148
The Sugarcoat Mills cereal company wants people to become loyal consumers of its new brand, Flaky Critters. According to dissonance theory, first-time purchasers are most likely to become loyal repeat customers if they
A.   get their first box free.
B.   are induced to buy the first box for only 10¢ off.
C.   receive a free gift at the time of their first purchase.
D.   try a free sample before buying a box of Flaky Critters.

(65) Answer D, Type FAC, Reference 148
According to research, you will feel the most cognitive dissonance if you are induced to commit a costly action
A.   that fits with your friends' attitudes.
B.   in exchange for a sizable reward.
C.   out of fear of a powerful threat.
D.   of your own free will.

(66) Answer D, Type FAC, Reference 149
In applying the principle of cognitive dissonance to have others develop their own internal standards for new behavior, managers, teachers, and parents should use _____ to elicit the desired behavior.
A.   reminders of their legitimate authority
B.   only social punishments and rewards
C.   promises rather than threats
D.   the smallest possible incentive

(67) Answer C, Type FAC, Reference 149
Research indicates that after making important decisions that involve choosing between equally attractive alternatives, we
A.   experience very little cognitive dissonance once the choice is made.

B.   reduce dissonance by trying to think about something else.
C.   reduce dissonance by downgrading the rejected alternative.
D.   reduce dissonance by verbalizing the weaknesses of the chosen alternative.

(68)   Answer C, Type FAC, Reference 149
Researcher Jack Brehm had women rate the desirability of various appliances
before and after they had chosen one to keep for themselves. Brehm found that,
after the women had chosen a particular appliance, they
A.   decreased their rating of its desirability.
B.   expressed increased interest in learning about the others.
C.   increased their rating of its desirability.
D.   increased their rating of how desirable the others were.

(69)   Answer D, Type CON, Reference 149
The effects of dissonance after decisions are best summarized by which of the
following statements?
A.   "You often hurt the one you love."
B.   "You always want what you can't have."
C.   "He who hesitates is lost."
D.   "The grass is greener on the side of the fence you've chosen."

(70)   Answer C, Type FAC, Reference 149
Deciding-is-believing causes voters to indicate more esteem and confidence in a
candidate
A.   long before they vote.
B.   just before they vote.
C.   just after they vote.
D.   just after the results are known.

(71)   Answer B, Type DEF, Reference 150
When your attitude toward something is weak or ambiguous, you observe your
own behavior to infer how you must really feel. This is the rationale of _____
theory.
A.   self-presentation
B.   self-perception
C.   self-justification
D.   self-monitoring

(72)   Answer B, Type CON, Reference 151
Based on the findings of James Laird's research on self-perception, if you want to
feel happier you should

A. compare yourself to those who are worse off.
B. act happy by smiling.
C. assume a nonhappy expression like frowning.
D. reward yourself after you have met your goals.

(73) Answer A, Type FAC, Reference 153
A self-perception view of empathy recommends that, to sense how other people are feeling, you should
A. let your own face mirror their expressions.
B. call their attention to their facial expressions.
C. ask them to verbalize their nonverbal experiences.
D. ask a friend to join you in observing their behavior.

(74) Answer D, Type FAC, Reference 153
Wells and Petty asked students to listen to a tape-recorded radio editorial while testing the fit of earphone headsets. The students later said they agreed more with the editorial they had heard on the tape if they had been
A. distracted and unable to listen carefully.
B. wearing the lightest, most comfortable headsets.
C. given the choice of which editorial they would hear.
D. instructed to test the headsets by nodding.

(75) Answer C, Type FAC, Reference 153
Cocioppo and his colleagues found that people rated Chinese characters more positively
A. in the presence of a stranger than in the presence of a friend.
B. if distracted by loud music or a power saw.
C. if they gave their ratings while pressing their arms upward rather than downward.
D. if they had just viewed the suffering of an innocent victim.

(76) Answer A, Type FAC, Reference 154
The overjustification effect is best explained in terms of _____ theory.
A. self-perception
B. cognitive dissonance
C. self-monitoring
D. self-presentation

(77) Answer A, Type CON, Reference 155
Jeremy loses his former interest in doing arithmetic after his teacher promises him $1 for each problem he solves correctly. Which theory best explains

Jeremy's loss of interest in arithmetic?
A.   self-perception theory
B.   cognitive dissonance theory
C.   self-presentation theory
D.   self-monitoring theory

(78)   Answer B, Type FAC, Reference 156
According to the overjustification effect, promise children a reward for doing what they intrinsically enjoy and you will
A.   turn their work into play.
B.   turn their play into work.
C.   increase the time and effort they put into the task.
D.   soon no longer be required to offer the reward.

(79)   Answer D, Type CON, Reference 156
Myra's neighbor, a little boy, practices his saxophone loudly and annoyingly. According to the overjustification effect, if Myra wants to get him to quit playing, she should
A.   threaten to make him miserable if he keeps playing.
B.   pay him to quit playing.
C.   pay him a small amount to quit playing and then offer him more and more.
D.   pay him to play and then offer him less and less.

(80)   Answer B, Type FAC, Reference 155
As self-perception theory implies, the overjustification effect can be avoided, because _____ reward does not diminish intrinsic interest in an action, since people can still attribute the action to their own motivation.
A.   an uninformative
B.   an unanticipated
C.   a social
D.   an excessive

(81)   Answer C, Type FAC, Reference 157
The major difference between dissonance theory and self-perception theory is that the former relies on the motivating effects of _____, while the latter does not.
A.   behavior
B.   self-awareness
C.   tension
D.   self-inference

(82)   Answer D, Type FAC, Reference 158
According to dissonance theory, which of the following is a condition under which you become <u>more</u> likely to undergo a self-justifying attitude change?
A.   The negative effects of your behavior are irrevocable.
B.   Your behavior has negative consequences for which you feel responsible.
C.   A person harmed by your behavior is someone you like.
D.   All of the above.

(83)   Answer A, Type FAC, Reference 159
A comparison of theories explaining attitude-behavior relationships concludes that dissonance conditions do indeed arouse tension, especially when those conditions threaten
A.   self-worth.
B.   physical discomfort.
C.   as-yet-unformed attitudes.
D.   None of the above.

(84)   Answer B, Type FAC, Reference 160
A comparison of dissonance theory and self-perception theory concludes that _____ theory really explains _____.
A.   dissonance; attitude formation
B.   dissonance; attitude change
C.   self-perception; attitude change
D.   self-perception; behavior change

(85)   Answer D, Type CON, Reference 160
Harry has always strongly believed that it is wrong to shoplift. But after he himself shoplifts some inexpensive jewelry, his attitude toward shoplifting becomes less harsh. Which theory best accounts for this attitude shift?
A.   role-playing theory
B.   self-monitoring theory
C.   self-perception theory
D.   cognitive dissonance theory

<u>THE FOLLOWING ITEMS ALSO APPEAR IN THE STUDY GUIDE:</u>

(86)   Answer D, Type FAC, Reference 127
Which of the following is a technique for measuring attitudes?
A.   self-monitoring pipeline
B.   foot-in-the-door phenomenon
C.   low-ball technique

D.   bogus pipeline

(87)   Answer D, Type FAC, Reference 130
Based on recent social-psychological research, which of the following statements is true?
A.   Our attitudes and our behavior are unrelated.
B.   Our attitudes determine our behavior but our behavior does not determine our attitudes.
C.   Our behavior determines our attitudes but our attitudes do not determine our behavior.
D.   Under certain circumstances attitudes do predict behavior.

(88)   Answer A, Type FAC, Reference 133
When a movie version was made of William Golding's novel <u>Lord of the Flies</u>,
A.   the youngsters who acted it out became the creatures prescribed by their roles.
B.   hypnosis was used to get the youngsters to live up to their roles.
C.   action therapy was necessary to get the youngsters to unlearn their roles
D.   the foot-in-the-door phenomenon led the youngsters who acted it out to become uncivilized and brutal.

(89)   Answer A, Type FAC, Reference 140
Which of the following is cited in the text as an example of how changing behavior can alter attitudes?
A.   civil rights legislation
B.   prohibition
C.   traffic laws
D.   capital punishment legislation

(90)   Answer C, Type DEF, Reference 144
The theory that states we adopt certain attitudes in order to justify our past actions is _____ theory.
A.   self-perception
B.   self-presentation
C.   cognitive dissonance
D.   psychological reactance

(91)   Answer B, Type FAC, Reference 141
The gradual escalation of demands and active participation were described as key elements in
A.   the overjustification effect.

B.   brainwashing.
C.   the underjustification effect.
D.   the low-balling effect.

(92)   Answer B, Type FAC, Reference 153
Both cognitive dissonance theory and self-perception theory provide an explanation for the
A.   hindsight bias.
B.   insufficient justification effect.
C.   overjustification effect.
D.   Both B and C.

(93)   Answer D, Type CON, Reference 125
Which of the following is a component of Mary's attitude toward smoking?
A.   Mary believes smoking is harmful to one's health.
B.   Mary dislikes the fact that people are permitted to smoke in vehicles of public transportation.
C.   Mary is actively working for legislation that would outlaw the sale of cigarettes.
D.   All of the above are part of Mary's attitude toward smoking.

(94)   Answer B, Type CON, Reference 137
A car salesman offers to sell a customer a new car for $14,000 which is a very attractive price. After the customer signs the papers to purchase at that price, the salesman seeks final approval from the manager. He returns to tell the customer that the manager will sell the car for $14,500. The customer still agrees to buy. The customer was a victim of
A.   the overjustification effect.
B.   low-balling.
C.   brainwashing.
D.   the door-in-the-face phenomenon.

(95)   Answer C, Type CON, Reference 155
Nicole loses her former interest in playing the piano after her father promises to pay her $2 for each hour of practice. This illustrates the _____ effect.
A.   insufficient justification.
B.   low-ball
C.   overjustification
D.   door-in-the-face

(96)   Answer C, Type CON, Reference 147

86

Although John is strongly opposed to stricter parking regulations on campus, he is asked to write a paper supporting them. Dissonance theory predicts that his attitude will undergo the most change if he
A.   refuses to write the paper.
B.   agrees to write the paper for $200.
C.   agrees to write the paper for no pay.
D.   refuses to write the paper even after being offered $20.

(97)   Answer A, Type CON, Reference 160
Milford has always strongly believed that it is wrong to cheat. But after he himself cheats on a chemistry quiz, his attitude toward cheating becomes significantly less harsh. What best accounts for this attitude shift?
A.   cognitive dissonance theory
B.   self-perception theory
C.   reinforcement theory
D.   role-playing theory

(98)   Answer A, Type CON, Reference 145
In unfamiliar social situations Philip always sizes up his audience before stating an opinion. He only makes statements he knows others will support. Philip would probably obtain a high score on a scale of
A.   self-monitoring.
B.   low-balling.
C.   internal control.
D.   social comparison.

(99)   Answer D, Type CON, Reference 149
In which of the following situations would cognitive dissonance theorists predict that the person is experiencing dissonance?
A.   Dan is trying to decide whether to buy a new or used bicycle.
B.   Just as Mike finishes mowing the lawn, it begins to rain.
C.   Sara has just been accepted into law school.
D.   Nancy has just chosen to attend City College rather than State University after receiving equally attractive scholarship offers from both.

(100) Answer B, Type CON, Reference 150
"Let me see, do I like Chinese food? I guess I do because I eat at a Chinese restaurant twice a month." The process reflected in this internal dialogue is best understood in terms of
A.   cognitive dissonance theory.
B.   self-perception theory.

C. reinforcement theory.
D. equity theory.

CHAPTER FIVE: SOCIAL COGNITION AND HUMAN WELL-BEING

Multiple Choice

(1)   Answer B, Type FAC, Reference 164
If you are a typical college student, you may occasionally feel mildly depressed, as indicated by all <u>except</u> which of the following symptoms?
A.   feeling dissatisfied with your life
B.   frequent uncontrollable weeping
C.   feeling discouraged about your future
D.   lacking appetite and energy

(2)   Answer A, Type FAC, Reference 164
Major depression occurs in about _____ percent of men and nearly ___ percent of women.
A.   10; 20
B.   20; 10
C.   5; 10
D.   10; 5

(3)   Answer D, Type DEF, Reference 164
_____ psychology is the study, assessment, and treatment of people with psychological difficulties.
A.   Psychometric
B.   Health
C.   Medical
D.   Clinical

(4)   Answer A, Type FAC, Reference 164
Which of the following is <u>not</u> one of the questions currently being addressed by research bridging social and clinical psychology?
A.   How have recent social changes affected cultural values?
B.   How can laypersons and psychologists improve their judgments and predictions about others?
C.   How do the ways in which we think about ourselves and others contribute to personal problems?
D.   How can maladaptive thought patterns be reversed?

(5)   Answer D, Type FAC, Reference 164
According to the text, professional clinical judgment is vulnerable to

A. illusory correlations.
B. overconfidence bred by hindsight.
C. self-confirming diagnosis.
D. All of the above.

(6)   Answer A, Type FAC, Reference 165
Chapman and Chapman had college students and professional clinicians study the relationship between patients' test performances and diagnoses. They found that
A.   if students or clinicians expected a particular association, they perceived it, regardless of whether the data was supportive.
B.   students and clinicians only saw relationships that were indeed supported by the data.
C.   professional clinicians were more accurate than students in assessing relationships.
D.   students and clinicians only recognized positive relationships if the actual correlations were greater than .75.

(7)   Answer B, Type FAC, Reference 165
Clinicians who believed that suspicious people draw peculiar eyes on the Draw-a-Person test perceived such a relationship in the data
A.   only if the data indicated that suspicious people drew peculiar eyes at least as often as nonsuspicious people did.
B.   even when shown cases in which suspicious people drew peculiar eyes less often than nonsuspicious people.
C.   as long as suspicious people drew some part of the body out of proportion.
D.   only if other respected colleagues provided support for this hypothesis after examining the data.

(8)   Answer A, Type DEF, Reference 165
Our tendency to notice confirming instances but not disconfirming instances of an expected relationship contributes to
A.   illusory correlation.
B.   perceptual connectivity.
C.   the attention heuristic.
D.   the ultimate attribution error.

(9)   Answer C, Type FAC, Reference 165
One experiment gave people a description of a depressed person who committed suicide. Compared to those not informed of the suicide, those told that the person committed suicide
A.   showed greater compassion for the victim's family.

90

B.   were more likely to accept an invitation to a comedy show.
C.   had more negative reactions to the victim's family.
D.   were more likely to respond favorably to a third party's request for help.

(10)   Answer D, Type CON, Reference 166
Dr. Phillips, a psychotherapist, is plagued by doubt and guilt after a client
commits suicide. These guilt feelings probably stem from _____ on the part of
the therapist.
A.   self-serving bias
B.   the ultimate attribution error
C.   self-handicapping
D.   hindsight bias

(11)   Answer B, Type FAC, Reference 166
Clinician David Rosenhan and his colleagues faked schizophrenic symptoms to
infiltrate mental hospitals. Once they had been admitted and no longer
complained of any fake symptoms,
A.   professional clinicians quickly distinguished them from the real patients
and released them from hospitalization.
B.   the clinicians sought and found evidence in their histories and behavior to
confirm their admitting diagnoses.
C.   the pseudopatients were ostracized by the hospital's real patients.
D.   the pseudopatients absorbed their "sick" roles and developed additional
symptoms in the course of their treatment.

(12)   Answer B, Type FAC, Reference 166
In the Rosenhan study, clinicians who dealt with pseudopatients who had faked
symptoms to get into mental hospitals demonstrated the error of
A.   the Barnum effect.
B.   hindsight bias.
C.   self-handicapping.
D.   overjustification.

(13)   Answer A, Type FAC, Reference 167
After reporting on the results of his study in which clinicians had difficulty
recognizing pseudopatients, Rosenhan informed some mental staff members that
during the next 3 months one or more pseudopatients would seek admission to
their hospital. He subsequently found that the staff members
A.   wrongly identified many real patients as being pseudopatients.
B.   correctly identified several pseudopatients.
C.   failed to recognize several pseudopatients.

D.   All of the above.

(14)   Answer C, Type FAC, Reference 167
Snyder and Swann gave interviewers some hypotheses to test concerning individuals' traits, and found that people often test for a trait by
A.   asking those being tested for a general self-evaluation.
B.   looking for information that will contradict it.
C.   looking for information that will confirm it.
D.   All of the above.

(15)   Answer C, Type CON, Reference 167
Darnell is a personnel officer instructed to probe job candidates for signs of ambition and self-motivation. If given the following list of questions to use in interviewing candidates, which question is Darnell most likely to choose?
A.   "In what kinds of situations are you most likely to feel discouraged and ready to give up?"
B.   "What do you believe is the single most important quality to have for this job?"
C.   "Can you give me examples of how you have taken initiative in the past and shown yourself to be a self-starter?"
D.   "Who is the person you most admire?"

(16)   Answer D, Type FAC, Reference 167
Russell Fazio and colleagues found that, when interviewers questioned subjects to determine how extroverted they were,
A.   the questions asked for evidence of extroversion.
B.   the interviewees later perceived themselves as more extroverted.
C.   the interviewees later became noticeably more outgoing.
D.   All of the above.

(17)   Answer A, Type FAC, Reference 167
Research indicates that when interviewers are instructed to test for a trait, they tend to ask questions that show evidence of
A.   the confirmation bias.
B.   the illusion of control.
C.   negative attributional style.
D.   illusory correlation.

(18)   Answer C, Type FAC, Reference 167
When Zva Zunda and colleagues asked university students, "Are you happy with your social life?" the students ended up feeling _____ than those

students asked, "Are you unhappy with your social life?"
A.   more lonely
B.   more depressed
C.   happier
D.   more introspective

(19)   Answer A, Type FAC, Reference 168
Snyder and his colleagues found that they could get interviewers to search for
behaviors that would disconfirm the trait they were testing for by
A.   telling them that it was relevant and informative to find out ways in which
the person might not be like the stereotype.
B.   promising $25 to the interviewer who developed the set of questions that
told the most about the interviewee.
C.   Both A and B resulted in interviewers overcoming their confirmation bias.
D.   None of the above worked in overcoming the confirmation bias of the
interviewers.

(20)   Answer D, Type FAC, Reference 168
Renaud and Estress conducted life history interviews of 100 healthy, successful
adult men and discovered that their subjects' childhood experiences were loaded
with
A.   stories of good luck and happy outcomes.
B.   incidences of self-defeat and self-handicapping.
C.   attribution error and self-fulfilling prophecy.
D.   traumatic events, tense relationships, and bad parenting.

(21)   Answer A, Type FAC, Reference 168
Some researchers believe that psychotherapists' susceptibility to confirmation bias
may explain
A.   their patients' recovered memories of sex abuse.
B.   the occurrence of transference in therapy.
C.   the sadder-but-wiser effect in depressed patients.
D.   the beneficial effects of patients' optimism.

(22)   Answer A, Type FAC, Reference 168
When researchers pit statistical prediction--such as predicting graduate school
success on a formula including grades and aptitude scores--against interviewers'
intuitive prediction,
A.   statistical prediction is usually superior to expert intuition.
B.   expert intuition is usually superior to statistical intuition.
C.   statistical prediction and expert intuition do equally well.

93

D.   both methods usually fare no better than chance.

(23)   Answer B, Type FAC, Reference 169
Robyn Dawes assessed the accuracy of interviewers' ratings of candidates for the University of Texas Medical School by measuring the candidates' later performance in medical school. Results indicated that interviewers' ratings of future competence were
A.   extremely accurate.
B.   worthless.
C.   better predictors than aptitude test scores.
D.   helpful in predicting candidates' success in relating to patients but not in predicting their academic success.

(24)   Answer D, Type FAC, Reference 169
Robyn Dawes suggests that graduate admissions officers think that personal interviews are better predictors of graduate school success than statistical methods because
A.   GRE scores have been demonstrated to have little validity.
B.   academic records reflect the judgments of too few people to be representative.
C.   the reputation of the Educational Testing Service is decreasing.
D.   of cognitive conceit on the part of interviewers.

(25)   Answer B, Type FAC, Reference 169
Where professional clinicians have been given the statistical prediction of someone's future academic performance or risk of suicide and asked to refine or improve on the prediction, results have indicated that
A.   clinical intuition combined with the statistical indicator leads to the best prediction.
B.   prediction turns out better if the "improvements" are ignored.
C.   clinical intuition improves the predictability of suicide but not of academic performance.
D.   the past experience of the clinician is crucial in determining the predictive value of suggested improvements.

(26)   Answer D, Type FAC, Reference 170
According to research evidence, professional clinicians
A.   can easily convince clients of worthless diagnoses.
B.   are frequently the victims of illusory correlation.
C.   are fooled by hindsight analysis and self-confirming diagnoses.
D.   All of the above.

94

(27)   Answer C, Type FAC, Reference 171
According to the text, an important implication of the research on illusory thinking is that
A.   intuition really has no legitimate place in doing science.
B.   the scientific method is the only legitimate way to answer significant human questions.
C.   research psychologists must test their preconceptions before propounding them as truth.
D.   the conventional wisdom is almost always wrong.

(28)   Answer D, Type FAC, Reference 172
Burton VanderLaan, a cancer specialist and medical director of a large staff of physicians, reports that
A.   physicians' reviews of the medical records of their colleagues sometimes elicit the "I knew it all along" phenomenon.
B.   the high pay physicians receive may lead them to lose the intrinsic motivation that led them to enter the profession.
C.   physicians sometimes exhibit self-serving bias by taking credit when patients get well but not when patients are misdiagnosed.
D.   All of the above.

(29)   Answer B, Type FAC, Reference 173
Alloy and Abramson had depressed and nondepressed students observe whether their pressing a button was linked with a light blinking and found that depressed students
A.   were too self-focused to complete the task.
B.   were quite accurate at assessing their control.
C.   exaggerated the extent of their control of the light.
D.   underestimated the extent of their control of the light.

(30)   Answer C, Type DEF, Reference 173
The work of Alloy and Abramson in studying how depressives view the extent of their personal control over events provides evidence of the phenomenon known as
A.   optimistic well-being.
B.   pessimistic exaggeration.
C.   depressive realism.
D.   learned helplessness.

(31)   Answer D, Type DEF, Reference 173

95

The tendency of mildly depressed people to make accurate rather than self-serving judgments is referred to as

A. accurate explanatory style.
B. the Barnum effect.
C. realistic pessimism.
D. depressive realism.

(32) Answer B, Type CON, Reference 173
Jane, college senior, is mildly depressed. Asked to describe herself, she notes both her positive and negative qualities. She recalls both past successes and failures and takes personal responsibility for both. Jane clearly illustrates the _____ effect.

A. rose-colored-glasses
B. sadder-but-wiser
C. head-in-the-clouds
D. feet-on-the-ground

(33) Answer A, Type FAC, Reference 173
Depressed people are more likely to _____ than are nondepressed people.

A. take personal responsibility for experiences of failure
B. suffer from the illusion of control
C. maintain unrealistic visions of the future
D. None of the above.

(34) Answer C, Type FAC, Reference 174
In a hundred-plus studies involving 15,000 subjects, depressed people have been more likely than nondepressed people to exhibit "_____ explanatory style."

A. optimistic
B. illusory
C. negative
D. positive

(35) Answer B, Type DEF, Reference 174
"Explanatory style" refers to

A. the complexity of one's persuasive arguments.
B. one's habitual way of explaining life events.
C. the pitch and speed with which one communicates.
D. whether one relies primarily on reason or emotion in debating an issue.

(36) Answer A, Type DEF, Reference 174
Depressed persons are likely to attribute their failures or setbacks to causes that

are
A. stable, global, and internal
B. unstable, specific, and external
C. stable, specific, and internal
D. stable, global and external

(37) Answer C, Type CON, Reference 174
Maxwell, a college junior, suffers from chronic depression. After learning that he has performed poorly on his chemistry test, he is most likely to say,
A. "The test was not a fair assessment of what I actually know."
B. "My chemistry professor does not grade his tests fairly."
C. "I'm incompetent and probably always will be."
D. "I am sure most people did poorly on the test."

(38) Answer D, Type CON, Reference 174
Which of the following attributions regarding a failure or a setback illustrates the global quality of a depressed person's explanatory style?
A. "It's all my fault."
B. "It's going to last forever."
C. "The whole world is against me."
D. "It's going to affect everything I do."

(39) Answer D, Type FAC, Reference 174
After reviewing the available research on depression and attributional style, Taylor and Brown say that mental health derives from all except which of the following attitudes?
A. overly positive self-evaluations
B. exaggerated perceptions of control or mastery
C. unrealistic optimism
D. accuracy in perceiving oneself and the world

(40) Answer A, Type FAC, Reference 175
Hirt and his colleagues found that after Indiana University basketball fans became depressed by watching their team lose, they subsequently offered more _____ assessments of the team's future performance and more _____ assessments of their own future performance at throwing darts, solving anagrams, and getting a date.
A. negative; negative
B. negative; positive
C. positive; negative
D. positive; positive

(41)   Answer B, Type FAC, Reference 175
Strack and Coyne found that depressed people were realistic in thinking that other people
A.   possessed more accurate self-concepts.
B.   did not appreciate their behavior.
C.   would welcome their friendship and trust.
D.   were less influenced by fear of social disapproval.

(42)   Answer A, Type FAC, Reference 175
College students who have depressed roommates tend to become
A.   somewhat depressed themselves.
B.   more accepting of people suffering psychological disorder.
C.   more optimistic about their own lives.
D.   more studious and committed to achieving academic success.

(43)   Answer C, Type FAC, Reference 176
Research on the relationship between depression and negative thinking indicates that depression is
A.   a consequence but not a cause of negative cognitions.
B.   a cause but not a consequence of negative cognitions.
C.   both a cause and a consequence of negative cognitions.
D.   unrelated to negative cognitions.

(44)   Answer A, Type FAC, Reference 176
According to Lewinsohn and colleagues, the negative self-image, attributions, and expectations of a depressed person are an essential link in a vicious cycle of depression that is usually triggered by
A.   negative experiences.
B.   self-focus and self-blame.
C.   depressed mood.
D.   cognitive and behavior consequences.

(45)   Answer C, Type FAC, Reference 177
In North America, today's young adults are _____ as likely as their grandparents ever to have suffered depression.
A.   one-half
B.   twice
C.   three times
D.   five times

(46)   Answer B, Type FAC, Reference 177
According to researcher Martin Seligman, near-epidemic levels of depression in America today, ironically, can be blamed in part on the promotion of attitudes that say,
A.   "Everybody needs somebody sometime."
B.   "You can make it on your own."
C.   "You're nobody if nobody loves you."
D.   "Eat, drink, and be merry, for tomorrow we die."

(47)   Answer D, Type FAC, Reference 177
According to Martin Seligman's analysis of the attitudes that promote near-epidemic levels of depression in America, most of us feel that, if we don't "make it" in today's world, we can blame
A.   our parents.
B.   the government.
C.   the alienation of the modern world.
D.   only ourselves.

(48)   Answer B, Type FAC, Reference 177
In comparison to those in Western cultures, depressed people in Japan are more likely to report feeling
A.   guilt and self-blame over personal failure.
B.   shame over letting down their family or co-workers.
C.   sad about social problems such as poverty and discrimination.
D.   All of the above.

(49)   Answer C, Type DEF, Reference 177
Loneliness is best described as a state created by the awareness that you
A.   are alone most of the time.
B.   have lost a significant relationship.
C.   have less numerous or meaningful social relationships than you desire.
D.   are not really respected even though you have many acquaintances.

(50)   Answer D, Type FAC, Reference 177
In her study of Dutch adults, Jenny de Jong-Gierveld observed that _____ are more likely to feel lonely.
A.   married people with children
B.   childless married couples
C.   married women who do not work outside the home
D.   unmarried and unattached people

(51)   Answer B, Type FAC, Reference 177
When beeped by an electronic pager at various times during a week and asked to record what they were doing and how they felt, _____ were most likely to report feeling lonely when alone.
A.   children
B.   adolescents
C.   adults
D.   women

(52)   Answer D, Type FAC, Reference 178
Studies of gender differences in loneliness reveal that _____ are more likely to feel lonely when _____.
A.   males; they are deprived of respect
B.   males; they are deprived of close one-to-one relationships
C.   females; they are isolated from group interaction
D.   females; they are deprived of close one-to-one relationships

(53)   Answer D, Type FAC, Reference 178
Chronically lonely people seem to have the same _____ as chronically depressed people.
A.   unrealistic vision of the future
B.   need to achieve perfection
C.   illusion of control
D.   negative explanatory style

(54)   Answer D, Type FAC, Reference 178
Which of the following statements about lonely people is true?
A.   They perceive others in negative ways.
B.   They tend to be low in self-esteem.
C.   When talking with strangers, they spend more time talking about themselves and take less interest in the other person.
D.   All of the above.

(55)   Answer A, Type FAC, Reference 179
While some situations would make almost anyone feel anxious, some people, especially those who are shy or easily embarrassed, feel anxious in almost any situation in which they might be
A.   evaluated.
B.   observed.
C.   approached.
D.   ignored.

(56)   Answer B, Type DEF, Reference 179
Which of the following theories most clearly predicts that we will feel anxious
when we are motivated to impress others but doubt our ability to do so?
A.   social learning theory
B.   self-presentation theory
C.   self-perception theory
D.   cognitive dissonance theory

(57)   Answer B, Type DEF, Reference 179
According to the text, shyness is a form of _____ characterized by self-
consciousness and worry about what others think.
A.   loneliness
B.   social anxiety
C.   depression
D.   social incompetence

(58)   Answer B, Type FAC, Reference 180
Highly self-conscious people have a tendency to _____, a tendency that breeds
anxious concern and, in extreme cases, paranoia.
A.   displace their anger
B.   overpersonalize social situations
C.   repress their fears
D.   rationalize their failures

(59)   Answer B, Type FAC, Reference 180
According to the text, labeling oneself as shy, depressed, or under the influence
of alcohol can serve a _____ function.
A.   anger-reducing
B.   self-handicapping
C.   concurrence-seeking
D.   group-identification

(60)   Answer A, Type FAC, Reference 180
Brodt and Zimbardo found that shy women who were bombarded with loud noise
and told that it would leave them _____ were subsequently _____ in
interacting with a handsome male.
A.   with a pounding heart; no longer so shy
B.   unaffected; no longer so shy
C.   with a pounding heart; even more shy
D.   unaffected; even more shy

(61)	Answer D, Type DEF, Reference 180

_____ is an interdisciplinary field that integrates and applies behavior and medical knowledge regarding health and disease.
A.	Clinical psychology
B.	Health psychology
C.	Medical psychology
D.	Behavioral medicine

(62)	Answer C, Type CON, Reference 180

Dr. Matthews is a psychologist who studies the factors that influence patient's willingness to follow their physicians' instructions. Dr. Matthews is most likely a _____ psychologist.
A.	physiological
B.	humanistic
C.	health
D.	developmental

(63)	Answer A, Type FAC, Reference 181

The _____ of the Type A personality is the characteristic most closely associated with heart disease.
A.	anger
B.	anxiety
C.	depression
D.	loneliness

(64)	Answer D, Type FAC, Reference 181

According to the text, which of the following is being studied by health psychologists as a strategy for controlling or reducing stress?
A.	regular aerobic exercise
B.	relaxation training
C.	confiding in close friends
D.	All of the above.

(65)	Answer D, Type FAC, Reference 181

Research indicates that patients are more willing to follow treatment instructions when
A.	they have a warm relationship with their doctor.
B.	they help plan their own treatment.
C.	their health care options are framed attractively.
D.	All of the above.

(66)   Answer B, Type FAC, Reference 183
Experiments that subject animals to mild but uncontrollable electric shocks, loud noises, or crowding have shown that such experiences
A.   directly cause diseases like cancer.
B.   lower the body's resistance to disease.
C.   strengthen the animals' capacity to deal with future stressors.
D.   lead to the animals becoming more aggressive in interacting with members of their own species.

(67)   Answer B, Type FAC, Reference 183
A growing body of evidence reveals that people who undergo highly stressful experiences become
A.   more resistant to low-level illnesses like colds and flu.
B.   become more vulnerable to disease.
C.   less self-disclosing and more socially isolated.
D.   stronger and more socially skilled than unstressed people.

(68)   Answer C, Type FAC, Reference 183
Research has reported that newlywed couples who become angry while discussing problems
A.   experience catharsis and better long-term relationships with their spouses.
B.   are subsequently more susceptible to problems of depression and loneliness.
C.   suffer more immune system suppression the next day.
D.   are more prone to develop colon cancer in the subsequent six months.

(69)   Answer C, Type FAC, Reference 183
A large Swedish study has found that, compared with unstressed workers, those with a history of workplace stress
A.   are better prepared to deal with stress in their family lives.
B.   tend to have a more pessimistic explanatory style.
C.   are at much greater risk of developing colon cancer.
D.   develop stronger immune defenses.

(70)   Answer B, Type CON, Reference 183
Which of the following is not an example of one of the components of an pessimistic explanatory style?
A.   "This is all my fault."
B.   "I've learned my lesson."
C.   "This is going to ruin everything."
D.   "Things are going to be terrible from now on."

(71)   Answer D, Type FAC, Reference 183
Peterson and Seligman analyzed the press quotes of baseball Hall of Famers and found that those who routinely offered pessimistic explanations for bad events, like losing big games, were more likely to
A.   earn lower salaries.
B.   experience divorce.
C.   play aggressively.
D.   die at younger ages.

(72)   Answer C, Type FAC, Reference 184
Research by Scheier and Carver indicates that people who agree with statements like _____ are less often bothered by various illnesses and even recover faster from operations like coronary bypass surgery.
A.   "My fate is out of my hands."
B.   "Human life is fragile."
C.   "I usually expect the best out of life."
D.   "I rarely count on good things happening to me."

(73)   Answer A, Type FAC, Reference 184
A study of 86 women undergoing breast cancer therapy found that survival time was nearly doubled among those who
A.   participated in morale-boosting weekly support groups.
B.   were involved in some competitive team sport.
C.   developed a new hobby that captured their interest.
D.   participated in daily relaxation exercises.

(74)   Answer C, Type CON, Reference 184
Julie has been recently diagnosed as having breast cancer and is receiving the best medical treatment available. Research suggests that her chances of survival may also be enhanced if her attitude is
A.   disciplined and cooperative.
B.   realistic and impassive.
C.   hopeful and determined.
D.   pessimistic and combative.

(75)   Answer A, Type FAC, Reference 184
Research investigating the nature of the connection between explanatory style and health has shown that people who routinely use the pessimistic style
A.   have weaker bodily immune defenses.
B.   boost the morale of others via a contrast effect.

C. also tend to be impulsive and resistant to influence.
D. complain more but are not really sicker than optimists.

(76) Answer B, Type FAC, Reference 185
Both assertiveness training and rational-emotive therapy are cited in the text as examples of psychotherapeutic techniques that
A. utilize social support to change behavior.
B. utilize the attitudes-follow-behavior principle.
C. encourage changes in explanatory style.
D. use counter-conditioning strategies.

(77) Answer D, Type FAC, Reference 186
Mirels and McPeek induced students to write self-laudatory essays, and found that, compared to students who wrote about social issues, they were more likely later to
A. feel guilty.
B. behave assertively in competitive games.
C. offer help to a stranger.
D. privately rate themselves higher in self-esteem.

(78) Answer A, Type FAC, Reference 186
Mendonca and Brehm found that overweight children were more likely to lose weight and keep it off after an eight-week program if they
A. felt responsible for choosing their weight-loss program.
B. were regularly monitored and penalized for breaking rules.
C. were praised and rewarded for even minor weight loss.
D. had been assigned to their "least preferred" treatment program and thus exercised the greatest effort in losing weight.

(79) Answer B, Type FAC, Reference 186
Axom and Cooper put women who wanted to lose weight through some supposedly therapeutic tasks, such as making perceptual judgments. Results indicated that those who _____ lost the most weight.
A. were most authoritarian
B. committed the most effort to the tasks
C. felt the most social pressure to perform the tasks
D. found the tasks most interesting

(80) Answer D, Type FAC, Reference 187
A study by Haemmerlie and Montgomery enticed shy college men to participate in laboratory exercises in which they were able to perceive themselves as socially

competent after they
A.   were taught specific communication skills.
B.   took a short course on positive thinking.
C.   delivered self-laudatory speeches to strangers.
D.   had several successful conversations with women.

(81) Answer B, Type FAC, Reference 187
Haemmerlie and Montgomery conclude that the success of their social skills training with shy men may very well have occurred because their program
A.   employed skilled counselors who took responsibility for inspiring the men to feel confident and competent.
B.   included no counseling, so the participants had to act on their own.
C.   protected the men from having to participate in actual conversations until they had been extensively trained first.
D.   paved the way for conversational success by providing many external reasons for initiating conversation.

(82) Answer D, Type FAC, Reference 188
The vicious cycles that maintain depression, loneliness, and shyness can be broken by
A.   training in more effective social skills.
B.   positive experiences that alter self-perceptions.
C.   changing negative thought patterns.
D.   All of the above.

(83) Answer A, Type FAC, Reference 188
In the treatment phase of Mary Anne Layden's explanatory style therapy for depressed college students, the participants were instructed to
A.   keep a diary recording internal reasons for success and external explanations for failure.
B.   keep a written record of mistakes they had made, reviewing them with a therapist to plan how to avoid them in the future.
C.   regularly recite phrases like "I can do it" to themselves.
D.   role-play the part of self-confident people for observers.

(84) Answer C, Type FAC, Reference 188
Improvements achieved through changing thought or behavior patterns are most likely to endure if people
A.   redesign their behavioral contexts.
B.   are required to report back to their therapist on a regular basis.
C.   attribute such changes to factors under their own control.

106

D.   recognize that success depends on a power beyond themselves.

(85)   Answer B, Type CON, Reference 189
Bill, a middle-aged insurance salesman, has recently managed to lose 50 pounds while on a weight-control program. Research suggests that he is most likely to maintain the weight loss if he
A.   attributes his changed eating behavior to the program.
B.   credits his success to his own efforts at self-control.
C.   successfully persuades several friends to participate in the same treatment program.
D.   subsequently participates in an assertiveness training program.

THE FOLLOWING ITEMS ALSO APPEAR IN THE STUDY GUIDE:

(86)   Answer D, Type FAC, Reference 164
According to the text, social psychology has contributed to
A.   our understanding of psychological disorders.
B.   the treatment of psychological disorders.
C.   improving the process of clinical judgment and prediction.
D.   All of the above.

(87)   Answer D, Type FAC, Reference 165
The text suggests that clinicians may continue to have confidence in uninformative or ambiguous tests because of human susceptibility to
A.   the inoculation effect.
B.   learned helplessness.
C.   the representativeness heuristic.
D.   illusory correlation.

(88)   Answer C, Type FAC, Reference 171
According to the text, the pervasiveness of illusory thinking points to the need for a _____ study of thought and behavior.
A.   psychohistorical
B.   literary
C.   scientific
D.   humanistic

(89)   Answer B, Type FAC, Reference 174
Which of the following attributions regarding a failure or setback illustrates the stable quality of a depressed person's explanatory style?
A.   "It's all my fault."

B.   "It's going to last forever."
C.   "The whole world is against me."
D.   "It's going to affect everything I do."

(90)   Answer B, Type FAC, Reference 173
Which of the following is not one of the psychological difficulties discussed in the text in terms of social cognitions?
A.   depression
B.   schizophrenia
C.   loneliness
D.   social anxiety

(91)   Answer A, Type FAC, Reference 180
Brodt and Zimbardo found that shy women were no longer shy when they
A.   were provided an alternative explanation for their social anxiety.
B.   were provided alcohol before interacting with others.
C.   discovered most people feel shy.
D.   were taught to blame their failures on circumstances beyond their control.

(92)   Answer D, Type FAC, Reference 185
Which of the following is not given as an example of a therapy that utilizes the "attitudes-follow-behavior" principle?
A.   assertiveness training
B.   rational-emotive therapy
C.   self-help groups
D.   psychoanalysis

(93)   Answer D, Type FAC, Reference 169
Robyn Dawes, writing in <u>House of Cards: Psychology and Psychotherapy Built on Myth</u>, reports that interviewers' ratings of medical school applicants were highly predictive of the applicants'
A.   likelihood of receiving the M.D.
B.   eventual performance in their first year of residency.
C.   likelihood of graduating from medical school with honors.
D.   None of the above.

(94)   Answer C, Type FAC, Reference 178
Chronically lonely people tend to blame _____ for their poor social relationships.
A.   their parents and early childhood experiences
B.   the uncaring attitudes of those presently around them

C. themselves
D. cultural patterns

(95) Answer D, Type CON, Reference 180
Dr. Jones is a psychologist who specializes in the causes and control of stress.
Dr. Jones is most likely a(n) _____ psychologist.
A. consumer
B. educational
C. forensic
D. health

(96) Answer D, Type CON, Reference 174
Philip suffers from chronic depression. How is he likely to respond when told
that he failed the test to renew his driver's license?
A. "Yesterday was just my unlucky day."
B. "I imagine very few people have passed that same test."
C. "The person giving the test is incompetent."
D. "I am a poor driver and always will be."

(97) Answer D, Type CON, Reference 183
Mary wants advice on how to cope with the stress of a new job. She would be
best advised to approach her new job with a sense of
A. skepticism and humility.
B. ambition and competitiveness.
C. urgency and time-consciousness.
D. control and optimism.

(98) Answer A, Type CON, Reference 188
As a result of participating in a program to help him quit smoking, Bill has not
had a cigarette for three weeks. He is least likely to return to smoking if he
attributes his success in quitting the habit to
A. his own motivation.
B. the therapist who helped him quit.
C. the support of his friends.
D. the unique nature of the therapeutic program.

(99) Answer C, Type CON, Reference 173
Valerie is a severely depressed college student. From research presented in the
text on depression she
A. probably suffers from the better-than-average phenomenon.
B. assumes that her behavior is well-accepted by others.

C.   demonstrates the sadder-but-wiser effect.
D.   is below average in intelligence.

(100) Answer C, Type CON, Reference 168
Gayle, a Freudian analyst, finds that, without exception, her patients report dreams closely related to their emotional problems and that are easily understood in terms of Freud's theory of personality. From research presented in the text, what may best explain why the dreams and problems of Gayle's patients are so consistent with Freudian theory?
A.   Freud's theory is the oldest and most comprehensive of all the theories of personality.
B.   Freud's theory is more ambiguous than any other theory, and thus any problem fits into its framework.
C.   The patients are perhaps induced to give information that is consistent with Gayle's theoretical orientation.
D.   Freudian psychotherapists are "true believers" and Gayle's report is an attempt to convert other therapists to her orientation.

CHAPTER SIX: GENDER, GENES, AND CULTURE

Multiple Choice.

(1)   Answer B, Type FAC, Reference 194
Given the prevalence of ethnic conflict and racial hostilities worldwide, it is not surprising that historian Arthur Schlesinger calls _____ "the explosive problem of our times."
A.   social anarchy
B.   social diversity
C.   totalitarianism
D.   mindless conformity

(2) Answer B, Type FAC, Reference 194
As similar as human beings are in many ways, according to your text the most important of all our similarities is probably our
A.   anxious response to unfamiliar peoples and cultures.
B.   capacity to learn and adapt.
C.   standards for conducting personal relationships.
D.   definition of social justice.

(3)   Answer C, Type DEF, Reference 194
_____ is the enduring behaviors, ideas, attitudes, and traditions shared by a large group of people and transmitted from one generation to the next.
A.   Ethnic philosophy
B.   Anthropology
C.   Culture
D.   Ingroup ideology

(4)   Answer D, Type FAC, Reference 194
Which of the following is shaped by where and when we live?
A.   how we define beauty
B.   how we define social justice
C.   whether we tend to be expressive or reserved
D.   All of the above.

(5)   Answer A, Type CON, Reference 195
Human kinship is to the _____ perspective as social diversity is to the _____ perspective.
A.   evolutionary; cultural
B.   cognitive; psychoanalytic

C. humanistic; cultural
D. biological; humanistic

(6) Answer D, Type CON, Reference 195
The cultural perspective is to _____ as the evolutionary perspective is to _____.
A. Brown; Darwin
B. social norms; human adaptability
C. social roles; hormonal factors
D. human adaptability; natural selection

(7) Answer D, Type DEF, Reference 195
Evolutionary psychology is the study of the evolution of _____ using the principles of _____.
A. cultures; natural selection
B. behavior; conditioning
C. cultures; conditioning
D. behavior; natural selection

(8) Answer C, Type FAC, Reference 195
The fact that all human societies engage in communal sharing, rank people by authority and status, and have ideas about economic justice would be emphasized by the _____ perspective.
A. psychoanalytic
B. communitarian
C. evolutionary
D. cultural

(9) Answer A, Type FAC, Reference 195
The fact that people worldwide vary greatly in their dress habits and the specific foods they eat would be emphasized by the _____ perspective.
A. cultural
B. individualistic
C. evolutionary
D. psychoanalytic

(10) Answer D, Type FAC, Reference 196
Males and females are alike in
A. vocabulary.
B. intelligence.
C. self-esteem.

D.   All of the above.

(11)   Answer A, Type FAC, Reference 196
Compared to men, women are more vulnerable to
A.   anxiety disorders.
B.   suicide.
C.   alcoholism.
D.   None of the above.

(12)   Answer C, Type FAC, Reference 196
Compared to women, men are more vulnerable to
A.   anxiety disorders.
B.   depression.
C.   suicide.
D.   None of the above.

(13)   Answer B, Type FAC, Reference 196
During the 1970s, many scholars worried that studies of gender differences might
A.   lead to the conclusion that males and females are fundamentally the same, and thus to social upheaval.
B.   reinforce stereotypes, and that gender differences might be interpreted as women's deficits.
C.   lead to the conclusion that males are inferior to women, and thus to a reverse form of sexism.
D.   replace more basic and important research on processes of social influence and interpersonal relationships.

(14)   Answer A, Type FAC, Reference 196
In rating their feelings regarding "men" and "women," most
A.   people rate women more favorably than men.
B.   people rate men more favorably than women.
C.   people rate men and women the same.
D.   men rate men more favorably, and most women rate women more favorably.

(15)   Answer D, Type FAC, Reference 197
Despite the fact that individual men and women display attitudes and behavior that span the complete range of human potential, several psychologists contend that women more than men give priority to
A.   individual self-fulfillment.
B.   personal freedom.

113

C.   intellectual honesty.
D.   relationships.

(16)   Answer C, Type FAC, Reference 197
As children, girls are more likely than boys to
A.   play in groups.
B.   display conflict.
C.   display sharing.
D.   All of the above.

(17)   Answer C, Type FAC, Reference 197
In groups, men talk more _____, while women talk more
_____.
A.   about others; about themselves
B.   about people; about issues
C.   to give information; to show support
D.   to show support; to criticize

(18)   Answer A, Type FAC, Reference 197
When surveyed, women are far more likely than men to describe themselves as having
A.   empathy for others.
B.   difficulty with important relationships.
C.   envy of others.
D.   problems expressing their emotions.

(19)   Answer C, Type CON, Reference 197
After seeing victims of an earthquake on television, women are more likely than men to
A.   become withdrawn and irritable.
B.   demonstrate the just world phenomenon.
C.   express empathy.
D.   distract themselves with some leisure activity.

(20)   Answer D, Type FAC, Reference 198
When they want empathy and understanding, men turn to _____ and women turn to _____.
A.   men; women
B.   women; men
C.   men; men
D.   women; women

114

(21) Answer A, Type CON, Reference 198
Which of the following couples is likely to experience the greatest marital satisfaction?
A. gentle Bill and empathic Sue
B. ambitious Nick and assertive Lucy
C. warm Mike and independent Jan
D. competitive Rob and nurturant Jane

(22) Answer C, Type FAC, Reference 199
In every known society, men, relative to women
A. have poorer vocabularies.
B. are more communitarian.
C. are socially dominant.
D. have higher self-esteem.

(23) Answer D, Type FAC, Reference 199
In group situations, men are more likely than women to
A. interrupt others.
B. smile less.
C. touch with the hand.
D. All of the above.

(24) Answer A, Type FAC, Reference 200
Research on gender differences indicates that
A. throughout the world hunting and fishing are primarily men's activities.
B. in some parts of the world women are as likely to murder women as men are to murder men.
C. in Canada, the male-to-female arrest rate for murder is 3 to 1.
D. All of the above.

(25) Answer D, Type FAC, Reference 200
Research on sexual behavior indicates that
A. in their physiological and subjective responses to sexual stimuli, women and men are "more similar that different."
B. males are more likely than females to initiate sexual activity.
C. about half as many men as women cite affection for the partner as a reason for first intercourse.
D. All of the above.

(26) Answer C, Type DEF, Reference 202

115

Evolutionary psychology studies how natural selection predisposes organisms to develop traits that
A.	give them the competitive advantages over other members of their species.
B.	are physically but not psychologically more "fit."
C.	predispose them to adapt to their environment.
D.	None of the above.

(27)	Answer A, Type FAC, Reference 202
In their theory and research, evolutionary psychologists emphasize the fact that
A.	common social tasks have resulted in members of the human species being more alike than different.
B.	different environments have resulted in members of the human species being more different than alike.
C.	the principle of natural selection explains the evolution of cultural differences but not the evolution of gender differences.
D.	the principle of natural selection operates very differently in humans from the way it does in animals.

(28)	Answer A, Type CON, Reference 202
Seven-year-old Mary says "Thank you" after opening each birthday present she receives because her family considers it to be proper behavior. This best illustrates the influence of a
A.	norm.
B.	schema.
C.	role.
D.	stereotype.

(29)	Answer D, Type FAC, Reference 202
The text suggests that social norms
A.	grease the social machinery.
B.	sometimes seem arbitrary and confining.
C.	may control us so successfully that we hardly sense their presence.
D.	All of the above.

(30)	Answer C, Type FAC, Reference 202
The incest taboo
A.	is very difficult for evolutionary psychologists to explain.
B.	is no longer considered a universal norm.
C.	is violated more often than psychologists once believed.
D.	All of the above.

(31)   Answer D, Type FAC, Reference 203
Roger Brown claims that a universal norm governs the tendency for
people to
A.   excuse themselves when they accidentally make physical contact with
strangers.
B.   avoid eye contact with people they do not know.
C.   feel indebted to a friend or relative who does them a favor.
D.   talk to higher-status people and strangers in the same respectful way.

(32)   Answer D, Type FAC, Reference 203
In languages that distinguish between the two forms of "you," the familiar form
is used with _____ and the respectful form is used with _____.
A.   children; adults
B.   intimates; strangers
C.   inferiors; superiors
D.   All of the above.

(33)   Answer C, Type CON, Reference 204
Which of the following illustrates a violation of Roger Brown's universal norm?
A.   Peter and Millicent, who are first cousins, get married.
B.   Veronica often stares at strangers she passes on the street.
C.   The first week of his new job as janitor, Joel invites the office
administrator over for dinner.
D.   On their first date, Les offers Marty a bite of her dessert.

(34)   Answer C, Type FAC, Reference 204
When a 1990 Gallup survey asked respondents whether upbringing or biology
accounted for gender differences,
A.   most said "upbringing."
B.   most said "biology."
C.   nearly equal numbers said "upbringing" and "biology."
D.   most men said "biology," and most women said "upbringing."

(35)   Answer B, Type FAC, Reference 205
Evolutionary psychologists suggest that males are sexually assertive while females
are more selective of sexual partners because
A.   worldwide, males outnumber females.
B.   each strategy is likely to promote gene survival.
C.   males and females are socialized differently.
D.   of differences in brain chemistry.

(36)   Answer A, Type FAC, Reference 206
Studies in 37 cultures of women's and men's mate preferences reveal that
A.   women preferred men with resources and status while men preferred women with physical features suggesting fertility.
B.   men preferred women with resources and status while women preferred men with physical features suggesting fertility.
C.   both men and women preferred mates with resources and status.
D.   both men and women preferred mates with physical features suggesting fertility.

(37)   Answer B, Type CON, Reference 206
Given their present analysis of gender differences, evolutionary psychologists would have greatest difficulty explaining why
A.   a young man would engage in casual sex with many female partners.
B.   a young woman would engage in casual sex with many male partners.
C.   a woman would prefer to marry a man who is slightly older than herself.
D.   a woman would rather marry a man who is wealthy than one who is physically attractive.

(38)   Answer B, Type FAC, Reference 208
National Football League players have been found to have higher than normal levels of
A.   blood glucose.
B.   testosterone.
C.   progesterone.
D.   endorphins.

(39)   Answer A, Type FAC, Reference 208
From courtship through early parenthood to middle age, gender differences in personality
A.   decrease.
B.   increase.
C.   remain stable.
D.   first decrease and then increase.

(40)   Answer A, Type FAC, Reference 208
A person who is both _____ would be considered androgynous.
A.   assertive and nurturant
B.   intelligent and athletic
C.   moral and competent

D.   good and evil

(41)   Answer C, Type CON, Reference 208
Cameron has qualities like assertiveness, a traditionally masculine trait, as well as nurturance, a quality associated with traditional femininity. Cameron could be described as
A.   gender-ambivalent.
B.   role-conflicted.
C.   androgynous.
D.   gender-diffused.

(42)   Answer B, Type FAC, Reference 209
Evolutionary explanations of gender differences have been criticized because they
A.   underestimate the role of genetic factors.
B.   do not explain cultural changes in behavior that occur over relatively short periods of time.
C.   deny the role of hormonal factors.
D.   rely too heavily on the experimental method in formulating and testing hypotheses.

(43)   Answer A, Type FAC, Reference 210
Evolutionary psychology has been criticized for
A.   hindsight bias.
B.   unethical treatment of human subjects.
C.   use of unrepresentative samples.
D.   functional fixedness.

(44)   Answer D, Type FAC, Reference 211
Compared to people from a Mediterranean culture, those from a northern European culture are likely to be _____ expressive and _____ punctual.
A.   more; more
B.   less; less
C.   more; less
D.   less; more

(45)   Answer C, Type DEF, Reference 211
The buffer zone we like to maintain around our bodies is called
A.   private territory.
B.   protective covering.
C.   personal space.
D.   intimacy quotient.

(46)   Answer B, Type CON, Reference 211
Although there are many unoccupied tables in the restaurant, Rudolph decides to sit at the same table in the chair right next to James. James feels uncomfortable because Rudolph has violated
A.   his social role.
B.   his personal space.
C.   Brown's universal norm.
D.   the personal rights taboo.

(47)   Answer A, Type FAC, Reference 212
Research indicates that _____ prefer more personal space than do _____.
A.   Scandinavians; French
B.   Latin Americans; Americans
C.   French; British
D.   Arabs; Americans

(48)   Answer C, Type FAC, Reference 212
A pervasive culture difference arises from social values that stress either individual control and achievement or
A.   personal helplessness.
B.   human rights.
C.   social solidarity.
D.   personal morality and altruism.

(49)   Answer D, Type FAC, Reference 213
Western industrialized cultures typically value _____, while Asian and third-world cultures place a great value on _____.
A.   morality; power
B.   cooperation; competence
C.   duty; self-fulfillment
D.   individualism; collectivism

(50)   Answer A, Type CON, Reference 213
Individualism is to _____ as collectivism is to _____.
A.   self-reliance; social duty
B.   wisdom; power
C.   family security; world peace
D.   work; leisure

(51) Answer C, Type FAC, Reference 214
In comparison to collectivists, individualists are more likely to emphasize the importance of
A.   cooperation.
B.   interdependence.
C.   personal well-being.
D.   social expectations.

(52) Answer B, Type FAC, Reference 214
A willingness to leave jobs, homes, and churches in search of better opportunities is most clearly one of the consequences of
A.   collectivism.
B.   individualism.
C.   communitarianism.
D.   socialism.

(53) Answer C, Type CON, Reference 214
Which of the following advertising appeals is more likely to be used in a collectivist culture than in an individualist culture?
A.   "She's got a style all her own."
B.   "Your deserve a break today."
C.   "We have a way of bringing people closer together."
D.   "You only live once--so enjoy yourself."

(54) Answer B, Type FAC, Reference 215
Child rearing in a collectivist culture is especially likely to emphasize the importance of
A.   nonconformity.
B.   cooperation.
C.   personal achievement.
D.   values clarification.

(55) Answer D, Type FAC, Reference 215
Which of the following does not describe the social relations characteristic of people in collectivist cultures?
A.   During the day they talk with fewer people for longer periods of time.
B.   They show respect and allow others to save face.
C.   They avoid blunt honesty and stay away from touchy topics.
D.   They warn against the dangers of stereotyping and prefer not to judge people by their backgrounds and affiliations.

(56)   Answer A, Type FAC, Reference 215
Compared to those in a collectivist culture, those in an individualist culture are more likely to be judged on the basis of their
A.   physical attractiveness.
B.   gender.
C.   family background.
D.   educational background.

(57)   Answer D, Type FAC, Reference 216
According to research by Triandis, Brislin, and Hui, which of the following would not be good advice to individualists visiting collectivist cultures?
A.   Avoid confrontation.
B.   Pay attention to people's positions in their group hierarchies.
C.   Let them know your own social position.
D.   Get right to business.

(58)   Answer D, Type FAC, Reference 216
People living in a culture that values individualism are more likely than those in collectivist cultures to experience
A.   loneliness.
B.   stress-related disease.
C.   divorce.
D.   All of the above.

(59)   Answer A, Type FAC, Reference 216
Compared to people living in individualist cultures, those in collectivist cultures are likely to experience _____ depression and _____ privacy.
A.   less; less
B.   less; more
C.   more; less
D.   more; more

(60)   Answer B, Type DEF, Reference 217
The attempt to balance individual rights with the collective right to communal well-being is referred to as
A.   communism.
B.   communitarianism.
C.   collective synergy.
D.   responsible totalitarianism.

(61)   Answer A, Type FAC, Reference 217

"Liberty, equality, and fraternity" best reflects the perspective of
A. communitarianism.
B. individualism.
C. collectivism.
D. fascism.

(62) Answer C, Type FAC, Reference 218
Britain's attempt to strengthen the individual incentives of a free market economy while restricting individual rights of gun ownership is clearly consistent with the goals of
A. individualism.
B. collectivism.
C. communitarianism.
D. egalitarianism.

(63) Answer D, Type DEF, Reference 219
A _____ is a set of norms that defines how people in a given social position ought to behave.
A. role
B. social status
C. tradition
D. performance standard

(64) Answer C, Type CON, Reference 219
Which of the following is least likely to be regarded as a social role?
A. student
B. husband
C. typist
D. mother

(65) Answer D, Type DEF, Reference 219
It takes a whole cluster of _____ to define a role.
A. traditions
B. relationships
C. positions
D. norms

(66) Answer B, Type FAC, Reference 219
The more you occupy and internalize a role,
A. the more socially awkward you may feel.
B. the less self-conscious you feel.

C. the more discrepant your attitudes and actions become.
D. All of the above.

(67) Answer A, Type FAC, Reference 219
The changes undergone by heiress-turned-revolutionary Patricia Hearst in the early 1970s illustrate the power exerted by situations in defining roles. Commenting on this phenomenon, social psychologist Philip Brickman notes, "Nowhere is social psychology farther apart from public consciousness than in its understanding of _____."
A. how things become real for people.
B. the destructiveness of which humans are capable.
C. the differences between being rich and poor.
D. the pervasiveness of social class in one's consciousness.

(68) Answer D, Type FAC, Reference 220
In many everyday and laboratory situations, people assigned a superior status come to see themselves as
A. overwhelmed by responsibilities that detract from the quality of life.
B. underqualified and in jeopardy of losing their position.
C. having a special obligation to follow the social responsibility norm.
D. superior performers who merit favorable treatment.

(69) Answer B, Type FAC, Reference 220
After Ronald Humphrey randomly assigned the roles of managers and clerks to participants in a simulated business office, both clerks and managers agreed that
A. the clerks' positions were more challenging and leaderlike.
B. the managers had been more intelligent, assertive, and supportive.
C. each thought the other's role was the more difficult one.
D. status differences only interfered with their work, and business did better when they ignored role divisions.

(70) Answer A, Type FAC, Reference 220
Pairs of New York City women first solved arithmetic problems as individuals and then worked together on additional problems, with one of the women designated "boss" and the other "assistant." When the women returned to working individually, the former "bosses" now solved _____ problems and the former "assistants" solved _____ problems than they had in the first round.
A. more; fewer
B. fewer; more
C. more; more

D.   fewer; fewer

(71)   Answer C, Type FAC, Reference 220
Having people play a demeaning role seems to undermine their feelings of
A.   individualism.
B.   collectivism.
C.   self-efficacy.
D.   empathy.

(72)   Answer C, Type FAC, Reference 220
According to the text, role reversal can
A.   increase conflict between partners.
B.   lead to a loss of self-efficacy.
C.   be used to improve communication and understanding.
D.   make role conflict more severe.

(73)   Answer B, Type DEF, Reference 222
A set of behavior expectations for males or females defines a gender
A.   type.
B.   role.
C.   identity.
D.   position.

(74)   Answer B, Type FAC, Reference 222
From studies of gender differences worldwide, it would seem that gender
socialization gives girls _____ and boys _____.
A.   "arms"; "legs"
B.   "roots"; "wings"
C.   "feet"; "hands"
D.   "ears"; "eyes"

(75)   Answer A, Type FAC, Reference 222
Compared to boys, girls spend more time _____ and less time
_____.
A.   helping with housework; in unsupervised play
B.   in unsupervised play; in school
C.   helping with child care; helping with housework
D.   playing; working

(76)   Answer A, Type FAC, Reference 222
When Zanna and Pack led women to believe that they would meet an attractive,

unattached, nonsexist man who liked strong, ambitious women, the women
A.   behaved more intelligently and solved more problems.
B.   presented themselves in "traditionally feminine" terms.
C.   experienced a great deal of conflict over how they should present themselves.
D.   denigrated him as being probably not very attractive at all.

(77)   Answer B, Type FAC, Reference 223
When Williams, Best, and their collaborators asked university students in 14 cultures questions such as "Should women do the housework?" and "Should women be more concerned with promoting their husband's career than their own?" they found that in nearly every culture women students had _____ egalitarian views than their male peers.
A.   significantly more
B.   slightly more
C.   slightly less
D.   significantly less

(78)   Answer A, Type FAC, Reference 223
Gender roles are more distinct in _____ societies than in _____ societies.
A.   agricultural; nomadic, food-gathering
B.   nomadic, food-gathering; industrialized
C.   industrialized; agricultural
D.   pastoral; agrarian

(79)   Answer A, Type FAC, Reference 224
Which of the following is <u>true</u> of American gender roles?
A.   Since 1970, increasing numbers of women have been training to become lawyers, doctors, and dentists.
B.   In 1993, only a minority of Americans still stated that the "ideal family situation" is one in which "father has a job and mother stays home and cares for the children."
C.   From 1965 to 1985, the proportion of housework done by men remained constant.
D.   All of the above.

(80)   Answer B, Type FAC, Reference 225
According to the text, what term best describes the relationship between biology and culture?
A.   competition

B.   interaction
C.   interpolation
D.   reciprocation

(81)   Answer C, Type CON, Reference 225
If the presence of others improves performance on easy tasks but hinders
performance on difficult tasks, the presence of others and task difficulty are said
to
A.   compete.
B.   accentuate.
C.   interact.
D.   interpolate.

(82)   Answer D, Type FAC, Reference 226
A very strong cultural norm dictates that males should be taller than their female
mates. This height norm is cited in your text as evidence that
A.   relationship behavior is influenced more by biology than culture.
B.   gender roles are essentially cultural and thus completely arbitrary.
C.   what is biologically "fit" may be culturally disastrous.
D.   biology and culture interact to develop gender-role norms.

(83)   Answer A, Type FAC, Reference 226
In her book Sex Differences in Social Behavior, Alice Eagly theorizes that in
adult life, the immediate causes of gender differences in social behavior are
A.   the roles that reflect a sexual division of labor.
B.   biologically-based differences in power and aggressiveness.
C.   learned habits reinforced by social rewards like affection.
D.   rules and laws that legislate and maintain the status quo.

(84)   Answer D, Type FAC, Reference 227
What conclusion does the text reach regarding the relationship between persons
and situations?
A.   Individuals vary in how they interpret and react to a given situation.
B.   People choose many of the situations that influence them.
C.   People often create their social situations.
D.   All of the above.

(85)   Answer B, Type FAC, Reference 228
In the final analysis, the text suggests that it is wisest for us to view ourselves as
_____ and others as _____.
A.   influenced by our environments; free agents

127

B.   free agents; influenced by their environments
C.   free agents; free agents
D.   influenced by our environments; influenced by their environments

THE FOLLOWING ITEMS ALSO APPEAR IN THE STUDY GUIDE:

(86)   Answer B, Type DEF, Reference 202
Norms, according to the text,
A.   are composed of a set of roles.
B.   prescribe proper behavior.
C.   are social behaviors of typical or average people.
D.   are laws that govern the distribution of social rewards.

(87)   Answer C, Type FAC, Reference 202
Which of the following is true?
A.   There are really no truly universal norms.
B.   Religion does not exist in some societies.
C.   Norms can liberate us from preoccupation with what we are saying and
        doing.
D.   A "pedestrian" would be an example of a role.

(88)   Answer D, Type FAC, Reference 203
Which of the following friendship norms seems to be universal?
A.   Respect the friend's privacy.
B.   Make eye contact while talking.
C.   Don't divulge things said in confidence.
D.   All of the above.

(89)   Answer C, Type DEF, Reference 195
The study of how natural selection predisposes adaptive traits and behavior is
called
A.   behavioral genetics.
B.   biological behaviorism.
C.   evolutionary psychology.
D.   genetic psychology.

(90)   Answer D, Type FAC, Reference 198
Research indicates that a gender difference exists in
A.   vocabulary.
B.   intelligence.
C.   age at which infants walk.

D.   smiling.

(91)   Answer A, Type FAC, Reference 196
A noticeable difference has <u>not</u> been found between males and females in
A.   happiness.
B.   judging emotion on people's faces.
C.   suicide rate.
D.   frequency of smiling.

(92)   Answer B, Type FAC, Reference 208
Research on possible hormonal influences on aggression has indicated that
A.   testosterone levels influence animal aggression but not human aggression.
B.   violent male criminals have higher than normal testosterone levels.
C.   gender differences in aggression are clearly unrelated to hormonal differences.
D.   administering testosterone reduces aggression in most animals.

(93)   Answer C, Type FAC, Reference 212
Who among the following maintain the least personal space?
A.   British
B.   Americans
C.   Arabs
D.   Scandinavians

(94)   Answer A, Type FAC, Reference 198
A study of Australian married couples found that marital satisfaction was highest when
A.   both partners possessed feminine traits.
B.   both partners possessed androgynous traits.
C.   both partners possessed masculine traits.
D.   the male possessed feminine traits and the female possessed masculine traits.

(95)   Answer B, Type FAC, Reference 227
Which of the following terms best describes the relationship between persons and situations?
A.   indeterminate
B.   interactive
C.   attributional
D.   biocultural

(96)	Answer B, Type CON, Reference 204
Which of the following illustrates Roger Brown's "universal norm"?
A.	Brothers do not have sexual relations with their sisters in Daneria.
B.	The King of Sindab invites subjects to his castle for dinner before they invite him to their huts for dinner.
C.	Friends in Transylvania do not divulge things said in confidence.
D.	Males rather than females initiate sexual relations in Wallonia.

(97)	Answer A, Type CON, Reference 208
William is gentle and affectionate with his children but independent and assertive in running his business. What term best describes his personality?
A.	Androgynous
B.	Gender diffused
C.	Gender schematic
D.	Interrole patterned

(98)	Answer A, Type CON, Reference 202
"Drivers are expected to keep to the right on a two-lane road" would be an example of what the text calls a
A.	norm.
B.	role.
C.	position.
D.	status.

(99)	Answer B, Type CON, Reference 219
Which of the following would be least likely to be considered a role?
A.	College president
B.	Bicyclist
C.	Father
D.	Wife

(100)	Answer D, Type CON, Reference 217
Herman is a middle-aged attorney who supports legislation that would restrict gun ownership and restrain violent pornography. At the same time, he strongly supports a free market economy and wants to see new incentives for individuals to set up small businesses. Herman's attitudes seem to reflect a(n)
_____ orientation.
A.	collectivistic
B.	communistic
C.	individualistic
D.	communitarian

CHAPTER SEVEN: CONFORMITY

<u>Multiple Choice</u>

(1)   Answer B, Type FAC, Reference 232
American and European psychologists view going along with group pressure in such a way that they customarily refer to it with all <u>except</u> which of the following terms?
A.   conformity
B.   cooperation
C.   compliance
D.   submission

(2)   Answer A, Type FAC, Reference 232
In Japan, going along with others is a sign of
A.   maturity.
B.   mindlessness.
C.   incompetence.
D.   irresponsibility.

(3)   Answer A, Type DEF, Reference 233
_____ is a change in behavior or belief as a result of real or imagined group pressure.
A.   Conformity
B.   Consensus
C.   Obedience
D.   Submission

(4)   Answer B, Type DEF, Reference 233
Conformity that involves publicly acting in accord with social pressure while privately disagreeing is called
A.   acceptance.
B.   compliance.
C.   mindlessness.
D.   reactance.

(5)   Answer A, Type DEF, Reference 233
Conformity that involves both acting and believing in accord with social pressure is called
A.   acceptance.
B.   cooperation.

C. compliance.
D. social sensitivity.

(6)   Answer D, Type CON, Reference 233
Sincere inward conformity is to _____ as insincere outward conformity is to
_____.
A. acceptance; reactance
B. reactance; submission
C. obedience; compliance
D. acceptance; compliance

(7)   Answer A, Type CON, Reference 233
Professor Jones hates to attend faculty meetings and does so merely to avoid the
disapproval of the college dean. Professor Jones's behavior reflects the process
of
A. compliance.
B. acceptance.
C. reactance.
D. informational social influence.

(8)   Answer B, Type CON, Reference 233
After hearing respected medical authorities lecture about the importance of
regular exercise, Heidi begins to jog regularly and finds she enjoys it. This
change in Heidi's behavior reflects the process of
A. compliance.
B. acceptance.
C. reactance.
D. social facilitation.

(9)   Answer D, Type CON, Reference 233
Denise disliked exercising but started attending an aerobics class at the urging of
her friends. She continued to attend, knowing they would give her a hard time if
she dropped out. Now her friends have dropped out, but Denise keeps going and
would not think of missing class. What principle does Denise's behavior
illustrate?
A. the boomerang effect
B. the foot-in-the-door principle
C. Acceptance can increase cohesion.
D. Acceptance sometimes follows compliance.

(10)   Answer B, Type FAC, Reference 233

132

If we have stood up for something, we usually become sympathetic to that position unless
A.   our position is controversial.
B.   we feel no responsibility for our behavior.
C.   our stand was made in public.
D.   our stand is already socially popular.

(11)   Answer C, Type FAC, Reference 235
In his classic study of _____, Sherif had subjects in groups call out estimates of the distance a small point of light appeared to move in a dark room.
A.   obedience
B.   group cohesiveness
C.   norm formation
D.   psychological reactance

(12)   Answer D, Type CON, Reference 235
At one time, aircraft had constant rather than blinking lights on the wingtips. When pilots in formation tried to follow the constant lights of the aircraft in front of them, they veered off course. This is perhaps best explained by
A.   illusory correlation.
B.   normative influence.
C.   psychological reactance.
D.   the autokinetic effect.

(13)   Answer B, Type DEF, Reference 235
The autokinetic effect refers to
A.   a false group consensus.
B.   an illusion of perceived movement.
C.   a form of self-efficacy.
D.   an influential bias in social judgment.

(14)   Answer A, Type FAC, Reference 235
In Muzafer Sherif's study, subjects concentrated on a small point of light in a dark room and called out estimates of the distance it had moved. As time passes, the subjects gave answers that
A.   converged.
B.   diverged.
C.   remained constant.
D.   first converged and then diverged.

(15)   Answer D, Type FAC, Reference 236

A year after his original study, Sherif's subjects were retested alone and gave answers that supported the original group's norm. This suggests that the process involved was really
A. reactance.
B. compliance.
C. obedience.
D. acceptance.

(16) Answer C, Type FAC, Reference 236
Jacobs and Campbell repeated the Sherif experiment and planted a confederate in the group who called out inflated estimates. Results showed that the confederate's influence
A. was minimized by his status as a deviant.
B. was temporary and vanished when the confederate was replaced.
C. persisted for several generations after the confederate had been replaced.
D. was greatest when the confederate was male.

(17) Answer B, Type FAC, Reference 236
In spring of 1954, Seattle residents were alarmed by widespread reports of damage by a mysterious windshield-pitting agent. The true cause of public concern was most likely
A. fallout from recent Pacific testing of the H-bomb.
B. mass suggestibility.
C. psychological reactance.
D. the autokinetic phenomenon.

(18) Answer D, Type FAC, Reference 236
Sociologist David Phillips and colleagues report that _____ increase after well-publicized and celebrity suicides.
A. suicides
B. private airplane crashes
C. fatal auto accidents
D. All of the above.

(19) Answer C, Type FAC, Reference 236
Solomon Asch's insights into conformity may have been inspired by a story he tells about being particularly susceptible to suggestion while participating in
A. a university commencement ceremony.
B. a psychology conference in a big city.
C. his family's traditional Jewish seder at Passover.
D. a famous experiment on obedience to authority.

(20)   Answer C, Type FAC, Reference 237
Solomon Asch's studies of conformity differ in important ways from those of
Muzafer Sherif because
A.   Asch's subjects faced a more ambiguous task.
B.   Sherif's subjects were dealing with facts rather than opinions.
C.   Asch's subjects could clearly see the correct judgment.
D.   Sherif's subjects were in the physical presence of the pressuring group
while Asch's subjects were not.

(21)   Answer B, Type FAC, Reference 237
While control subjects were correct about line-length judgments more than 99
percent of the time in Asch's conformity study, his naive subjects conformed to a
false consensus _____ of the time.
A.   12 percent
B.   37 percent
C.   65 percent
D.   87 percent

(22)   Answer B, Type FAC, Reference 238
Richard Crutchfield's variation on Asch's original experiment was different from
Asch's procedure because, in Crutchfield's study,
A.   all the subjects had above average IQ.
B.   all the group participants were real subjects.
C.   subjects judged matters of fact, not opinion.
D.   All of the above.

(23)   Answer D, Type FAC, Reference 239
Crutchfield's studies of conformity indicated that
A.   military officers are particularly resistant to group influence.
B.   only a group of real confederates who are unanimous in their false
judgments can influence a naive subject.
C.   people conform to a unanimous majority only on trivial issues.
D.   None of the above.

(24)   Answer D, Type FAC, Reference 239
The Sherif, Asch, and Crutchfield results are all startling because none of the
studies employed any
A.   judgments about ambiguous stimuli.
B.   groups larger than four persons.
C.   experimental realism.

D.   open, obvious pressure to conform.

(25)   Answer B, Type FAC, Reference 240
Commenting on the experiments conducted by _____, psychologist Lee Ross
notes, "Perhaps more than any other empirical contributions in the history of
social science, they have become part of our society's shared, intellectual legacy,"
a classic work with important revelations about human nature.
A.   Asch
B.   Milgram
C.   Sherif
D.   Crutchfield

(26)   Answer C, Type FAC, Reference 240
Subjects in Stanley Milgram's famous experiment believed they were required to
administer electric shocks as part of a study of
A.   obedience to authority.
B.   group conformity.
C.   learning and memory.
D.   violence and aggression.

(27)   Answer B, Type FAC, Reference 241
The experimenter in Milgram's study used all but which of the following verbal
prods to encourage subjects to continue?
A.   "It is absolutely essential that you continue."
B.   "You will be penalized if you refuse to go on."
C.   "You have no other choice, you must go on."
D.   "The experiment requires that you continue."

(28)   Answer B, Type FAC, Reference 241
When Milgram asked 100 psychiatrists, college students, and middle-class adults
to predict the results of his experiment, the respondents said that they thought
_____ would _____.
A.   they themselves; never begin to administer shock
B.   they themselves; disobey by about 135 volts
C.   other people; disobey by about 210 volts
D.   other people; would go all the way to 450 volts

(29)   Answer C, Type FAC, Reference 242
When Milgram conducted his first series of experiments with a sample of 20- to
50-year-old men, he found that over 60 percent of them
A.   refused to deliver shocks beyond 150 volts.

136

B.   refused to deliver shocks past the 300-volt level.
C.   went clear to 450 volts.
D.   asked to be released from the experiment by 135 volts.

(30)   Answer A, Type FAC, Reference 242
In a follow-up series of experiments after his initial study, Milgram made the learner's protests more compelling by having him complain of a heart condition, then scream and plead for release, and finally refuse to answer. With this added condition,
A.   most subjects still fully obeyed the experimenter's demands.
B.   teachers were more reluctant to deliver initial shocks.
C.   learners became more real and personal to the teacher.
D.   fewer subjects went to 450 volts.

(31)   Answer A, Type FAC, Reference 243
When the subjects in Milgram's studies were surveyed afterward about their participation in the obedience experiment, most said
A.   they did not regret having participated.
B.   they deeply regretted having participated.
C.   they were glad to have helped but felt the study should never be repeated.
D.   they experienced guilt over their actions as subjects.

(32)   Answer D, Type FAC, Reference 243
Which of the following was found to be a factor that influenced obedience in Milgram's research?
A.   the victim's emotional distance
B.   the closeness of the authority
C.   the presence of other defiant teachers
D.   All of the above.

(33)   Answer C, Type FAC, Reference 243
When Milgram varied his experiment so that teachers had to physically force the learner's hand onto a shock plate in order to administer punishment, compliance to the experimenter's orders
A.   dropped to almost zero.
B.   dropped to 10 percent.
C.   dropped to 30 percent.
D.   actually increased to almost 80 percent.

(34)   Answer D, Type FAC, Reference 243
It is easiest to debase someone who is

A.   a close, convenient target.
B.   in range of physical contact.
C.   personalized.
D.   distant and anonymous.

(35)   Answer B, Type CON, Reference 244
From the results of Milgram's studies that manipulated the distance between teacher and learner, one could conclude that
A.   it would be more disturbing to ignore many people starving in a foreign land than a single neighbor who needs food.
B.   it would be more disturbing to kill another with one's bare hands than with a gun.
C.   ironically it may be more difficult to dehumanize a stranger than a close friend.
D.   group cohesiveness breeds aggression.

(36)   Answer B, Type FAC, Reference 244
In Milgram's research, when the experimenter gave the commands by telephone instead of in person, full obedience
A.   dropped to zero.
B.   dropped to 21 percent.
C.   dropped to 50 percent.
D.   increased to 73 percent.

(37)   Answer A, Type FAC, Reference 244
Research shows that when people are given a _____, they are more likely to lend a dime, sign a petition, or sample a new pizza.
A.   light touch on the arm
B.   handwritten rather than a typed letter
C.   letter rather than a telephone call
D.   sense of anonymity

(38)   Answer A, Type FAC, Reference 244
In order for a person to be more willing to obey authoritative orders that conflict with his or her own personal standards,
A.   the authority must be perceived as legitimate.
B.   the probable victims must be as close as possible.
C.   the authority figure must be as distant as possible.
D.   All of the above.

(39)   Answer D, Type FAC, Reference 245

In one variation on his original experiment, Milgram arranged for a confederate to pose as a fellow subject in the group and to assume command in the experimenter's absence. As a result of this manipulation,
A.   most teachers agreed to comply with the orders of their fellow group member.
B.   the teachers competed with him and with each other for the role of leader.
C.   subjects became more positive about their roles in this cohesive group, and some even became enthusiastic.
D.   80 percent of the teachers refused to comply fully.

(40)   Answer D, Type FAC, Reference 245
In a study by Hofling and colleagues, 22 hospital nurses were telephoned by an unknown physician and ordered to administer an obvious drug overdose. Results showed that
A.   most would not act on the order unless the caller named a familiar physician as reference.
B.   most nurses refused to comply unless given the order in writing.
C.   less experienced nurses complied but more experienced ones challenged the order.
D.   all but one proceeded to comply without delay.

(41)   Answer B, Type FAC, Reference 246
When Milgram's experimental series was reenacted in Bridgeport, Connecticut, far from the prestige and authority of Yale University, the proportion of subjects who fully complied with orders to shock the learner _____ compared to the Yale rate.
A.   remained unchanged
B.   decreased to 48 percent
C.   decreased to 25 percent
D.   decreased to 10 percent

(42)   Answer B, Type FAC, Reference 246
When Milgram assigned two confederates to act as fellow teachers with a third teacher, the real subject, and then had the two confederates defy the experimenter, the presence of defiant peers
A.   pressured the subject to comply more fully with the experimenter's orders.
B.   led 90 percent of the subjects to also disregard the experimenter.
C.   led 60 percent of the subjects to also disregard the experimenter.
D.   made it easier for subjects to feel anonymous while shocking the learner.

(43)   Answer D, Type FAC, Reference 244

In Milgram's research, subjects were most likely to obey the experimenter's commands when the experimenter was _____ and the victim was _____.
A.   distant; distant
B.   close; close
C.   distant; close
D.   close; distant

(44)   Answer A, Type FAC, Reference 247
As demonstrated by the classic experiments on conformity, one reason our attitudes often fail to determine our behavior is that
A.   external influences sometimes override inner convictions.
B.   we seldom have attitudes or values about the behaviors in question.
C.   the behaviors in question are so trivial that we really do not have attitudes about them.
D.   attitudes are not specific to the behavior in question.

(45)   Answer D, Type FAC, Reference 248
The increments in voltage indicated by the labeled switches of the shock generator suggest that, in Milgram's obedience research, the teachers' behavior was influenced by
A.   psychological reactance.
B.   the availability heuristic.
C.   the fundamental attribution error.
D.   the foot-in-the-door principle.

(46)   Answer A, Type FAC, Reference 249
Milgram and Sabini had students ask New York subway riders to give up their seats. Results showed that
A.   most riders complied, even when no justification was given.
B.   most complied if given a reasonable justification for doing so.
C.   female but not male riders were slightly more likely to comply.
D.   newcomers to New York complied but not native New Yorkers.

(47)   Answer B, Type FAC, Reference 250
The text suggests that in our everyday lives, the experience of _____ illustrates an unintended drift toward self-harm, similar to the same incremental action experienced by Milgram's subjects and the German civil servants who worked for the Nazis.
A.   mistrust
B.   procrastination
C.   overeating

D.   social rejection

(48)   Answer B, Type FAC, Reference 251
To believe that Milgram's compliant subjects were particularly aggressive people is
A.   a correct inference.
B.   to commit the fundamental attribution error.
C.   to ignore the power of behavior to shape attitudes.
D.   to ignore the strength of positive character traits.

(49)   Answer C, Type FAC, Reference 252
According to Milgram, the most fundamental lesson to be learned from his study of obedience is that
A.   people are naturally inclined to be hostile and aggressive.
B.   the desire to be right is one of the strongest human motives.
C.   even ordinary people, who are not particularly hostile, can become agents of destruction.
D.   people value their freedom and uniqueness and react negatively when it is taken from them.

(50)   Answer B, Type FAC, Reference 253
Which of the following is not one of the factors that has been found to significantly influence one's conformity to the group?
A.   requiring the individual's response to be made in public
B.   increasing the size of the group from 6 to 10 members
C.   increasing the attractiveness of the group
D.   having the group's agreement be unanimous rather than reflect some disagreement

(51)   Answer A, Type FAC, Reference 253
In a study by Milgram, Bachman, and Berkowitz, groups of people paused on a busy New York sidewalk and looked up. As the size of the original group grew from _____ people, the percentage of passers-by who also looked up increased.
A.   1 to 5
B.   5 to 10
C.   10 to 15
D.   All of the above.

(52)   Answer A, Type DEF, Reference 253
Bibb Latané's _____ theory proposes that social influence increases with the immediacy and size of the group.

A.   social impact
B.   individuation
C.   reactance
D.   elaboration likelihood

(53)   Answer B, Type FAC, Reference 254
Research on group size and conformity has shown that
A.   as group size increases, conformity decreases.
B.   two groups of three persons elicit more conformity than one group of six persons.
C.   group size influences conformity in teenagers but not in adults.
D.   the conformity of females is more significantly influenced by group size than is the conformity of males.

(54)   Answer C, Type FAC, Reference 254
According to conformity research, a group's social power is deflated when it loses its
A.   agenda.
B.   anonymity.
C.   unanimity.
D.   heterogeneity.

(55)   Answer D, Type FAC, Reference 255
A practical lesson of much conformity research is that it is easier to stand up for something if you
A.   believe the matter is trivial.
B.   do so all at once instead of paving the way with smaller actions and hints.
C.   go it alone and face the criticism independently.
D.   get someone else to stand up with you.

(56)   Answer B, Type FAC, Reference 255
It is hard to disagree in _____ groups because we don't want the other members to _____.
A.   large; notice us
B.   close-knit; reject us
C.   problem-solving; ignore us
D.   work; loaf

(57)   Answer B, Type FAC, Reference 256
In Milgram's original studies of obedience, he found that subjects who were _____ were most likely to be obedient and deferential.

142

A.   the victims of past abuse
B.   of low status
C.   female
D.   professionals used to giving orders

(58)   Answer A, Type FAC, Reference 256
In experiments, people have been found to conform more when they must _____ than when they are allowed to _____.
A.   respond publicly; write down their responses in private
B.   commit themselves in writing; announce their responses in public
C.   think before acting; react spontaneously
D.   explain their responses; keep silent

(59)   Answer D, Type FAC, Reference 257
In a variation on the Asch experiments, you announce your answer to a question but you do so before anyone else in the group has a chance to respond. All the subsequent responses disagree with yours. Now you have a chance to reconsider and possibly change your answer. According to research, you will probably
A.   question the procedure and ask to be last in line next time.
B.   modify your response so that it comes closer to everyone else's but is still different.
C.   tell yourself privately that you were right the first time but publicly change your response.
D.   stick to your original answer.

(60)   Answer D, Type FAC, Reference 257
In calling sports decisions, umpires and referees rarely change their decisions as a result of a player's objection. This may be an example of how
A.   status produces psychological reactance.
B.   a we-they feeling has evolved between professional sports players and officials.
C.   the umpire or referee seeks to maintain emotional distance from players.
D.   public commitment reduces susceptibility to social influence.

(61)   Answer D, Type FAC, Reference 257
When simulated juries make decisions, _____ are more likely to occur when jurors are polled by a show of hands rather than by secret ballot.
A.   acquittals
B.   convictions
C.   death sentences
D.   hung juries

(62) Answer B, Type CON, Reference 256

Once the President has announced his position on a major foreign policy matter, he is unlikely to change his mind. This most likely reflects the fact

A. of we-they polarity between the political parties.
B. that public commitment reduces susceptibility to social influence.
C. that the high status of the office elicits a need for uniqueness.
D. that higher-status people are more susceptible to psychological reactance.

(63) Answer D, Type DEF, Reference 259

_____ influence is based on a person's desire to be _____.

A. Normative; correct
B. Informational; accepted
C. Informational; respected
D. Normative; accepted

(64) Answer B, Type DEF, Reference 259

_____ influence is based on a person's desire to be _____.

A. Normative; correct
B. Informational; correct
C. Informational; accepted
D. Normative; unique

(65) Answer D, Type CON, Reference 259

Normative social influence is to the need to be _____ as informational social influence is to the need to be _____.

A. unique; free
B. accepted; unique
C. free; correct
D. accepted; correct

(66) Answer C, Type CON, Reference 259

Dr. Jennings hates to wear a suit to teach his classes. Nevertheless he does so to win the approval of the senior faculty at his institution. Dr. Jennings' behavior is an example of

A. identification.
B. informational social influence.
C. normative social influence.
D. acceptance.

(67) Answer A, Type CON, Reference 259

144

Jodi wears slacks or jeans almost all the time, rejecting skirts and dresses as too formal and sexist. However, when she is invited to attend an honors reception, she borrows a skirt to wear so she will fit in with the other guests. This is an example of
A.   normative social influence.
B.   self-efficacy.
C.   psychological reactance.
D.   informational social influence

(68)   Answer C, Type FAC, Reference 259
Commenting on the pervasiveness of _____, President John F. Kennedy once remarked that, when he first joined Congress, he was told that "the way to get along is to go along."
A.   reactance
B.   acceptance
C.   normative influence
D.   consensual validation

(69)   Answer A, Type CON, Reference 260
Normative influence commonly leads to _____, while informational influence leads to _____.
A.   compliance; acceptance
B.   acceptance; compliance
C.   persuasion; reactance
D.   reactance; consensus

(70)   Answer B, Type CON, Reference 260
You see a person lying in the street in apparent discomfort. Unsure of whether he needs help, you observe that while other people notice him, no one else stops to offer help. Because no one else stops, you conclude that he must not need help but is probably only drunk. Your decision shows the effects of
A.   normative social influence.
B.   informational social influence.
C.   compliance.
D.   the boomerang effect.

(71)   Answer C, Type FAC, Reference 261
Eagly and Wood believe that gender differences in conformity may actually be a product of
A.   sexism on the part of researchers who expect it to occur.
B.   hormonal influences and unlearned predispositions.

145

C.   men's and women's typical social roles.
D.   feelings of intimidation by males' greater physical power.

(72)   Answer C, Type FAC, Reference 261
The conclusion of conformity research conducted in the 1960s and 1970s seemed
to be that, if you wanted to know how conforming or aggressive or helpful
someone was going to be, you should find out
A.   person's age and gender.
B.   person's scores on a battery of psychological tests.
C.   details of the situation the person was in.
D.   attitudes of the person's closest friends.

(73)   Answer D, Type FAC, Reference 262
Personality predicts behavior better than situational forces do when
A.   researchers are studying a diverse variety of individuals.
B.   the trait is specific to a particular situation.
C.   social influences are generally weak.
D.   All of the above.

(74)   Answer A, Type FAC, Reference 263
According to research by Ickes, Monson, and others, when the influence of the
situation is _____, the consequent behavior is likely to be a result of _____.
A.   weak; individual personalities
B.   weak; external circumstances
C.   strong; internal forces
D.   strong; dispositions

(75)   Answer C, Type FAC, Reference 263
According to theorist Kurt Lewin, "every psychological event" depends on
A.   cultural filtering.
B.   learned behavior patterns.
C.   both the person and the environment.
D.   instinctive emotional predispositions.

(76)   Answer D, Type FAC, Reference 264
Which of the following statements about cross-cultural research on conformity is
true?
A.   Findings using the Asch procedure have found similar conformity rates in
most countries, except among the Bantu of Zimbabwe, a tribe with strong
sanctions against nonconformity.
B.   When Milgram compared the conformity of French and Norwegian

students, the Norwegians consistently conformed more.
C.   Recent conformity studies in Britain, Canada, and the United States have indicated less conformity than was observed two or three decades ago.
D.   All of the above.

(77)   Answer A, Type CON, Reference 264
Euro-American cultures are to _____ as Asian cultures are to _____.
A.   individualism; collectivism
B.   conformity; reactance
C.   acceptance; compliance
D.   mundane realism; experimental realism

(78)   Answer B, Type FAC, Reference 264
Compared to people in individualistic countries, those in collectivist countries are
A.   more likely to express psychological reactance.
B.   more responsive to others' influence.
C.   more susceptible to the fundamental attribution error.
D.   None of the above.

(79)   Answer B, Type FAC, Reference 265
When social pressure threatens a person's sense of _____, he or she is likely to rebel.
A.   belonging
B.   freedom
C.   achievement
D.   meaning or purpose in life

(80)   Answer D, Type CON, Reference 265
High school students Chas and Marnie have been dating each other casually. When Marnie's parents urge her to stop seeing Chas and ask her to go out with "nicer boys," Marnie announces that she and Chas are actually "in love" and have decided to go steady. Marnie's behavior most likely illustrates the effects of
A.   the false uniqueness effect.
B.   the fundamental attribution error.
C.   the self-serving bias.
D.   psychological reactance.

(81)   Answer C, Type CON, Reference 266
The theory of psychological reactance would advise parents who wish to keep their children from taking up the habit of smoking cigarettes that their best

strategy would be to

A.   threaten their children with severe punishment if they are ever caught smoking.

B.   promise large rewards to their children for not smoking.

C.   explain why they are opposed to smoking and then allow their children to decide for themselves whether they will smoke or not.

D.   forbid their children to see, talk about, or have any contact with cigarettes or other tobacco products.

(82)   Answer B, Type FAC, Reference 267
In research by Snyder and Fromkin and others, subjects who heard others express attitudes that were identical to their own

A.   experienced an increase in their own self-esteem.

B.   altered their own attitudes to seem different.

C.   suspected the others were confederates and no longer trusted the experimenter.

D.   actively sought leadership roles when placed in newly formed groups.

(83)   Answer D, Type FAC, Reference 267
In a study by Snyder, students who were told that their personal attitudes were nearly identical to those of 10,000 other students _____ when they participated in a conformity experiment.

A.   were judged most attractive by their fellow subjects

B.   were more willing to obey the experimenter's request to make a public commitment to a popular cause

C.   took on additional attitudes as well as the mannerisms of the majority

D.   asserted their individuality by being nonconformist

(84)   Answer C, Type FAC, Reference 267
When William McGuire and his Yale University colleagues invited children to "tell us about yourself," they found that the children were most likely to mention their

A.   sex.

B.   nationality.

C.   distinctive attributes.

D.   most common personal characteristics.

(85)   Answer C, Type CON, Reference 267
Milly has blonde hair, a sister and a brother, and parents who are both teachers. Milly was born in the Netherlands and her family moved to New York when she was six. She attends a state university in the Midwestern United States and majors

in journalism. If you asked Milly to "tell us about yourself," she is most likely
to mention that
A.   she has blonde hair.
B.   she has a brother and a sister.
C.   she was born in the Netherlands.
D.   her parents both attended college.

THE FOLLOWING ITEMS ALSO APPEAR IN THE STUDY GUIDE:

(86)   Answer B, Type FAC, Reference 236
Studies involving _____ most clearly demonstrate social influence
taking the form of acceptance.
A.   judgments of the length of lines
B.   judgments of the autokinetic phenomenon
C.   shocking innocent victims
D.   none of the above demonstrate acceptance

(87)   Answer C, Type FAC, Reference 247
Which of the following social-psychological principles is not illustrated by the
conformity literature?
A.   Behavior shapes attitudes.
B.   the fundamental attribution error
C.   the inoculation effect
D.   the power of the situation

(88)   Answer C, Type FAC, Reference 246
How social pressure may lead us to perform immoral acts is best illustrated by
studies of
A.   psychological reactance.
B.   spontaneous self-concept.
C.   obedience to authority.
D.   informational influence.

(89)   Answer D, Type FAC, Reference 253
The effect of group size on conformity has been explained by _____
theory.
A.   cognitive dissonance
B.   social norm
C.   psychological reactance
D.   social impact

(90)   Answer B, Type CON, Reference 259
Normative influence is to informational influence as _____ is to
_____.
A.   autokinetic effect; cohesiveness
B.   compliance; acceptance
C.   conformity; reactance
D.   acceptance; reactance

(91)   Answer A, Type FAC, Reference 260
Which of the following is true regarding individual differences in conformity?
A.   Females conform slightly more than males.
B.   French subjects conform slightly more than Norwegian subjects.
C.   People's self-esteem test scores are excellent predictors of conformity.
D.   American subjects conform slightly more than German subjects.

(92)   Answer B, Type FAC, Reference 264
Compared to Euro-American cultures, Asian cultures are more likely to teach
their children
A.   independence.
B.   collectivism.
C.   to follow their own conscience.
D.   to respect another's privacy.

(93)   Answer C, Type CON, Reference 259
After hearing a respected medical authority lecture about the value of eating
fresh fruits and vegetables, Joshua includes more of them in his diet. This change
in Joshua's eating patterns is an example of
A.   normative social influence.
B.   psychological reactance.
C.   informational social influence.
D.   social facilitation.

(94)   Answer C, Type CON, Reference 259
Peter hates to wear ties anywhere. Nevertheless he wears one to his sister's
wedding to avoid the disapproval of his family. This is an example of
A.   identification.
B.   informational social influence.
C.   normative social influence.
D.   psychological reactance.

(95)   Answer A, Type CON, Reference 235
Ancient astronomers who observed the stars occasionally saw a star that seemed
to move very abruptly. This is probably an example of
A.   the autokinetic effect.
B.   the inoculation effect.
C.   astronomical impact theory.
D.   normative social influence.

(96)   Answer A, Type CON, Reference 251
In light of the Milgram studies, to believe that soldiers who shoot innocent
civilians as a consequence of following orders are unusually cruel is to
A.   make the fundamental attribution error.
B.   engage in self-serving bias.
C.   overlook the effect of cultural differences on conformity.
D.   underestimate the influence of personality differences on conformity.

(97)   Answer B, Type CON, Reference 233
Philip hated to attend concerts but went because his wife wanted him to. After
three years Philip came to genuinely enjoy concerts. This is an example of
A.   how acceptance can lead to compliance.
B.   how compliance can lead to acceptance.
C.   the boomerang effect.
D.   how psychological reactance can lead to acceptance.

(98)   Answer A, Type FAC, Reference 265
Psychological reactance theory provides an explanation for
A.   resistance to authority.
B.   obedience to authority.
C.   why compliance is more common than acceptance.
D.   why people are most likely to conform when the group is unanimous.

(99)   Answer C, Type CON, Reference 265
Molly generally likes to go home to visit her family during vacation. However,
after her father tells her she must be home during spring vacation, Molly decides
to remain at college. We can probably best understand Molly's behavior in terms
of
A.   reaction formation.
B.   regression.
C.   psychological reactance.
D.   self-serving bias.

(100) Answer B, Type CON, Reference 267

John has red hair, has two brothers, one sister, and was born in Chicago. Both his parents were born in this country and are lawyers. If you asked John to "tell us about yourself," he is most likely to mention that

A.   he has two brothers.
B.   he has red hair.
C.   his father has a college education.
D.   he was born in this country.

CHAPTER EIGHT: PERSUASION

<u>Multiple Choice</u>

(1)   Answer C, Type FAC, Reference 272
According to the text, those who wish to influence our behavior will seek to change our
A.   experiences.
B.   environments.
C.   attitudes.
D.   social relationships.

(2)   Answer D, Type FAC, Reference 272
As a result of the anti-Semitic propaganda campaigns engineered by Propaganda Minister Josef Goebbels and journalist Julius Streicher in Nazi Germany, most Germans
A.   were persuaded to feel deep hatred for the Jews.
B.   were left utterly unaffected and kept their original views.
C.   privately reacted with genuine sympathy for the Jews.
D.   were uncertain or intimidated enough to permit the Holocaust.

(3)   Answer D, Type FAC, Reference 272
According to the text, persuasion efforts to change attitudes toward
_____ have been successful while efforts to change attitudes toward
_____ have been unsuccessful.
A.   marijuana use; tobacco use
B.   seat belt use; tobacco use
C.   tobacco use; marijuana use
D.   marijuana use; seat belt use

(4)   Answer A, Type FAC, Reference 272
The response of most Americans to massive media campaigns urging automobile seat belt use suggests that our behavior is strongly influenced by
A.   the illusion of invulnerability.
B.   the availability heuristic.
C.   the vivid or emotion-arousing appeal.
D.   television as an irresistible medium of propaganda.

(5)   Answer A, Type FAC, Reference 273
According to the text, the factor that determines whether we call attempts at persuasion "education" or "propaganda" is whether

A. we believe them or not.
B. we know the communicator or not.
C. the message is rational or emotional in tone.
D. the message is one-sided or two-sided.

(6) Answer C, Type FAC, Reference 273
To answer questions about effective persuasion, social psychologists usually study persuasion the way some geologists study erosion:
A. by surveying the populations most directly affected.
B. by conducting massive, wide-scale observational studies.
C. by observing the effects of various factors in brief controlled experiments.
D. by designing simulations of real-world effects and analyzing the components of the most accurate models.

(7) Answer D, Type FAC, Reference 274
According to the text, actual social psychological studies of the various factors that influence persuasion produce effects that are _____ and that are most potent on _____.
A. large; our central values
B. small; our central values
C. large; weak attitudes that don't touch our values
D. small; weak attitudes that don't touch our values

(8) Answer D, Type FAC, Reference 274
Persuasion researchers Petty and Cacioppo and Eagly and Chaiken report that there are two basic routes to persuasion: a(n) _____ route and a(n) _____ route.
A. direct; indirect
B. active; passive
C. primary; secondary
D. central; peripheral

(9) Answer B, Type DEF, Reference 275
Persuasion that occurs when people are influenced by incidental cues, such as a speaker's attractiveness, is referred to as _____ route persuasion.
A. central
B. peripheral
C. subconscious
D. emotional

(10) Answer A, Type DEF, Reference 275
Which of the following is a characteristic of central route persuasion?

154

A. It uses systematic arguments.
B. It relies heavily on the communicator's attractiveness.
C. It employs rule-of-thumb heuristics to persuade.
D. Its effectiveness depends on a two-step flow of communication.

(11) Answer B, Type CON, Reference 275
An automobile manufacturer who produces advertisements associating his cars with a young, attractive family enjoying picnics is most clearly using
A. central route persuasion.
B. peripheral route persuasion.
C. two-step flow of communication.
D. social implosion.

(12) Answer A, Type CON, Reference 275
A refrigerator manufacturer who produces advertisements comparing his product with other competing models on features and prices is most clearly using
A. central route persuasion.
B. peripheral route persuasion.
C. attitude inoculation.
D. sleeper effect.

(13) Answer C, Type DEF, Reference 277
A(n) _____ communicator is one who is necessarily perceived as both expert and trustworthy.
A. high status
B. attractive
C. credible
D. analytical

(14) Answer B, Type DEF, Reference 277
The "sleeper effect" refers to the tendency of people who have heard a persuasive message to
A. forget to counterargue.
B. be more persuaded over time by a low-credibility source.
C. respond more to subliminal cues than to the overt message.
D. be influenced through a two-step flow of communication.

(15) Answer A, Type FAC, Reference 278
According to the text, a communicator who begins a message by saying things that the audience agrees with will likely be perceived as
A. smart.

B.   manipulative.
C.   irrelevant.
D.   wasting time.

(16)   Answer D, Type FAC, Reference 278
What characteristic of "women's speech" may make it seem less credible than
"men's speech"?
A.   higher pitch
B.   faster speed
C.   emotional quality
D.   hesitating manner

(17)   Answer A, Type FAC, Reference 278
According to Helmsley and Doob, videotaped witnesses who _____ impressed
people as being more believable.
A.   looked their questioners straight in the eye
B.   hesitated and paused thoughtfully before each response
C.   summarized their recollections slowly and carefully
D.   used expressive gestures and body language

(18)   Answer A, Type CON, Reference 278
A congressman argues that the government should be more aggressive in its
campaign to get citizens to stop smoking. He will appear more credible and
persuasive if he
A.   represents a district dependent on tobacco farming.
B.   is a former employee of the American Cancer Society.
C.   has once been a lobbyist for the television industry.
D.   comes from a religiously conservative region where many people believe it
is wrong to smoke.

(19)   Answer A, Type CON, Reference 278
A citizens' group that favors strict restriction of gun sales is preparing a
communication to present to various community groups. If they want their
message to seem most credible and sincere, which member of their group should
present it?
A.   Smitty, who owns a local sports store and sells guns
B.   Betty, an x-ray technician who works at the local hospital
C.   Jacob, whose son was killed by an accidental gunshot
D.   Maurice, a psychologist and expert on human aggression

(20)   Answer C, Type FAC, Reference 279

156

In a study by Miller and colleagues, Los Angeles residents who listened to tape-recorded messages on topics like "the dangers of drinking coffee" rated fast speakers as being _____ than slow speakers.
A.   less objective
B.   less intelligent
C.   more believable
D.   more manipulative

(21)   Answer B, Type FAC, Reference 279
One reason why fast speech may be more persuasive is that it
A.   typically has a higher pitch.
B.   tends to prevent counterarguing.
C.   is associated with greater intensity.
D.   is more comprehensible.

(22)   Answer C, Type FAC, Reference 280
Physical appeal and similarity are two important factors that determine a communicator's
A.   credibility.
B.   status.
C.   attractiveness.
D.   trustworthiness.

(23)   Answer D, Type FAC, Reference 280
What seems to determine whether a credible or a similar communicator will prove more persuasive?
A.   the age of the audience
B.   the intelligence of the audience
C.   whether the topic is pleasant or unpleasant
D.   whether the topic is of subjective preference or objective reality

(24)   Answer D, Type CON, Reference 280
People who are similar to ourselves will be more influential than those who are dissimilar to us in persuading us about all of the following questions except:
A.   Which soft drink tastes best?
B.   Is being honest more important than being loving?
C.   Who would make the best President?
D.   What North American city gets the most annual rainfall?

(25)   Answer C, Type FAC, Reference 281
_____ people are more responsive to rational appeals and are more persuaded by

reasoned arguments.
A. Self-monitoring
B. Authoritarian
C. Highly analytical
D. Highly empathic

(26) Answer D, Type FAC, Reference 281
_____ audiences are more persuaded by _____.
A. Well-educated; rational appeals
B. Uninvolved; how much they like the communicator
C. Highly involved; reasoned arguments
D. All of the above.

(27) Answer A, Type FAC, Reference 281
One can best predict Americans' voting preferences by knowing their
A. emotional reactions to the candidates.
B. beliefs about the candidates' likely behavior.
C. beliefs about the candidates' traits.
D. past voting record.

(28) Answer B, Type FAC, Reference 281
Janis and his colleagues found that if Yale students were allowed to consume peanuts and Pepsi while reading persuasive messages, they
A. felt manipulated and resisted influence.
B. were more convinced by the messages.
C. were distracted and showed poorer comprehension of the messages.
D. viewed the communicator as more attractive but less credible.

(29) Answer B, Type FAC, Reference 281
Compared to happy people, unhappy people ruminate more before reacting to a persuasive message and thus are
A. more vulnerable to emotional appeals.
B. less easily swayed by weak arguments.
C. less involved in judging persuasive messages.
D. more vulnerable to one-sided messages.

(30) Answer D, Type FAC, Reference 282
Fear-arousing messages have proven potent in convincing people to
A. cut down on smoking.
B. brush their teeth more often.
C. drive carefully.

D. All of the above.

(31) Answer A, Type FAC, Reference 282
Fear-arousing messages are effective if they
A. also tell people how to avoid the danger.
B. raise a moderate but not high level of fear.
C. are presented by similar rather than dissimilar communicators.
D. follow the peripheral rather than the central route of persuasion..

(32) Answer B, Type FAC, Reference 283
According to the text, health warnings on cigarette ads are ineffective because they
A. lack source credibility.
B. lack vividness.
C. generate too much fear.
D. lack logical appeal.

(33) Answer C, Type FAC, Reference 284
One study found that people who disagree with conclusions drawn by a newscaster rate the newscaster as being more
A. stimulating.
B. authoritarian.
C. untrustworthy.
D. manipulative.

(34) Answer A, Type FAC, Reference 284
Aronson, Turner, and Carlsmith reasoned that only a _____ source would elicit considerable opinion change when advocating a position greatly discrepant from the recipient's.
A. credible
B. physically appealing
C. fear-arousing
D. personally familiar

(35) Answer C, Type FAC, Reference 284
Communicators with little credibility are most effective in changing the opinions of other people when they advocate positions that
A. arouse the emotions of the audience.
B. arouse intense dissonance in the audience.
C. differ only moderately from the positions of the audience.
D. differ markedly from the positions of the audience.

(36)   Answer C, Type FAC, Reference 284
Which of the following statements best summarizes the effect of a highly discrepant message on an audience that disagrees with it?
A.   Discrepant messages cause discomfort in the audience, which then discounts all associated arguments.
B.   Discrepancy arouses audience attention and increases analysis and elaboration of the message, so it is accepted.
C.   Discrepancy and credibility interact, so that the effect of a large or small discrepancy depends on communicator credibility.
D.   None of the above.

(37)   Answer A, Type FAC, Reference 284
A highly discrepant message is least likely to be persuasive if the audience
A.   is deeply involved in the issue.
B.   is youthful.
C.   views the communicator as credible.
D.   is in a happy mood.

(38)   Answer C, Type FAC, Reference 285
A message presenting only one side of an issue will be more effective than a two-sided communication if
A.   the issue is of great personal significance to the audience and tends to elicit strong emotion.
B.   the communicator has only moderate credibility or attractiveness.
C.   the audience tends to agree with the advocated position and will not hear the opposing side.
D.   the audience is well-informed and is already aware of the opposing arguments.

(39)   Answer D, Type FAC, Reference 285
After Germany's defeat in World War II, radio broadcasts were designed to warn Army infantry that the war in the Pacific would probably last another two years. Soldiers who already initially agreed with that message were more persuaded by a(n) _____ version.
A.   logical
B.   emotional
C.   two-sided
D.   one-sided

(40)   Answer C, Type FAC, Reference 285

160

A two-sided communication is more effective than a one-sided appeal when the audience is
A. male.
B. highly opinionated.
C. well informed.
D. friendly.

(41) Answer A, Type DEF, Reference 286
Information presented early in an argument strongly affects people's judgments, a phenomenon known as
A. the primacy effect.
B. the initiation principle.
C. the shaping effect.
D. priming.

(42) Answer B, Type FAC, Reference 286
In experiments where people succeed on a guessing task half the time and fail half the time, people perceive those whose successes come early as
A. likely to have cheated.
B. more able than those whose early experience is failure.
C. less attractive than those whose successes come later.
D. having lost interest in the task.

(43) Answer B, Type CON, Reference 287
In an election campaign debate, Kelly makes her statement to the audience first and is immediately followed by her opponent, Stuart. The election is not held till two weeks later. If both messages were persuasive and the debate was the deciding factor, the election results should show the influence of
A. the recency effect.
B. the primacy effect.
C. a two-step flow of communication.
D. the credibility-discrepancy effect.

(44) Answer B, Type FAC, Reference 286
Using the transcript of an actual criminal case, Gary Wells and his colleagues found that a defense attorney's opening statement was more effective if presented before, rather than after, the prosecution's presentation of evidence. This finding illustrates
A. the recency effect.
B. the primacy effect.
C. the sleeper effect.

D. social implosion.

(45) Answer C, Type DEF, Reference 287
The fact that information presented last sometimes has the most effect is referred to as the
A. halo phenomenon.
B. fading effect.
C. recency effect.
D. serial position effect.

(46) Answer C, Type FAC, Reference 287
Which of the following statements about the recency effect is true?
A. Recency effects are more common than primacy effects.
B. It is more likely to occur when a delay occurs before the audience is asked to commit to a choice.
C. It probably occurs because early arguments have faded from memory.
D. All of the above.

(47) Answer A, Type DEF, Reference 287
How a message is presented--whether face-to-face, in writing, on film, or in some other way--constitutes the _____ of communication.
A. channel
B. route
C. flow
D. process

(48) Answer B, Type FAC, Reference 287
Compared to attitudes formed passively, experience-based attitudes are
A. less complex.
B. more stable.
C. more vulnerable to attack.
D. less rational.

(49) Answer B, Type FAC, Reference 288
In comparing the actions of 180 different students before and after a "Keep Our Campus Beautiful" poster campaign, Paloutzian found that _____ more passers-by picked up test litter after the campaign than had done so before the campaign.
A. no
B. two
C. 25 percent
D. 80 percent

162

(50)   Answer D, Type FAC, Reference 288
According to the text, which of the following is one of the hurdles a persuasive message must clear in order to change attitudes and behavioral intentions?
A.   Is the message comprehended?
B.   Is the message believed?
C.   Is the message remembered?
D.   All of the above.

(51)   Answer D, Type FAC, Reference 288
Joseph Grush analyzed campaign activities in all the 1976 Democratic presidential primaries and found that those candidates who _____ usually got the most votes.
A.   were most physically appealing
B.   presented themselves as most similar to their constituents
C.   used emotional instead of rational appeals
D.   spent the most money

(52)   Answer A, Type FAC, Reference 289
A simple rule summarizes the effects of the media's influence on attitude change: Persuasion decreases as _____ of the issue increase(s).
A.   significance and familiarity
B.   complexity
C.   novelty and ambiguity
D.   triviality

(53)   Answer C, Type FAC, Reference 289
Persuasion studies demonstrate that the major influence on important beliefs and attitudes appears to be
A.   television.
B.   print media like newspapers and magazines.
C.   our contact with people.
D.   major social institutions and the values they foster.

(54)   Answer C, Type FAC, Reference 289
In 1954 Eldersveld and Dodge studied the influence of political campaigns on Ann Arbor, Michigan, citizens who had intended not to vote for a revision of the city charter. Those who got their information from _____ were most likely to be persuaded to vote for the revision.
A.   mass media promotion
B.   four separate mailings
C.   a personal visit

D.   a mass rally

(55)   Answer B, Type FAC, Reference 290
In reflecting on their college experience, most former students say they learned more from _____ than from any other source.
A.   class assignments and in-class experiences
B.   contacts with friends and fellow students
C.   specific books and readings
D.   professors and other role models

(56)   Answer D, Type DEF, Reference 291
The process by which media influence often occurs through opinion leaders, who in turn influence others, is referred to as
A.   the sleeper effect.
B.   an indirect channel of communication.
C.   the opinion leader effect.
D.   a two-step flow of communication.

(57)   Answer D, Type CON, Reference 291
Which of the following illustrates media influence through a two-step flow of communication?
A.   A teenager buys a video game she saw advertised both on television and in a favorite magazine.
B.   A domestic car manufacturer sponsors a television program about the defectiveness of many foreign imports.
C.   A candidate for political office answers questions from members of a studio audience on live television.
D.   A man buys a new laundry detergent after hearing it recommended by a friend who read that it was both effective and environmentally safe in a consumer magazine article.

(58)   Answer C, Type FAC, Reference 291
Chaikin and Eagly note that research shows that _____ messages are most likely to be _____.
A.   face-to-face; forgotten
B.   written; forgotten
C.   written; comprehended and remembered
D.   audiotaped; distorted in memory

(59)   Answer C, Type CON, Reference 291
Peter is opposed to capital punishment and has, on the basis of extensive research,

developed some complex but compelling arguments to support his position. In attempting to persuade others of the validity of his arguments, he should present them

A.   on a videotape.
B.   on an audiotape.
C.   in writing.
D.   on live television.

(60)   Answer B, Type FAC, Reference 292
Research suggests that people with _____ are the easiest to influence.
A.   low self-esteem
B.   moderate self-esteem
C.   high self-esteem
D.   None of the above; there is no relationship between self-esteem and susceptibility to influence.

(61)   Answer A, Type DEF, Reference 292
The idea that attitudes change as people grow older is known as the _____ explanation of age differences in attitudes.
A.   life cycle
B.   generational
C.   belief differentiation
D.   psychosocial crisis

(62)   Answer C, Type FAC, Reference 292
According to David Sears, researchers have almost invariably found and confirmed _____ effects in studying age differences in attitudes.
A.   maturation
B.   life cycle
C.   generational
D.   conservatism

(63)   Answer C, Type FAC, Reference 293
Which of the following is true regarding age differences in attitudes?
A.   People's racial attitudes tend to be most liberal in their 30s and 40s.
B.   People in their 50s and 60s tend to have more conservative sexual attitudes than they had in their 30s and 40s.
C.   Attitudes formed in the teens and 20s tend to be stable thereafter.
D.   All of the above are true.

(64)   Answer D, Type FAC, Reference 293

Schuman and Scott found that when they asked people to name the most important national or world events of the last half century, most recalled
A.   tragedies like war and assassinations.
B.   achievements like peace accords and moon landings.
C.   recent rather than long-ago news events.
D.   events from their teens and early adulthood.

(65)   Answer D, Type FAC, Reference 293
Freedman and Sears found that California high schoolers did not change their attitudes in response to a talk entitled "Why Teenagers Should Not Be Allowed to Drive" if they
A.   had a moderate, rather than a high or low, level of self-esteem.
B.   were of lower intelligence.
C.   were male.
D.   had been forewarned that the talk was coming.

(66)   Answer A, Type CON, Reference 294
Keela wants to persuade her parents to help pay for a study trip abroad this summer. She will have a more difficult time succeeding if
A.   her parents are forewarned of her intent to convince them.
B.   she has the trip coordinator call to reassure them.
C.   her parents are not particularly intelligent or analytical.
D.   her parents have a moderate level of self-esteem.

(67)   Answer B, Type CON, Reference 294
In which of the following issues would you be least likely to construct counterarguments and most likely to accept the premise suggested by the communicator?
A.   the best career option for you to follow after college
B.   which brand of toothpaste you should buy
C.   which health care insurance policy you should choose
D.   whether eating your favorite food has negative health consequences

(68)   Answer D, Type FAC, Reference 294
Political ads that use words to promote the candidate while visual images keep the viewer occupied to prevent analysis of the words are most clearly employing
A.   the technique of classical conditioning.
B.   the two-step flow of communication.
C.   the sleeper effect.
D.   distraction to inhibit counterarguing.

166

(69)   Answer A, Type CON, Reference 294
Analytical people are to _____ as image-conscious people are to
_____.
A.   central route persuasion; peripheral route persuasion
B.   the primacy effect; the recency effect
C.   life-cycle explanation; generational explanation
D.   personal influence; media influence

(70)   Answer D, Type FAC, Reference 294
Which of the following techniques has been used to stimulate people's thinking in
response to a persuasive message?
A.   having different speakers present separate arguments rather than the same
speaker present all the arguments
B.   using rhetorical questions such as, "Are you better off for having voted for
so-and-so four years ago?"
C.   making people in the audience feel responsible for passing along the
persuasive message
D.   All of the above.

(71)   Answer C, Type FAC, Reference 294
Asking rhetorical questions, repeating the message, and using multiple speakers to
deliver a message all stimulate the audience's thinking and make _____ messages
_____ persuasive.
A.   strong; more
B.   weak; less
C.   Both A and B.
C.   None of the above.

(72)   Answer A, Type FAC, Reference 299
In many cults, new converts are quickly made active members of the team and
required to participate in disciplined rituals. According to the text, this strategy
utilizes the principle
A.   that compliance breeds acceptance.
B.   of the sleeper effect.
C.   of social implosion.
D.   of the two-step flow of communication.

(73)   Answer B, Type FAC, Reference 299
The recruitment strategy of the Unification Church and the tithing schedule of the
Rev. Jim Jones's Peoples' Temple both illustrate the effectiveness of applying
A.   the sleeper effect.

B.   the foot-in-the-door phenomenon.
C.   the two-step flow of communication.
D.   attitude inoculation.

(74)   Answer A, Type FAC, Reference 301
According to cult researcher Margaret Singer, middle-class Caucasian youths are most vulnerable to cult recruitment because they are more _____ than older or lower-class targets.
A.   trusting
B.   alienated
C.   liberal
D.   unstable

(75)   Answer A, Type DEF, Reference 302
Stark and Bainbridge suggest that a "social implosion" may occur within a cult when
A.   members are separated from previous support systems and kept isolated with other cultists.
B.   charismatic leaders are challenged by cult members.
C.   too many new converts join in a short time.
D.   cult leaders attempt to change familiar rituals too quickly.

(76)   Answer D, Type FAC, Reference 303
According to psychiatrist Jerome Frank, the psychotherapy setting, like cults and zealous self-help groups, provides which of the following experiences?
A.   an offer of expertise and hope
B.   a special rationale or myth that explains one's difficulties and offers a new perspective
C.   a set of rituals and learning experiences that promises a new sense of peace and happiness
D.   All of the above.

(77)   Answer B, Type FAC, Reference 303
According to the text, by the 1990s, psychologists more and more accepted the idea that _____ is at the heart of therapy.
A.   prosocial action or altruism
B.   social influence
C.   modeling
D.   self-monitoring

(78)   Answer A, Type FAC, Reference 304

Recent analyses of psychotherapy suggest that the primary task of the therapist is to
A.   raise questions that stimulate the client's thinking.
B.   establish his or her credible expertise.
C.   use the peripheral rather than central route of persuasion in changing the client's behavior.
D.   elicit compliance that will eventually lead to acceptance.

(79)   Answer D, Type FAC, Reference 304
Most clients entering therapy are motivated to take the _____ route, thinking deeply about their problems under the therapist's guidance.
A.   indirect
B.   peripheral
C.   unconscious
D.   central

(80)   Answer B, Type FAC, Reference 304
Ernst and Heesacker reported that an assertiveness training workshop proved more effective if, in addition to learning and rehearsing concepts of assertiveness, participants
A.   were exposed to models of assertiveness on videotape.
B.   were stimulated to think favorable thoughts about assertiveness by recalling a time when they hurt themselves by being unassertive.
C.   heard from previous workshop participants whose lives were changed by learning to become more assertive.
D.   were exposed to both credible and attractive communicators who provided strong arguments for the benefits of assertiveness.

(81)   Answer A, Type FAC, Reference 305
Charles Kiesler recommends that one way to stimulate people's thinking so they become more committed to their positions is to
A.   mildly attack their position.
B.   strongly attack their position.
C.   mildly support their position.
D.   strongly support their position.

(82)   Answer B, Type DEF, Reference 306
Eliciting counterarguments by means of a mild attack on one's beliefs is known as
A.   counteracceptance.
B.   attitude inoculation.
C.   psychological reactance.

D.   the boomerang effect.

(83)   Answer C, Type FAC, Reference 306
The text indicates that inoculation procedures have been successful in
A.   increasing drivers' use of seat belts.
B.   reducing children's aggression.
C.   reducing teenage smoking rates.
D.   increasing adults' charitable contributions.

(84)   Answer D, Type FAC, Reference 308
Research on attitude inoculation suggests that religious educators are wise to avoid
A.   the two-step flow of communication.
B.   forewarning followers that outsiders will question their beliefs.
C.   using charismatic leaders to attract new converts.
D.   creating a germ-free ideological environment.

(85)   Answer C, Type FAC, Reference 309
Inoculation research suggests that to build resistance to persuasion one ought to
A.   insulate oneself from media influence.
B.   recognize that compliance often leads to acceptance.
C.   be an active listener and critical thinker.
D.   seek social support for one's beliefs.

THE FOLLOWING ITEMS ALSO APPEAR IN THE STUDY GUIDE:

(86)   Answer D, Type CON, Reference 275
The central route is to _____ as the peripheral route is to _____.
A.   analytical; motivated
B.   similarity; attractiveness
C.   heuristics; incidental cues
D.   high effort; low effort

(87)   Answer A, Type FAC, Reference 273
Social psychologists study persuasion primarily through
A.   experiments.
B.   surveys.
C.   case studies.
D.   participant observation.

(88)   Answer C, Type FAC, Reference 287
Which of the following is one of the four major factors studied by psychologists in research on effective persuasion?
A.   the function of communication
B.   the setting of communication
C.   the channel of communication
D.   the length of communication

(89)   Answer B, Type FAC, Reference 279
Wood and Eagly reported that when a speaker presents _____, we are more likely to attribute the message to compelling evidence and thus to be persuaded by it.
A.   a popular rather than an unpopular position
B.   an unexpected rather than an expected position
C.   an emotional rather than a rational appeal
D.   a political rather than a religious position

(90)   Answer D, Type FAC, Reference 278
People who argue against their own self-interest are
A.   effective in persuading a female audience but not in persuading a male audience.
B.   effective with an intelligent audience but not with an unintelligent audience.
C.   viewed as inconsistent and thus lose their effectiveness.
D.   viewed as more credible and are thus more influential.

(91)   Answer D, Type FAC, Reference 280
"Similar" communicators are more effective in persuading on
_____ than on _____.
A.   radio; television
B.   judgments of fact; matters of value
C.   political issues; religious beliefs
D.   matters of value; judgments of fact

(92)   Answer D, Type FAC, Reference 303
Most recent analyses of social influence in psychotherapy have focused on how
A.   therapists establish credible expertise and trustworthiness.
B.   the peripheral route to persuasion can produce enduring attitude and behavior change.
C.   the various channels of communication affect the therapeutic process.
D.   the interaction between therapist and client affects the client's thinking.

(93)   Answer A, Type FAC, Reference 288
When researchers went to the homes of people from 12 churches shortly after
they heard sermons opposing racial bigotry, they found that ____ percent
spontaneously recalled the sermons.
A.   10
B.   30
C.   50
D.   70

(94)   Answer B, Type FAC, Reference 292
Life-cycle and generational explanations both attempt to explain
A.   why the content of messages changes over time.
B.   why people have different attitudes depending on their age.
C.   why a particular communicator has a different effect on people of different
ages.
D.   how an emotional appeal builds to a climax in terms of its impact.

(95)   Answer D, Type CON, Reference 280
An attractive or similar communicator would be most effective in changing
beliefs about the
A.   health benefits of eating fruits and vegetables.
B.   dangers of marijuana use.
C.   dangers of driving without wearing seat belts.
D.   advantages of living in a small town versus the country or a large city.

(96)   Answer B, Type CON, Reference 277
A gun manufacturer delivers a speech against stricter gun legislation. Because he
clearly has a vested interest, his arguments have little initial impact on the
audience. However, several weeks later, a survey of the audience indicates that
his impact was much greater than first thought. This would be an example of
A.   the recency effect.
B.   the sleeper effect.
C.   social implosion.
D.   attitude inoculation.

(97)   Answer D, Type CON, Reference 282
You have been asked to design an advertising campaign urging people to stop
drinking alcohol. To be most effective, your message should arouse
A.   no fear.
B.   a moderate level of fear.
C.   a low level of fear.

D.   a high level of fear.

(98)   Answer B, Type CON, Reference 285
You have been asked to prepare a speech opposing capital punishment. To be most effective in convincing those who strongly favor the death penalty, you should present
A.   a one-sided communication.
B.   a two-sided communication.
C.   an emotional appeal.
D.   an audiotaped appeal.

(99)   Answer B, Type CON, Reference 287
You are one of two candidates being interviewed for a position as superintendent of the city school system. You are notified that one candidate will be interviewed tomorrow evening and the other a week later. The school board will make a decision immediately after the second candidate has been interviewed. If you want the job
A.   you should try to be interviewed first.
B.   you should try to be interviewed last.
C.   you should try to be interviewed first but only if the school board is composed of college graduates and the other candidate is controversial.
D.   you should try to be interviewed first but only if you are more attractive than the other candidate.

(100) Answer C, Type CON, Reference 289
According to research presented in the text, the mass media may be most effective in influencing
A.   whether one becomes a Democrat or Republican.
B.   whether a person believes in God or not.
C.   the brand of shampoo a person buys.
D.   one's attitude toward capital punishment.

CHAPTER NINE: GROUP INFLUENCE

<u>Multiple Choice</u>

(1)   Answer D, Type DEF, Reference 314
According to group dynamics expert Marvin Shaw, one thing that all groups have in common is that their members
A.   share a common goal.
B.   have well-defined roles.
C.   enjoy free and open communication.
D.   interact.

(2)   Answer D, Type DEF, Reference 314
Which of the following is a defining characteristic of a group?
A.   Two or more people belong to it.
B.   Its members influence one another.
C.   Its members perceive one another as "us."
D.   All of the above.

(3)   Answer D, Type CON, Reference 314
Which of the following is probably <u>not</u> a group as that term is defined in your text?
A.   two people dancing
B.   three people playing cards but not talking much
C.   four people discussing how to solve a problem at work
D.   five people reading magazines in a dentist's waiting room

(4)   Answer A, Type DEF, Reference 315
Which of the following can occur in a minimal group situation?
A.   social facilitation
B.   minority influence
C.   group polarization
D.   groupthink

(5)   Answer C, Type FAC, Reference 315
What does your text refer to as "social psychology's most elementary question"?
A.   Why do we form groups?
B.   Is social interaction beneficial?
C.   How are we affected by the mere presence of another person?
D.   How do we meet another's need to belong?

(6)   Answer A, Type DEF, Reference 315
A coactor is someone who
A.   does the same task as you at the same time.
B.   helps and cooperates with you.
C.   competes with you on a single task.
D.   imitates you.

(7)   Answer A, Type CON, Reference 315
Who among the following would be considered coactors?
A.   20 people doing situps in an exercise class
B.   two people playing chess against each other
C.   12 competitors running in a cross-country race
D.   three friends chatting pleasantly before class starts

(8)   Answer C, Type FAC, Reference 315
In one of social psychology's earliest experiments, Norman Triplett found that
children told to wind string on a fishing reel as quickly as possible did their task
much faster when
A.   competing with other children.
B.   each worked alone.
C.   they worked in the presence of coactors.
D.   they had first practiced with their teammates.

(9)   Answer A, Type FAC, Reference 315
The mere presence of others has been found to boost people's performance when
they are
A.   crossing out designated letters on printed pages.
B.   memorizing nonsense syllables.
C.   performing complex multiplication problems.
D.   completing a maze.

(10)   Answer D, Type FAC, Reference 315
The social-facilitation effect has been found to apply to
A.   people performing simple motor tasks.
B.   chickens eating grain.
C.   ants excavating sand.
D.   All of the above.

(11)   Answer B, Type FAC, Reference 315
Which of the following statements best states the puzzling findings of early
research on social facilitation?

A. The presence of certain people facilitates performance, and the presence of other people hinders it.
B. The presence of others sometimes facilitates performance and sometimes hinders it.
C. The presence of others makes tasks easier but tempts group members to contribute less effort.
D. The presence of others facilitates verbal performance but hinders motor performance.

(12) Answer A, Type FAC, Reference 316
Zajonc resolved the conflicting findings on how the presence of others influences performance with the help of the well-established principle in experimental psychology that arousal
A. enhances whatever response tendency is dominant.
B. interferes with the performance of simple tasks.
C. inhibits coordination of efforts.
D. weakens competing motives.

(13) Answer B, Type CON, Reference 316
The presence of others is likely to lead to better performance in _____ and to worse performance in _____.
A. solving a crossword puzzle; sweeping a sidewalk
B. raking leaves; solving complex mathematical problems
C. playing golf; raking leaves
D. solving complex mathematical problems; solving a crossword puzzle

(14) Answer B, Type FAC, Reference 317
Zajonc and Sales asked people to pronounce nonsense words between 1 and 16 times each, and then told them to guess which of these words appeared briefly on a screen. When subjects were shown random black lines, they reported having seen
A. the least familiar nonsense words.
B. the most familiar nonsense words.
C. the longest nonsense words.
D. the shortest nonsense words.

(15) Answer B, Type FAC, Reference 317
Michaels and his colleagues watched students play pool in the student union at Virginia Tech. When four observers came up to watch the pool players, _____ players did _____ than they had when playing without the audience.
A. good; slightly worse

B. good; even better
C. poor; slightly better
D. poor; significantly better

(16) Answer C, Type FAC, Reference 318
Which of the following is supported by the research findings?
A. Stutterers stutter less in front of larger audiences.
B. College basketball players are somewhat more accurate in free-throw shooting in a packed field house.
C. In professional and college sports, home teams win the majority of games.
D. All of the above.

(17) Answer B, Type FAC, Reference 319
When people sit close together, friendly people are _____, and unfriendly people are _____.
A. liked more; disliked less
B. liked more; disliked more
C. liked less; disliked less
D. liked less; disliked more

(18) Answer C, Type FAC, Reference 319
Freedman and his colleagues had an accomplice listen to a humorous tape or watch a movie with other subjects. When all sat close together, the accomplice
A. was liked less by males and liked more by females.
B. could more readily induce the group to express hostility toward the experimenter.
C. could more readily induce the group to laugh and clap.
D. could more readily distract the group from attending to the tape or movie.

(19) Answer B, Type FAC, Reference 319
Evans tested 10-person groups of University of Massachusetts students in either a small, crowded room or a larger, more spacious room. Those in the crowded room were found to
A. make more errors on both simple and complex tasks.
B. make more errors on complex tasks but not on simple tasks.
C. complete both simple and complex tasks more quickly.
D. complete simple tasks more quickly and complex tasks more slowly.

(20) Answer A, Type FAC, Reference 320
Cortrell found that when observers were blindfolded, their presence
A. did not boost the well-practiced responses of others.

B.   still boosted the well-practiced responses of others.
C.   was a distraction and led others to poorer performance of both simple and complex tasks.
D.   boosted the performance of motor but not verbal tasks.

(21)   Answer B, Type DEF, Reference 320
Social psychologists refer to our concern for how others are evaluating us as
A.   social fear.
B.   evaluation apprehension.
C.   evaluation phobia.
D.   coactor anxiety.

(22)   Answer A, Type FAC, Reference 320
In one experiment, joggers on a jogging path at the University of California at Santa Barbara sped up as they came upon a woman seated on the grass--but only if she was
A.   facing them.
B.   facing away from them.
C.   someone they knew.
D.   a stranger.

(23)   Answer C, Type FAC, Reference 320
People seem to perform best when their coactor is
A.   slightly inferior.
B.   equal in ability.
C.   slightly superior.
D.   significantly superior.

(24)   Answer C, Type FAC, Reference 320
Sanders and his colleagues have suggested that we are aroused in the presence of others, not only because of evaluation apprehension, but because we
A.   engage in social comparison.
B.   become deindividuated.
C.   get distracted.
D.   need to belong.

(25)   Answer A, Type FAC, Reference 320
According to the "distraction hypothesis," the mere presence of others can cause arousal because one experiences a conflict between
A.   paying attention to the task and paying attention to the other people.
B.   wanting to perform well and wanting to complete the task.

C.   one's social role and one's personal self-image.
D.   following instructions and making one's own decisions.

(26)   Answer B, Type FAC, Reference 320
According to the text, the idea that the mere presence of others produces some arousal even without evaluation apprehension or distraction is supported by the finding that
A.   some people publicly violate social norms.
B.   people's color preferences are stronger when they make judgments with others present.
C.   social facilitation effects occur among children.
D.   social facilitation effects occur among strangers.

(27)   Answer C, Type CON, Reference 321
Research on social facilitation suggests that the design of new office buildings in which private offices are replaced with large, open areas may
A.   invade privacy and disrupt worker morale.
B.   improve communication and build employee morale.
C.   disrupt creative thinking on complex tasks.
D.   disrupt performance of routine clerical tasks.

(28)   Answer D, Type DEF, Reference 322
Social loafing refers to the tendency for people to
A.   perform an unfamiliar task more poorly when others are present.
B.   violate social norms when no one is watching.
C.   be insensitive to the needs of others.
D.   exert less effort when they pool their efforts toward a common goal.

(29)   Answer D, Type DEF, Reference 322
Social loafing occurs in situations in which people
A.   pool their efforts toward a common goal.
B.   are not accountable as individuals.
C.   work on additive tasks.
D.   All of the above.

(30)   Answer A, Type FAC, Reference 322
When people cooperate on additive tasks, pooling their efforts toward a common goal,
A.   they may be less motivated to perform well.
B.   their efforts are usually boosted by a social bonding.
C.   they develop a stronger sense of self-efficacy.

D.   individual effort is facilitated by social arousal.

(31)   Answer D, Type FAC, Reference 322
In a study by Ingham, blindfolded participants were placed in the first position in a tug-of-war apparatus. Subjects pulled hardest when they
A.   were part of a five-person team.
B.   were part of a three-person team.
C.   were part of a two-person team.
D.   knew they were pulling alone.

(32)   Answer A, Type CON, Reference 322
Social loafing would be most likely to occur in
A.   college students working on a group project for which they will all receive the same grade.
B.   factory workers who are each paid according to how many lamps they assemble.
C.   a group of golfers competing for first place in a tournament.
D.   political candidates who hope to win a seat on the city council.

(33)   Answer A, Type FAC, Reference 323
_____ occurs when observation increases evaluation apprehension; _____ occurs when the pooling of effort lowers evaluation apprehension.
A.   Social facilitation; social loafing
B.   Social loafing; group polarization
C.   Deindividuation; social loafing
D.   Social loafing; deindividuation

(34)   Answer B, Type FAC, Reference 324
Making group members' performance individually identifiable seems to be one effective strategy for reducing
A.   social facilitation.
B.   social loafing.
C.   minority influence.
D.   group polarization.

(35)   Answer A, Type FAC, Reference 326
Research indicates that _____ exhibit less social loafing than _____.
A.   groups of friends; groups of strangers
B.   women; men
C.   people in collectivist cultures; people in individualist cultures
D.   All of the above.

(36) Answer B, Type FAC, Reference 326
Experiments have shown that people in groups loaf less when
A.   people have moderate levels of self-esteem.
B.   the task is involving.
C.   they work on an additive task with strangers.
D.   the task is familiar.

(37) Answer A, Type FAC, Reference 326
Research suggests that social loafing does not occur in
A.   Israel's kibbutz farms.
B.   China's collective factories.
C.   Cuba's collective farms.
D.   Russia's central government offices.

(38) Answer C, Type FAC, Reference 326
The behavior of the four Los Angeles police officers who were videotaped
beating unarmed Rodney King in the spring of 1991 illustrates the possible effects
of
A.   social loafing.
B.   groupthink.
C.   deindividuation.
D.   group polarization.

(39) Answer D, Type DEF, Reference 327.
Which of the following circumstances contributes to people becoming
deindividuated?
A.   They are immersed in a large group.
B.   They are physically anonymous.
C.   They are involved in arousing, distracting activities.
D.   All of the above.

(40) Answer D, Type DEF, Reference 327
_____ occurs as a result of the loss of self-awareness and evaluation
apprehension, typically as a result of group situations that foster anonymity and
draw attention away from the individual.
A.   Social facilitation
B.   Groupthink
C.   Group polarization
D.   Deindividuation

(41) Answer B, Type FAC, Reference 328
In his report on lynch mobs, Brian Mullen notes that the bigger the mob, the more its members _____ and become willing to commit atrocities, such as burning, lacerating, or dismembering the victim.
A.   undergo groupthink
B.   lose self-awareness
C.   take a "free ride"
D.   experience social facilitation

(42) Answer C, Type FAC, Reference 328
Zimbardo explained the greater vandalism of an abandoned car left in New York than one left in Palo Alto in terms of the greater _____ of the large city.
A.   poverty
B.   frustration
C.   anonymity
D.   competitiveness

(43) Answer A, Type FAC, Reference 328
Zimbardo reported that women who were masked and hooded in KKK-style hoods and robes tended to _____ than women who were visible and wore name tags.
A.   administer longer shocks to a victim
B.   engage in greater social loafing
C.   make riskier decisions
D.   make more contact and reveal more personal information

(44) Answer B, Type FAC, Reference 328
In a study on Halloween night, Diener and colleagues conducted a study of trick-or-treat theft at homes scattered throughout the Seattle area. Given a chance to steal candy, the children who were _____ were most likely to commit transgressions.
A.   anonymous and alone
B.   anonymous and in a group
C.   frustrated and alone
D.   frustrated and in a group

(45) Answer B, Type FAC, Reference 329
Robert Watson scrutinized anthropological files and discovered that the cultures with depersonalized warriors were also the cultures that
A.   seldom made war.
B.   were brutal to the enemy.

C.   were least democratic in electing leaders.
D.   were particularly susceptible to social loafing.

(46)   Answer C, Type FAC, Reference 329
In a study at the University of Georgia, women who donned nurses' uniforms and were made anonymous became _____ than when their names and personal identities were emphasized.
A.   less sympathetic to patients' needs
B.   more sympathetic to patients' needs
C.   less aggressive in administering shock
D.   more aggressive in administering shock

(47)   Answer A, Type FAC, Reference 330
In a study by Gergen, Gergen, and Barton, subjects who spent an hour in a dark room with other strangers found that their relative anonymity _____ compared to control subjects in a well-lighted room.
A.   permitted greater intimacy and affection
B.   led to more aggressive and hostile tendencies
C.   enabled them to talk more
D.   created greater social anxiety

(48)   Answer C, Type CON, Reference 330
"It was such an exciting game," your friend insists. "We were all shouting and clapping together, everyone was in sync. When our team won, I realized I was jumping up and down, screaming, right along with everyone else. I don't know what got into me!" Your friend's reactions best illustrate the process of
A.   social loafing.
B.   minority influence.
C.   deindividuation.
D.   groupthink.

(49)   Answer A, Type CON, Reference 331
In which of the following groups is deindividuation least likely to occur?
A.   in a jury where a guilty verdict requires unanimous agreement
B.   at a Ku Klux Klan rally where new members are being inducted
C.   in a high school pep rally attended by almost all students
D.   in the audience at an Independence Day parade celebrating the benefits of individual freedom

(50)   Answer D, Type CON, Reference 331
Which of the following pairs are most clearly opposites?

184

A. group polarization and group consensus
B. groupthink and the accentuation phenomenon
C. minority influence and leadership
D. deindividuation and self-awareness

(51) Answer B, Type FAC, Reference 331
People who are made self-aware, by acting in front of a mirror or TV camera, for example, have been found to
A. exhibit increased self-confidence.
B. behave more consistently with their attitudes.
C. be less thoughtful in analyzing complex social issues.
D. be more vulnerable to persuasive appeals that run counter to social norms.

(52) Answer A, Type CON, Reference 331
In recognizing the dangers of becoming deindividuated, a parent's parting advice to a teenager setting off for a party might well be, "Have fun, and _____."
A. remember who you are
B. stay with the group
C. remember you are only young once
D. don't worry about being popular

(53) Answer D, Type DEF, Reference 332
Group polarization occurs when group discussion _____ group members' initial inclinations.
A. challenges
B. reverses
C. neutralizes
D. strengthens

(54) Answer A, Type FAC, Reference 332
Studies of _____ eventually led to formulation of the group polarization hypothesis.
A. the risky shift
B. social comparison
C. social loafing
D. groupthink

(55) Answer B, Type FAC, Reference 333
Investigations of the risky shift eventually led to the conclusion that this group phenomenon was really a tendency for group discussion to
A. reverse the group's original leanings.

185

B.   accentuate group members' initial leanings.
C.   arouse and distract members so their self-awareness is reduced.
D.   favor illusory thinking in supporting the group's leader.

(56)   Answer D, Type FAC, Reference 334
Myers and Bishop organized groups of prejudiced and nonprejudiced high school
students and asked them to respond to issues involving racial attitudes, both
before and after group discussion. Results showed that after within-group
discussion, _____ became _____.
A.   all students; more prejudiced
B.   all students; less prejudiced
C.   between-group differences; smaller
D.   between-group differences; greater

(57)   Answer B, Type DEF, Reference 334
Which of the following describes the accentuation phenomenon?
A.   Initial differences among college student groups become less marked over
time in college as a result of exposure to new information.
B.   Initial differences among college student groups become sharper and
greater with more time in college.
C.   Discussions with like-minded others stimulate creative thought and reduce
the extremism of opinions.
D.   The benefits of group membership become more apparent the longer one is
part of the group.

(58)   Answer A, Type FAC, Reference 335
The text suggests that the extremism of terrorist organizations is very likely the
result of the process of
A.   group polarization.
B.   pluralistic ignorance.
C.   social loafing.
D.   social facilitation.

(59)   Answer B, Type CON, Reference 335
Individuals who believe that physician-assisted suicide should be legalized meet to
discuss the issue. Research on group interaction suggests that after discussion the
individuals will be
A.   more likely to question the wisdom of legalizing physician-assisted suicide.
B.   even more convinced that physician-assisted suicide should be legalized.
C.   sharply divided over whether physician-assisted suicide should be legalized.
D.   opposed to the legalization of physician-assisted suicide.

(60)   Answer A, Type FAC, Reference 336
What two underlying processes seem to explain the occurrence of group
polarization?
A.   informational influence and normative influence
B.   minority influence and social facilitation
C.   psychological reactance and deindividuation
D.   social comparison and self-censorship

(61)   Answer C, Type FAC, Reference 337
Research suggests that the expectation that we will discuss an issue with an equally
expert person of an opposing view can motivate us to adopt a _____ position.
A.   compatible
B.   somewhat less contradictory
C.   more extreme
D.   neutral

(62)   Answer A, Type FAC, Reference 337
According to Festinger, it is human nature to want to evaluate our opinions by
A.   comparing ourselves with others.
B.   designing everyday tests of their validity.
C.   engaging in frequent introspection.
D.   actively studying the results of scientific research.

(63)   Answer C, Type DEF, Reference 338
_____ is a false impression of how other people are thinking, feeling, or
responding.
A.   Social rationalization
B.   Social censorship
C.   Pluralistic ignorance
D.   Group delusion

(64)   Answer A, Type FAC, Reference 339
When people learn others' positions--without discussion--and have not already
made a prior commitment to a particular response, seeing the others' responses
A.   stimulates a small polarization effect.
B.   causes a small reactance effect.
C.   has no influence on those who have yet to publicly commit themselves
D.   contributes to a more questioning attitude.

(65)   Answer C, Type FAC, Reference 339

Research on the underlying processes producing group polarization indicates that persuasive arguments predominate on issues having a(n) _____ basis and social comparison predominates on issues having a _____ basis.
A.   emotional; factual
B.   personal; social
C.   factual; value-laden
D.   economic; psychological

(66)   Answer D, Type CON, Reference 339
Norman Triplett is to _____ as Irving Janis is to _____.
A.   social facilitation; social loafing
B.   deindividuation; group polarization
C.   groupthink; social loafing
D.   social facilitation; groupthink

(67)   Answer D, Type FAC, Reference 340
Which of the following was not suggested by Janis to be a product of groupthink?
A.   the U.S. military's failure to be alert to the possibility of the Japanese attack on Pearl Harbor
B.   the Kennedy administration's disastrous decision to accept a CIA plan to invade Cuba at the Bay of Pigs in 1961
C.   President Johnson's decision to escalate the war in Vietnam during the late 1960s
D.   President Truman's formulation of the Marshall Plan for getting Europe back on its feet after World War II

(68)   Answer A, Type DEF, Reference 340
Groupthink can best be defined as
A.   a tendency to suppress dissent in the interests of group harmony.
B.   a tendency to sacrifice group cohesiveness in favor of task orientation and problem focus.
C.   enhancement of problem-solving capacity as a result of several persons joining together to work on the same problem.
D.   reduced self-awareness as a result of group immersion and social anonymity.

(69)   Answer D, Type FAC, Reference 340
A group that _____ is at risk for developing groupthink.
A.   is isolated from contrary viewpoints
B.   is amiably cohesive
C.   has a directive leader

D.   All of the above.

(70)   Answer C, Type FAC, Reference 341
Which of the following is <u>not</u> one of the symptoms of groupthink?
A.   unquestioned belief in the group's morality
B.   pressure to conform
C.   the illusion of vulnerability
D.   self-censorship

(71)   Answer A, Type CON, Reference 341
Which of the following comments is most likely to be made in a group characterized by groupthink?
A.   "We have been in agreement on matters in the past and I hope that will continue."
B.   "Joe, why don't you play devil's advocate and challenge the course of action most of us seem to prefer?"
C.   "I think we need some outsiders to come in and critique our decision before we proceed."
D.   "We have made some stupid mistakes in the past. Let's work carefully and not make the same errors again."

(72)   Answer B, Type FAC, Reference 342
"Mindguards" protect group leaders from
A.   unfair criticism.
B.   disagreeable facts.
C.   susceptibility to illusions.
D.   stereotyped views of the opponents.

(73)   Answer A, Type FAC, Reference 343
The text suggests that groupthink was clearly evident in
A.   NASA's decision to launch the space shuttle *Challenger* in January 1986.
B.   the Kennedy administration's handling of the U.S.S.R.'s attempts to install missile bases in Cuba.
C.   the Bush administration's decision to defend Kuwait against Iraq.
D.   the Clinton administration's decision to send U.S. troops into Haiti to restore democracy.

(74)   Answer B, Type FAC, Reference 345
Which of the following is <u>not</u> a prescriptive strategy to prevent groupthink from developing?
A.   One or more members should be assigned the position of devil's advocate.

B.   Group members should be kept together as one unit and not divided into separate discussion subgroups.
C.   Outsiders should attend the meetings and challenge the group's views.
D.   After reaching a preliminary decision, the group should call a second-chance meeting and ask each member to express remaining doubts.

(75) Answer B, Type FAC, Reference 346
Research on brainstorming has indicated that people working in a group will feel _____ productive and generate _____ good ideas than the same people working alone.
A.   more; more
B.   more; fewer
C.   less; more
D.   less; fewer

(76) Answer D, Type FAC, Reference 346
According to the text, the symptoms of groupthink illustrate the social psychological principle of
A.   conformity.
B.   self-serving bias.
C.   self-justification.
D.   All of the above.

(77) Answer D, Type FAC, Reference 348
According to Serge Moscovici, there are several determinants of minority influence in group interaction. Which of the following is not one of them?
A.   defections from the majority
B.   behavior that conveys self-confidence
C.   consistency in minority judgment
D.   behavior that conveys open-mindedness

(78) Answer B, Type FAC, Reference 348
Research indicates that minorities are most influential when they
A.   make use of two-sided rather than one-sided appeals.
B.   unswervingly stick to their position.
C.   argue positions that are greatly discrepant from the majority position.
D.   show respect for the majority position.

(79) Answer A, Type FAC, Reference 348
Moscovici and colleagues found that, in judging the color of slides, if members of a minority _____, then members of the majority occasionally agreed with them.

A. consistently judged blue slides to be green
B. occasionally wavered in their judgments
C. emphasized the importance of their judgments
D. verbalized their prior experience with the task

(80) Answer A, Type FAC, Reference 348
Moscovici believes that a minority's following the majority usually reflects _____ and a majority's following a minority usually reflects _____.
A. public compliance; genuine acceptance
B. genuine acceptance; public compliance
C. public compliance; public compliance
D. genuine acceptance; genuine acceptance

(81) Answer C, Type FAC, Reference 349
In research with University of Pittsburgh students, John Levine and colleagues found that a minority person who _____ was more persuasive than a consistent minority voice.
A. expressed some doubts about the minority position
B. merely conveyed self-confidence
C. had defected from the majority
D. acted polite and respectful

(82) Answer C, Type DEF, Reference 349
The process by which certain group members motivate and guide the group defines
A. social facilitation.
B. goal arousal.
C. leadership.
D. expert power.

(83) Answer D, Type FAC, Reference 350
_____ leaders have a directive style while _____ leaders have a democratic style.
A. Charismatic; social
B. Authoritarian; authoritative
C. Task; permissive
D. Task; social

(84) Answer B, Type FAC, Reference 351
Research on leadership indicates that
A. all great leaders share certain traits.

B.   effective supervisors tend to score high on both task and social leadership.
C.   the most effective leaders typically deviate significantly from a group's standards or norms.
D.   All of the above.

(85)   Answer D, Type DEF, Reference 351
Charismatic leaders typically have
A.   a compelling vision of some desired state of affairs.
B.   an ability to communicate goals in clear and simple language.
C.   enough optimism and faith in the group to inspire members to follow them.
D.   All of the above.

THE FOLLOWING ITEMS ALSO APPEAR IN THE STUDY GUIDE:

(86)   Answer D, Type FAC, Reference 315
Which form of social influence discussed in Chapter 9 does not necessarily involve an interacting group?
A.   group polarization
B.   groupthink
C.   minority influence
D.   social facilitation

(87)   Answer D, Type FAC, Reference 315
Which of the following is true?
A.   People's color preferences are stronger when they make judgments with others present.
B.   Ants excavate more sand in the presence of other ants.
C.   In the presence of others, students take less time to learn a simple maze and more time to learn one that is complex.
D.   All of the above.

(88)   Answer A, Type FAC, Reference 323
Social facilitation and social loafing have been explained in terms of difference in
A.   evaluation concern.
B.   informational influence.
C.   cognitive dissonance.
D.   group polarization.

(89)   Answer C, Type FAC, Reference 326
Which of the following is false?
A.   Groups of friends loaf less than groups of strangers.

B.   Israel's communal kibbutz farms have outproduced Israel's noncollective farms.
C.   Research completed in Japan, Thailand, and India indicates that social loafing does not occur in less individualistic, more group-centered cultures.
D.   Students pumped exercise bikes more energetically when they knew they were being individually monitored than when they thought their output was being pooled with that of other riders.

(90)   Answer A, Type FAC, Reference 326
Experiments show that people in groups loaf less when
A.   the task is challenging.
B.   they are in an unfamiliar setting.
C.   they have a strong sense of external control.
D.   the task is routine.

(91)   Answer A, Type FAC, Reference 332
The term "risky shift" was used to refer to the finding of
A.   groups being riskier than individuals.
B.   individuals being riskier than groups.
C.   males being riskier than females.
D.   people becoming less risky as they grow older.

(92)   Answer B, Type CON, Reference 349
Tom, a successful foreman in a large furniture factory, emphasizes the attainment of production goals and sets high standards for the workers under him. Tom's style is an example of _____ leadership.
A.   normative
B.   task
C.   autocratic
D.   Type A

(93)   Answer A, Type CON, Reference 316
The presence of others would be most likely to improve performance on
A.   raking up leaves.
B.   solving crossword puzzles.
C.   learning foreign language words.
D.   solving complex mathematical puzzles.

(94)   Answer A, Type CON, Reference 315
Who among the following would be considered coactors?
A.   four people doing push-ups in an exercise class

B.   two people playing bridge
C.   eight competitors running a 5-kilometer race
D.   All of the above.

(95)   Answer B, Type CON, Reference 327
After an exciting soccer game in which the home team loses, a crowd of fans throws garbage and begins to tear up the field. This behavior is best understood in terms of
A.   group polarization.
B.   deindividuation.
C.   groupthink.
D.   social facilitation.

(96)   Answer D, Type CON, Reference 314
Which of the following is least likely to be considered a group as defined in the text?
A.   a husband and wife talking over dinner
B.   a committee of eight discussing the problem of neighborhood crime
C.   four seven-year-olds playing hide-and-go-seek
D.   seven people waiting at a bus stop

(97)   Answer A, Type CON, Reference 316
The presence of others would be least likely to improve performance in
A.   playing chess.
B.   weight lifting.
C.   running.
D.   the broad jump.

(98)   Answer B, Type CON, Reference 324
Social loafing would be least likely to occur
A.   in a boys' club trying to raise money by holding a Saturday car wash.
B.   in a relay race in which each team member's performance is timed.
C.   in a community garden where each family is expected to contribute whatever free time they have.
D.   in a work crew building a new highway.

(99)   Answer A, Type CON, Reference 333
Individuals who tend to favor stiff penalties for drunk drivers come together to discuss various ways of dealing with the problem of intoxicated drivers. The group polarization hypothesis predicts that after group discussion,
A.   the individuals will favor even more severe penalties for drunk drivers.

B.   the individuals will tend to become more tolerant of drunk drivers.

C.   the individuals will be divided into two opposing groups as to the best way to deal with drunk drivers.

D.   the individuals will favor a rehabilitation program rather than a jail sentence for drunk drivers.

(100) Answer C, Type CON, Reference 341
Which of the following is a comment you are least likely to hear being made within a group characterized by groupthink?

A.   "Our critics are not very smart."

B.   "Our past decisions have always been right."

C.   "Let's make the decision and get out of here. I've got more important things to do."

D.   "It seems to me we are all in agreement on this, so let's proceed."

CHAPTER TEN: SOCIAL PSYCHOLOGY IN COURT

Multiple Choice

(1)   Answer A, Type FAC, Reference 356
The text identifies all of the following questions or topics as pertinent to both social psychology and the law except
A.   How is the judicial function of a government related to its legislative function?
B.   How do a culture's norms and traditions influence its legal decisions?
C.   What legal procedures strike people as fair?
D.   In cases of civil liability, why do clients and their attorneys spend such enormous sums on legal fees before reaching settlements?

(2)   Answer C, Type FAC, Reference 356
In contrast to most English-speaking countries, most non-English-speaking countries
A.   dispose of most criminal cases through plea bargaining rather than court trial.
B.   resolve most civil and criminal cases through third-party mediation.
C.   have a nonadversarial justice system in which the court plays a more active role.
D.   only allow eyewitness testimony into court if there are at least two witnesses to a given crime.

(3)   Answer D, Type FAC, Reference 357
Of criminal cases disposed of in U.S. District Courts, _____ never come to trial because of pretrial plea bargaining and other negotiations.
A.   one in five
B.   two in five
C.   three in five
D.   four in five

(4)   Answer B, Type FAC, Reference 358
At the University of Washington, Elizabeth Loftus found that eyewitnesses in a hypothetical robbery-murder case were influential
A.   unless their testimony was shown to be useless.
B.   even when their testimony was discredited.
C.   only if other evidence supported their story.
D.   only if they were similar to those making judgment.

(5)   Answer A, Type FAC, Reference 358
When Loftus presented University of Washington students with a hypothetical robbery-murder case based on circumstantial evidence but no eyewitness testimony, only 18 percent voted for conviction. When other students received the same information plus a single eyewitness ____ percent were in favor of conviction.
A.   72
B.   58
C.   45
D.   30

(6)   Answer B, Type FAC, Reference 358
Loftus found that when an eyewitness who had testified against the defendant in a hypothetical robbery-murder case was discredited because of having poor vision
A.   about half the jurors switched their votes from guilty to innocent.
B.   the majority of jurors still voted for conviction.
C.   jurors regarded the eyewitness testimony as useless and it had no impact on their verdict.
D.   a boomerang effect occurred with all jurors now voting for acquittal.

(7)   Answer A, Type CON, Reference 358
A prosecuting attorney is uncertain whether her eyewitness will seem credible to the jury. The eyewitness's testimony could help win a conviction, but the witness might be discredited by the defense attorney. What advice should the prosecutor accept?
A.   Put the witness on the stand, since even a discredited eyewitness is more convincing than no eyewitness at all.
B.   Don't put the witness on the stand, since a discredited eyewitness is worse than no eyewitness at all.
C.   Put the eyewitness on the stand but admit your reservations about the witness's credibility before the defense attorney raises the issue.
D.   Put the witness on the stand only if he or she is attractive and similar to the jurors.

(8)   Answer D, Type FAC, Reference 358
Wells, Lindsay, and their colleagues staged the theft of a calculator hundreds of times before eyewitnesses. In attempting to determine whether people could spot erroneous testimony, the researchers had mock jurors observe the eyewitnesses being questioned. Results indicated that the jurors believed correct eyewitnesses _____ percent of the time and incorrect eyewitnesses _____ percent of the time.
A.   60; 40

B.   60; 20
C.   80; 40
D.   80; 80

(9)   Answer D, Type FAC, Reference 358
Lindsay, Wells, and Rumpel staged the same calculator theft under conditions that
sometimes gave witnesses a clear view of the thief and sometimes didn't. When
conditions were so poor that most witnesses misidentified an innocent person,
_____ of the jurors believed the witness.
A.   none
B.   fewer than half
C.   about half
D.   most

(10)   Answer D, Type FAC, Reference 358
Studies of eyewitness testimony indicate that
A.   jurors have very good ability at discerning whether eyewitnesses have
mistakenly identified an innocent person.
B.   when witnessing conditions are shown to have been poor, jurors do not
usually believe eyewitness testimony.
C.   eyewitnesses who are shown to have poor eyesight have little effect on the
juror's judgment.
D.   None of the above are true.

(11)   Answer B, Type FAC, Reference 358
Jurors think that an eyewitness who can recall trivial details such as how many
pictures were hanging in the room probably
A.   gained information about these details by a second visit to the crime scene
and thus is less credible.
B.   was paying better attention than one who recalls no details.
C.   was not paying attention to the culprit or the crime itself.
D.   is no more accurate in recalling important information than witnesses with
no memory for details.

(12)   Answer C, Type FAC, Reference 358
Research indicates that eyewitnesses who remember trivial details of a crime
scene
A.   also tend to overestimate the degree of harm or damage done as a result of
the crime.
B.   also tend to be particularly suspicious of all unfamiliar faces.
C.   are less likely to have paid attention to the culprit's face.

D.   are also more likely to have paid attention to the culprit's face.

(13)   Answer B, Type CON, Reference 358
City police find that Mr. Caldwell, an eyewitness to a murder in a local bank,
correctly remembers many trivial details of the crime scene, including the
specific time on the clock and the paintings on the wall. Research findings
suggest that Mr. Caldwell's recall of trivial details means
A.   it is more likely that he can also correctly identify the murderer.
B.   it is less likely that he can also correctly identify the murderer.
C.   nothing in terms of his ability to correctly identify the murderer.
D.   it is more likely that he can also correctly identify the murderer, provided
Mr. Caldwell is also highly educated.

(14)   Answer A, Type CON, Reference 358
A prosecuting attorney learns that a crucial eyewitness to a grocery store robbery
correctly remembers trivial details of the crime scene. If the prosecutor hopes to
convince the jury that the eyewitness is credible, research suggests
A.   he should make the jury aware of the witness's ability to remember trivial
details.
B.   he should deliberately avoid making the jury aware of the witness's ability
to remember trivial details.
C.   it will make no difference whether the jury knows that the witness can
remember trivial details.
D.   he should make the jury aware of the witness's ability to remember trivial
details only if the jury is composed of all males.

(15)   Answer D, Type FAC, Reference 360
When students witnessed an "assault" on a professor and seven weeks later were
asked to identify the assailant from a group of six photographs, _____ of the
students chose an innocent person.
A.   none
B.   fewer than half
C.   about half
D.   more than half

(16)   Answer C, Type FAC, Reference 360
Wells and his colleagues report that it's the _____ eyewitness whom witnesses
jurors find to be most believable.
A.   older
B.   younger
C.   confident

D.   emotional

(17)   Answer B, Type CON, Reference 360
Of the following eyewitnesses to a crime, which would probably appear most believable to a jury?
A.   Billy, a fifth-grader whose father is a lawyer
B.   Paul, a radio announcer who appears very confident about what he saw
C.   Moira, a retired teacher who has traveled widely to visit other countries
D.   Joyce, a shy student who smiles and speaks very softly

(18)   Answer A, Type FAC, Reference 360
Which of the following statements about eyewitness testimony is false?
A.   Eyewitnesses' certainty about what they have seen is closely related to their accuracy.
B.   Confident witnesses are more believable to jurors than those lacking confidence.
C.   Incorrect witnesses are virtually as self-assured as correct witnesses.
D.   In the United States alone, eyewitnesses accuse some 75,000 people a year of crimes.

(19)   Answer C, Type FAC, Reference 360
In 1972 the U.S. Supreme Court declared that among the factors to be considered in determining eyewitness accuracy is " the level of _____ demonstrated by the witness."
A.   impartiality
B.   interest
C.   certainty
D.   fluency

(20)   Answer C, Type FAC, Reference 360
Witnesses who are not correct typically express _____ confidence in their judgments as those who are correct.
A.   much less
B.   somewhat less
C.   the same level of
D.   more

(21)   Answer D, Type FAC, Reference 360
Mistaken eyewitnesses tend to be less _____ than accurate witnesses.
A.   willing to testify
B.   confident

C.   persuasive
D.   None of the above.

(22) Answer A, Type FAC, Reference 360
In a classic 1947 experiment, Allport and Postman showed subjects a picture of a
White man brandishing a razor while arguing with a Black man. After six
tellings of the story, subject to subject, the last version of the story said that
A.   the Black man held the razor.
B.   both the White man and the Black man held razors.
C.   both men were Black and fighting each other.
D.   both men were White and conversing with each other.

(23) Answer A, Type FAC, Reference 361
Loftus and her associates' studies of the misinformation effect provide a dramatic
demonstration of
A.   memory construction.
B.   repressed memory.
C.   proactive interference.
D.   state-dependent memory.

(24) Answer D, Type FAC, Reference 362
In research by Loftus and colleagues, University of Washington students were
shown slides depicting successive stages of an automobile-pedestrian accident.
Results showed that
A.   most witnesses did not notice the difference between a stop sign and a yield
sign.
B.   eyewitnesses were unable to determine whether the driver or the pedestrian
had been at fault.
C.   when the information was presented slowly, eyewitnesses' accuracy of
recall became nearly flawless.
D.   asking misleading questions caused distortion of eyewitnesses' memories.

(25) Answer B, Type DEF, Reference 362
The process of witnessing an event, receiving misleading information about it,
and then incorporating the misleading information into one's memory of the
event is referred to as the _____ effect.
A.   false memory
B.   misinformation
C.   inoculation
D.   interference

(26) Answer C, Type FAC, Reference 363
Police use of suggestive questions may distort witness's recall of a crime due to human susceptibility to
A.   retroactive interference.
B.   repression.
C.   the misinformation effect.
D.   state-dependent memory.

(27) Answer D, Type CON, Reference 363
After hearing a television report falsely indicating that drugs may have contributed to a recent auto accident, several eyewitnesses of the accident began to remember the driver as traveling at a faster rate of speed than was actually the case. This provides an example of
A.   flashbulb memory.
B.   state-dependent memory.
C.   the serial position effect.
D.   the misinformation effect.

(28) Answer D, Type FAC, Reference 363
Which of the following statements about asking eyewitnesses suggestive questions is true?
A.   After suggestive questioning, witnesses may believe that a red light was green or a clean-shaven robber had a mustache.
B.   Witnesses are most likely to incorporate misleading information into their memories if they think the questioner is well informed.
C.   Young children are more susceptible than adults to leading questions.
D.   All of the above.

(29) Answer C, Type FAC, Reference 363
Witnesses incorporate misleading information into their memories especially when they believe the questioner
A.   suspects them of the crime they are describing.
B.   does not believe them.
C.   is well informed.
D.   likes and respects them.

(30) Answer C, Type FAC, Reference 363
Research on the memories of young children indicates that
A.   they are better at remembering verbal than visual details.
B.   they tend to fabricate stories about their own victimization even when asked open-ended questions.

C.   they are especially susceptible to misinformation.
D.   None of the above.

(31)   Answer D, Type FAC, Reference 363
When Ceci and Bruck repeatedly asked preschoolers whether they could remember going to the hospital with a mousetrap on their finger, most
A.   demonstrated reactance and denied ever having been in a hospital for any reason.
B.   remembered this as having happened to a friend or relative but not to themselves.
C.   became increasingly assertive in denying that this had ever happened to them.
D.   eventually produced false and often detailed memories about this actually having happened.

(32)   Answer A, Type FAC, Reference 363
Ceci believes that young children's susceptibility to the misinformation effect raises the distinct possibility that
A.   some people have been falsely accused in sex abuse cases.
B.   many educators overestimate the competence of their students.
C.   repression leads children to forget that they were physically abused.
D.   many children are simply unable to experience empathy for dissimilar others.

(33)   Answer D, Type FAC, Reference 364
Retelling events
A.   commits people to their recollections, accurate or not.
B.   helps people resist suggestions that would change the story.
C.   increases the confidence of witnesses who are wrong.
D.   All of the above.

(34)   Answer C, Type FAC, Reference 364
Wells, Ferguson, and Lindsay had eyewitnesses to a staged theft rehearse their answers to questions before taking the witness stand. Doing so
A.   increased the accuracy of the eyewitness testimony.
B.   decreased the confidence of those who were correct.
C.   increased the confidence of those who were wrong.
D.   increased the confidence of those who were correct and decreased the confidence of those who were wrong.

(35)   Answer C, Type FAC, Reference 364

Sheppard and Vidmar had some students serve as witnesses to a fight, while others took the roles of lawyers and judges. When they had been interviewed by the defense lawyer, the witnesses
A.   gave testimony condemning the defendant as guilty.
B.   gained self-confidence and claimed to remember more details.
C.   gave testimony that was favorable to the defendant.
D.   were less susceptible to the misinformation effect.

(36)   Answer B, Type FAC, Reference 364
Vidmar and Lair found that witnesses who thought they were testifying on behalf of the defendant rather than on behalf of the plaintiff
A.   omitted facts that might have hurt the defendant's case.
B.   subtly changed their voice and choice of words while they testified.
C.   acted no differently from those who thought they were testifying for the plaintiff.
D.   remembered more facts that ironically hurt the defendant's case.

(37)   Answer C, Type FAC, Reference 364
Which of the following is not one recommended strategy for increasing the accuracy of eyewitnesses and jurors?
A.   Train police interviewers to elicit unbiased accounts.
B.   Educate jurors about the limitations of eyewitness testimony.
C.   Ask witnesses to scan a lineup of several suspects or mug shots simultaneously rather than one at a time.
D.   Have police acknowledge that the offender may not even be in the lineup.

(38)   Answer B, Type FAC, Reference 364
To elicit the most unbiased testimony, police interviewers should
A.   begin with specific questions that can be answered with yes-no responses.
B.   allow eyewitnesses to begin with their own unprompted recollections.
C.   tell witnesses what is already known before permitting them to add any information they might have.
D.   be open about their assumptions so witnesses can present their testimony in the most credible way.

(39)   Answer A, Type CON, Reference 364
Whose eyewitness testimony is probably the most reliable?
A.   Millie's report given immediately after a grocery store robbery. She was simply asked to tell the police what she saw.
B.   Fred's report given in court about a bank robbery a month ago. He has been interviewed several times by the defense attorney before appearing in court.

C.   Sue's report given immediately after observing an attempted rape. She was asked very specific questions by the police, who had identified a suspect immediately after the assault.

D.   All of the above are equally reliable.

(40)   Answer D, Type CON, Reference 365
A police interrogator questioning a robbery eyewitness hopes to learn whether the assailant was wearing a bright green hat similar to one seen in another robbery. According to research, which of the following questions will elicit the most detailed, undistorted recall from the eyewitness?

A.   "Did you see whether the robber was wearing a hat?"

B.   "Can you describe the hat the robber was wearing?"

C.   "What color was the robber's hat?"

D.   "How was the robber dressed?"

(41)   Answer C, Type FAC, Reference 366
Researchers have found that eyewitnesses' accuracy can improve when

A.   interrogators delay the interview at least one week.

B.   the witnesses scan a group of mug shots or a composite drawing before reviewing a lineup.

C.   they are presented with a sequence of individual people, one by one, instead of being presented with a group of photos or a lineup.

D.   the seriousness of the crime is highlighted.

(42)   Answer B, Type FAC, Reference 366
When eyewitnesses are presented with a lineup that contains no suspects, it is more likely that

A.   their memory about the real culprit's appearance will ultimately improve.

B.   witnesses who make false identifications can be screened out.

C.   an innocent person will be identified when a subsequent lineup contains the true culprit.

D.   eyewitnesses will become less confident of what they saw.

(43)   Answer D, Type FAC, Reference 366
Which of the following has been suggested as a strategy for reducing misidentifications in police lineups?

A.   Giving eyewitnesses a "blank" lineup that contains no suspects and screening out those who make false identifications

B.   Minimizing false identifications with instructions which acknowledge that the offender may not be in the lineup

C.   Composing the lineup of one suspect and several known innocent people

rather than a group of several suspects
D.   All of the above.

(44)   Answer A, Type FAC, Reference 366
According to the text, strategies such as using no-suspect lineups, wording
questions so they don't imply a particular response, and utilizing police officers
who don't know the real suspect will make police lineups resemble good
A.   experiments.
B.   detective stories.
C.   puzzles.
D.   games.

(45)   Answer C, Type FAC, Reference 366
Which of the following is <u>not</u> one of the explanations experts offer to educate
jurors to evaluate eyewitness testimony better?
A.   Eyewitnesses often perceive events selectively.
B.   Research using staged crimes shows that witnesses often choose the wrong
person in a lineup.
C.   The most confident eyewitness usually turns out to be the most accurate.
D.   Eyewitnesses are especially prone to error when trying to identify someone
of another race.

(46)   Answer B, Type FAC, Reference 367
Experts on eyewitness testimony occasionally give testimony on this research.
Experiments show that such expert testimony
A.   prompts jurors to be more accepting and less analytical about eyewitness
testimony.
B.   prompts jurors to analyze eyewitness reports more skeptically and discuss
them more fully.
C.   often backfires by making jurors reactant and more determined to show
their faith in the eyewitnesses.
D.   usually has no effect whatsoever on the jurors who hear it.

(47)   Answer C, Type FAC, Reference 367
According to famed trial lawyer Clarence Darrow, juries seldom convict a
person they
A.   are envious of.
B.   know.
C.   like.
D.   feel sorry for.

(48)   Answer C, Type FAC, Reference 367
A study of more than 3500 criminal cases and some 4000 civil cases found that
_____ the judge agreed with the jury's decision.
A.   two times in three
B.   three times in four
C.   four times in five
D.   nine times in ten

(49)   Answer D, Type FAC, Reference 367
Research into the factors that affect jury decisions indicates that, given relevant facts, jurors will focus most of their attention on
A.   how the defense presented the case.
B.   the characteristics of the accused.
C.   the social consequences of the possible verdicts.
D.   the evidence presented in the case.

(50)   Answer B, Type FAC, Reference 368
The more lenient treatment juries often give to _____ defendants suggests jurors' judgments continue to be contaminated by cultural bias.
A.   young
B.   high-status
C.   repentant
D.   poor

(51)   Answer A, Type FAC, Reference 368
When a researcher gave students a description of a case of student cheating and showed them a photograph of either an attractive or unattractive person accused of the crime, he found that attractive defendants were _____.
A.   recommended for least punishment
B.   more likely to be judged as guilty
C.   liked or respected
D.   perceived as more dangerous

(52)   Answer D, Type FAC, Reference 369
Baby-faced adults--with large round eyes and a small chin--who are accused of committing crimes are found
A.   to be too naive to be guilty of deliberate wrongdoing.
B.   more often guilty of crimes of negligence.
C.   less often guilty of intentional criminal acts.
D.   All of the above.

(53)   Answer C, Type FAC, Reference 369
If convicted, _____ people strike people as more dangerous, especially if they are sexual offenders.
A.   cute or baby-faced
B.   attractive
C.   unattractive
D.   underage

(54)   Answer B, Type FAC, Reference 369
In researching over 1700 defendants appearing in Texas misdemeanor cases, Downs and Lyons found that the judges _____ less attractive defendants.
A.   set lower bails for
B.   set greater fines for
C.   spent less time reviewing the cases of
D.   spent more time questioning

(55)   Answer A, Type FAC, Reference 370
Research shows that when people play the role of juror, they are more sympathetic to a defendant who
A.   shares their religion.
B.   is of another race.
C.   speaks a different language.
D.   is of the other gender.

(56)   Answer B, Type FAC, Reference 370
When Paul Amato had Australian students read evidence concerning a left- or right-wing person accused of a politically motivated burglary, they judged him less guilty if
A.   he claimed to have no religious preferences.
B.   his political views were similar to their own.
C.   he claimed he had been hired to commit the crime.
D.   he proved he had not profited by the burglary.

(57)   Answer D, Type FAC, Reference 371
A national survey before the O.J. Simpson trial reported that a majority of _____ but a minority of _____ found the case against him at least "fairly strong."
A.   women; men
B.   older adults; young adults and adolescents
C.   police; attorneys
D.   Whites; Blacks

(58) Answer B, Type FAC, Reference 371
According to the Sixth Amendment to the U.S. Constitution, "The accused shall enjoy the right to a speedy and public trial by
A.   jury of his peers."
B.   impartial jury."
C.   community jury."
D.   judge and jury."

(59) Answer B, Type FAC, Reference 371
Research shows that when a judge rules evidence to be inadmissible and admonishes the jury to ignore it,
A.   jurors are generally able to follow the judge's instructions.
B.   jurors have a hard time ignoring the evidence and its influence on their deliberations.
C.   jurors do so if the evidence damages the defendant's case but not if it hurts the prosecution's case.
D.   the evidence typically becomes the focus of debate in jury deliberations.

(60) Answer C, Type FAC, Reference 371
Sue, Smith, and Caldwell described a robbery-murder to university students and asked them to judge a defendant. When the prosecutor's case was weak, no one judged the defendant guilty. When the tape of an incriminating phone call made by the defendant was added to the testimony but ruled inadmissible by the judge, _____ of the students judged the defendant guilty.
A.   again, none
B.   about 10 percent
C.   one-third
D.   two-thirds

(61) Answer A, Type FAC, Reference 372
As a result of the judge's admonition that a jury disregard evidence ruled inadmissible, the stricken evidence may have even greater impact on the jury's decision than if it had not been ruled out. This is probably due to _____ in the jurors.
A.   reactance
B.   disinhibition
C.   self-efficacy
D.   self-monitoring

(62) Answer B, Type FAC, Reference 372

The concept of reactance has been used to explain why
A.   jurors show sympathy for an attractive defendant.
B.   a judge's instructions to a jury to ignore certain testimony can actually add to its impact.
C.   a severe potential punishment makes juries less likely to convict.
D.   experienced jurors' judgments differ from those of novice jurors.

(63)   Answer D, Type FAC, Reference 372
Research on pretrial publicity indicates that
A.   most people who have been influenced by pretrial publicity will admit its effect and exclude themselves from participation on a jury.
B.   getting mock jurors to verbally pledge their impartiality and their willingness to disregard prior information typically eliminates the pretrial publicity effect.
C.   judges' specific instructions to a jury to disregard pretrial publicity are typically successful in removing pretrial publicity effects.
D.   None of the above.

(64)   Answer B, Type FAC, Reference 373
To minimize the effects of inadmissible testimony, the text suggests that judges are best advised to
A.   wait until jurors have heard the testimony before ruling it inadmissible, so jurors specifically know what they are to disregard.
B.   forewarn jurors that certain types of evidence may be irrelevant and could be ruled inadmissible.
C.   meet with jurors during their deliberations after the trial to insure that inadmissible testimony is not influencing their judgments.
D.   immediately follow the trial by seeking a verbal pledge from each juror to ignore inadmissible evidence.

(65)   Answer B, Type FAC, Reference 373
Videotaped testimony
A.   does not have the same impact on jurors as live testimony.
B.   enables the judge to edit out inadmissible testimony.
C.   has been suggested as one of the best strategies for reducing court costs.
D.   All of the above.

(66)   Answer D, Type FAC, Reference 374
From research findings, which of the following statements appears to be true?
A.   A severe potential punishment makes jurors less willing to convict.
B.   Experienced jurors' judgments differ from those of novice jurors.

C.   Defendants are judged more harshly when the victim is attractive.
D.   All of the above.

(67)   Answer A, Type FAC, Reference 375
Research suggests that, in reaching their decisions, jurors first
A.   construct a story that makes sense of all the evidence.
B.   make separate mental lists of the two sides' arguments.
C.   engage in counterfactual thinking, imagining alternative scenarios and outcomes that might have happened but didn't.
D.   imagine themselves in both the defendant's and victim's place in an effort to develop objectivity.

(68)   Answer A, Type FAC, Reference 375
Research indicates that jurors are more likely to be persuaded when attorneys present evidence
A.   in the order of a narrative story.
B.   in the form of testing a hypothesis in an experiment.
C.   by numerically listing their specific arguments.
D.   without interpretation or drawing conclusions from it.

(69)   Answer A, Type FAC, Reference 376
In a Nevada study of people's ability to comprehend judicial instructions, viewers of videotaped criminal instructions could answer _____ percent of the 89 questions posed to them about what they had heard.
A.   15
B.   30
C.   50
D.   65

(70)   Answer D, Type FAC, Reference 377
An important step toward better jury decisions is devising clearer, more effective ways to present information, since jurors have been found to have particular difficulty understanding
A.   anecdotal evidence.
B.   crimes of passion.
C.   community standards.
D.   statistical arguments.

(71)   Answer B, Type FAC, Reference 377
According to the text, giving jurors transcripts of court proceedings can
A.   lead to stimulus overload and, in the long run, result in fewer people being

willing to serve on juries.
B.   aid the processing of complex information.
C.   shortcircuit their interest in the case and reduce their motivation to reach the best verdict.
D.   help them review the evidence less emotionally and thus suffer less burnout.

(72)   Answer B, Type FAC, Reference 378
In reviewing research on scientific jury selection, Saks and Hastie conclude that _____ is a substantially more potent determinant of jurors' verdicts than the individual characteristics of jurors.
A.   defendant characteristics
B.   evidence
C.   the group dynamics of jury deliberation
D.   All of the above.

(73)   Answer C, Type FAC, Reference 378
In experiments, jurors' personalities and general attitudes have been found to have the greatest effect on the verdict when
A.   the evidence is clearly prodefendant.
B.   the evidence is clearly antidefendant.
C.   the evidence is ambiguous.
D.   the crime is one that could warrant the death penalty.

(74)   Answer B, Type FAC, Reference 379
According to research on death-qualified juries, people who do not oppose the death penalty
A.   are more concerned with due process of law than with crime control.
B.   are more likely to oppose protecting the constitutional rights of defendants.
C.   are more prone to favor the defense.
D.   have a greater sense of self-efficacy.

(75)   Answer B, Type FAC, Reference 379
Conviction-prone jurors also tend to be
A.   less concerned about social approval.
B.   more authoritarian.
C.   higher in self-esteem.
D.   poorly educated.

(76)   Answer C, Type FAC, Reference 379
Research indicates that at the start of a jury's deliberations the chances are about

_____ that jurors will <u>not</u> agree on a verdict.

A.   one in three
B.   one in two
C.   two in three
D.   three in four

(77)   Answer B, Type FAC, Reference 380
Research suggests that a hung jury is likely unless at least _____ of the jurors agree at the outset of deliberation.

A.   one-half
B.   two-thirds
C.   three-quarters
D.   90 percent

(78)   Answer D, Type FAC, Reference 380
Research suggests that jurors in the minority will be most persuasive when they

A.   are consistent.
B.   are self-confident.
C.   win defections from the majority.
D.   All of the above.

(79)   Answer D, Type FAC, Reference 380
Bray and Noble found that as a result of group deliberation low authoritarians recommended a _____ prison term and high authoritarians recommended a _____ prison term.

A.   longer; longer
B.   shorter; shorter
C.   longer; shorter
D.   shorter; longer

(80)   Answer B, Type FAC, Reference 380
Hastie, Penrod, and Pennington showed subjects reenactments of an actual murder case, and asked them to deliberate until they agreed on a verdict. Prior to group deliberation, jurors who thought the defendant was guilty preferred a verdict of _____; after deliberation, they preferred a verdict of _____.

A.   second-degree murder; manslaughter
B.   manslaughter; second-degree murder
C.   first-degree murder; second-degree murder
D.   manslaughter; not guilty

(81)   Answer A, Type FAC, Reference 381

Kalven and Zeisel report that in those cases where a jury's majority does not prevail, it usually shifts to
A.   acquittal.
B.   conviction.
C.   acquittal if composed primarily of women and conviction if composed primarily of men.
D.   the position held by those with highest social status.

(82)   Answer B, Type FAC, Reference 382
Research on the effects of group deliberation by a jury suggests that
A.   groups do no better at recalling information from a trial than do their individual members.
B.   deliberation cancels out some of the biases that contaminate individual judgments.
C.   it increases the likelihood that jurors will use inadmissible evidence.
D.   all of the above are true.

(83)   Answer D, Type FAC, Reference 382
Research indicates that six-member juries
A.   are more likely to have hung verdicts.
B.   allow less participation per juror.
C.   encourage less balanced participation among jurors.
D.   are less likely to embody a community's diversity.

(84)   Answer B, Type FAC, Reference 383
Studies comparing juries required to reach consensus with those that are not indicates that
A.   different decision rules produce a very different distribution of verdicts.
B.   juries not required to reach consensus may discuss minority views rather superficially.
C.   juries not required to reach consensus experience greater social conflict.
D.   juries not required to reach consensus show the advantages of greater and more evenly balanced participation per juror.

(85)   Answer C, Type FAC, Reference 383
In order to close the gap between real courtroom processes and laboratory studies, researchers are using _____ as subjects and having them view _____.
A.   university students; videotapes of courtroom trials
B.   real jurors; dramas based on real-life cases
C.   members of real jury pools; enactments of actual trials
D.   real jurors; ongoing courtroom trials

(86)   Answer B, Type FAC, Reference 356
From the text, which of the following is a <u>true</u> statement regarding social psychology and the courtroom?
A.   Most of the government research funds available to social psychologists have been designated for the study of courtroom procedures.
B.   The courtroom is a miniature social world where people think about and influence each other.
C.   The study of criminal cases can provide important new insight into the causes of aggression and conflict.
D.   All of the above.

(87)   Answer C, Type FAC, Reference 367
Which of the following is not part of the literature discussed in the text on social psychology and the courtroom?
A.   how the defendant's characteristics can influence jurors' judgments
B.   how the jurors' own characteristics can influence their judgments
C.   how the physical environment of the jury room influences jurors' judgments
D.   how the judge's instructions influence jurors' judgments

(88)   Answer D, Type FAC, Reference 362
Research on memory construction indicates that suggestive questioning can lead people to believe that
A.   a yield sign was actually a stop sign.
B.   a red light was actually green.
C.   a robber had a moustache when he did not.
D.   All of the above.

(89)   Answer B, Type FAC, Reference 364
Research indicates that having eyewitnesses rehearse their answers to questions before taking the witness stand
A.   raises uncertainty in the minds of eyewitnesses as to what they actually saw.
B.   increases their confidence about what they saw.
C.   increases their confidence but also heightens their anxiety about appearing in court.
D.   invariably leads them to give a much more detailed and accurate account of what they saw.

(90)   Answer C, Type FAC, Reference 378
Survey researchers sometimes assist defense attorneys by using "scientific jury selection" to eliminate potential jurors likely to be unsympathetic. Results indicated that in the first nine important trials in which the defense relied on such methods, it
A.   won all nine.
B.   won two.
C.   won seven.
D.   lost all nine.

(91)   Answer B, Type FAC, Reference 379
In 1986 the U.S. Supreme Court in a split decision
A.   ruled that death-qualified jurors are a biased sample.
B.   overturned a lower court ruling that death-qualified jurors are a biased sample.
C.   ruled that Georgia's five-member juries were as reliable and accurate as twelve-member juries.
D.   overturned a lower court decision that six-member juries could decide cases involving the death penalty.

(92)   Answer C, Type FAC, Reference 370
Someone accused of a crime is judged more sympathetically
A.   by females than by males.
B.   if he or she appears to have personality characteristics that are complementary to the one who judges.
C.   if he or she appears similar to the one who judges.
D.   if there was a bystander who watched and did not intervene.

(93)   Answer D, Type DEF, Reference 380
What is meant by the "two-thirds-majority" scheme?
A.   Two-thirds of all people asked refuse to serve on a jury.
B.   Two out of three times judges agree with the jury's decision.
C.   A two-thirds majority is a better rule than consensus for a jury to follow in reaching a verdict.
       The jury verdict is usually the alternative favored by at least two-thirds of the jurors at the outset.

(94)   Answer A, Type FAC, Reference 383
According to the text, simulated juries
 A.   can help us formulate theories we can use to interpret the more complex

world.

B.   are almost identical to real juries so that we can readily generalize from one to the other.

C.   have been viewed by the majority of Supreme Court judges as valuable in predicting the behavior of actual juries.

D.   have mundane but not experimental realism.

(95)   Answer A, Type CON, Reference 364
Whose eyewitness testimony is probably the most reliable?

A.   Thressa's report immediately after a bank robbery. She was simply asked by police to tell in her own words what happened.

B.   Sheryl's testimony about a grocery store holdup. She has been interviewed eight times by the prosecuting attorney before appearing in court.

C.   David's testimony about a car accident. He has been interviewed three times by the defense attorney before his court appearance.

D.   Susan's report immediately after observing an attempted rape. She was asked very specific questions by the police, who believed they already had a suspect in custody.

(96)   Answer C, Type CON, Reference 379
Attorney Johnson will be defending James S., who is accused of raping a 22-year-old woman. Who among the following jurors is likely to be least sympathetic to his client's case?

A.   John, a 40-year-old plumber who once served a sentence for burglary

B.   Todd, a 22-year-old college student who is a political liberal

C.   Wilma, a 42-year-old mother of two who tends to be authoritarian

D.   Rita, a 32-year-old television executive who opposes the death penalty

(97)   Answer D, Type CON, Reference 368
Attorney Miller is defending Mary, a 20-year-old college student, who is being tried for failing to pay income tax. What should she do to boost Mary's chances of being acquitted?

A.   select Bill and Philip, who are also college students to serve as jurors

B.   have Mary appear in court as attractively dressed as possible

C.   select jurors who oppose the death penalty

D.   All of the above.

(98)   Answer B, Type CON, Reference 373
You have just been appointed to serve as a new county judge. You are concerned about the effect inadmissible evidence may have on the jury in an upcoming trial of a case involving rape. You anticipate that the defense attorney will seek to

introduce evidence regarding the victim's prior sexual history. To minimize the impact of such evidence on the jury, you should

A.   say nothing about such inadmissible evidence to the jury.

B.   remind the jury before the trial that the victim's previous sexual history is irrelevant.

C.   only tell the jury that the evidence is inadmissible after the defense attempts to introduce it.

D.   ask the defendant to refute any damaging evidence about her previous sexual history.

(99)   Answer A, Type CON, Reference 380

A 12-member jury has heard all the evidence in a child abuse case and is beginning to deliberate. At the outset five jurors favor acquittal of the defendant and seven favor conviction. Based on research in the text, the jury will probably

A.   be unable to reach a verdict and be a hung jury.

B.   bring in a guilty verdict.

C.   vote for acquittal.

D.   vote for acquittal if the defendant is female and for conviction if the defendant is male.

(100) Answer B, Type CON, Reference 380

After hearing evidence in a murder trial, 12 jurors tend to believe the evidence is insufficient to convict the 25-year-old Black defendant. According to the group polarization hypothesis, after the jurors deliberate,

A.   they will be more convinced the defendant is guilty.

B.   they will be more convinced the evidence is insufficient to convict.

C.   they will be evenly split, with some convinced he is guilty and others convinced he is innocent.

D.   they will be split, with a minority favoring acquittal and the majority favoring conviction.

CHAPTER ELEVEN: PREJUDICE: DISLIKING OTHERS

<u>Multiple Choice</u>

(1)   Answer B, Type DEF, Reference 390
A prejudice is defined in the text as
A.   any attitude based on insufficient or false information.
B.   an unjustifiable negative attitude toward a group and its members.
C.   an intentional or unintentional policy of discriminating against outgroups.
D.   a cognitive categorization based on simplified stereotypes.

(2)   Answer C, Type FAC, Reference 390
Prejudice biases us against a person based solely on
A.   the person's appearance and behavior.
B.   our past experience with similar persons.
C.   the person's identification with a particular group.
D.   our present emotional state.

(3)   Answer B, Type CON, Reference 391
Which of the following clearly meets the definition of a stereotype?
A.   Mary believes her employer is incompetent.
B.   Selma believes Hispanics are expressive.
C.   Toby believes Honda cars are well designed.
D.   All of the above.

(4)   Answer D, Type FAC, Reference 391
According to Lee Jussin and colleagues, stereotypes may be
A.   positive.
B.   accurate.
C.   desirable.
D.   All of the above.

(5)   Answer C, Type CON, Reference 391
Prejudice is to discrimination as attitude is to
A.   policy.
B.   belief.
C.   behavior.
D.   generalization.

(6)   Answer D, Type DEF, Reference 392
Racism refers to

A.	institutional practices that subordinate people of a given race.
B.	individuals' prejudicial attitudes toward people of a given race.
C.	individuals' discriminatory behavior toward people of a given race.
D.	All of the above.

(7)	Answer D, Type DEF, Reference 392
The term "sexism" applies to all of the following except
A.	individuals' prejudicial attitudes toward people of a given sex.
B.	institutional practices that subordinate people of a given sex.
C.	individuals' discriminatory behavior toward people of a given sex.
D.	individuals' stereotyping of males and females.

(8)	Answer A, Type CON, Reference 392
A state police force has set a height requirement of 5 feet 10 inches for all officers. This requirement is irrelevant to job effectiveness but generally excludes Hispanics, Asians, and women from the force. Such a requirement most clearly reflects
A.	racism and sexism.
B.	scapegoating and ingroup bias.
C.	stereotyping and prejudice.
D.	Gause's law and realistic conflict theory.

(9)	Answer B, Type FAC, Reference 392
To judge from what Americans tell survey takers, racial prejudice toward African-Americans
A.	is today worse than ever.
B.	has plummeted since the early 1940s.
C.	has actually increased since the early 1980s.
D.	decreased from 1940 to 1960, then increased until 1980, and has since stabilized.

(10)	Answer B, Type FAC, Reference 392
In making its historic 1954 decision declaring segregation unconstitutional, the Supreme Court found it noteworthy that, when researchers Kenneth Clark and Mamie Clark gave African-American children a choice between Black dolls and White dolls,
A.	most chose the Black dolls.
B.	most chose the White dolls.
C.	most refused to choose between them.
D.	most used the dolls in aggressive symbolic play.

(11)   Answer C, Type FAC, Reference 392
Which of the following statements best summarizes the present status of racial prejudice in the United States?
A.   Racial prejudice abounds and is verbally expressed by a majority of the population.
B.   While well-educated people are less likely to show prejudice, most others admit to being both racist and sexist.
C.   Though no longer fashionable, racial prejudice exists below the surface and is sometimes expressed in action.
D.   Racial prejudice is virtually extinct in American life.

(12)   Answer B, Type FAC, Reference 393
The phenomenon of "greatest prejudice in the most _____ social realms" seems universal.
A.   public
B.   intimate
C.   profitable
D.   traditional

(13)   Answer C, Type FAC, Reference 394
A researcher had White students observe a videotape of one man shoving another during an argument. When a White man shoved a Black man, only 13 percent of the observers labeled the act as
A.   competitiveness.
B.   playing around.
C.   violent behavior.
D.   impatience.

(14)   Answer D, Type FAC, Reference 394
White people who were asked to use electric shocks to "teach" a task, delivered no more shock to a Black person than to a White person except when
A.   they were angered.
B.   the recipient could not retaliate.
C.   the recipient did not know who did it.
D.   any of the above conditions were true.

(15)   Answer B, Type FAC, Reference 394
Research on discriminatory behavior in the U.S. indicates that it
A.   is practiced primarily by White males against Black males.
B.   occurs when it can hide behind the screen of some other motive.
C.   occurs wherever it is not legally prohibited.

223

D.   is primarily motivated by economic gain.

(16)   Answer C, Type FAC, Reference 394
In France, Britain, Germany, and the United States, _____ is replacing
_____.
A.   authoritarianism; permissiveness
B.   sexism; racism
C.   subtle prejudice; blatant prejudice
D.   self-efficacy; stereotype vulnerability

(17)   Answer A, Type FAC, Reference 395
Patricia DeVine suggest that even for the low-prejudice person, overcoming
prejudice is like learning to
A.   break a bad habit.
B.   play a musical instrument.
C.   write a novel.
D.   walk a tightrope.

(18)   Answer D, Type FAC, Reference 396
Racism researcher Thomas Pettigrew has commented that many people confess to
feeling prejudiced at a deep emotional level although they do not consciously
agree with racist ideas, and summarizes, "These feelings are left over from what
they learned
A.   from their experiences in the working world."
B.   in the course of their formal education."
C.   in interacting with their most intimate friends."
D.   in their families as children."

(19)   Answer A, Type DEF, Reference 397
_____ are people's ideas about how women and men ought to behave.
A.   Gender-role norms
B.   Gender stereotypes
C.   Sexist attitudes
D.   Sexual preferences

(20)   Answer A, Type CON, Reference 397
The belief that Italians are passionate is an example of _____; the refusal to hire
Hispanics is an example of _____.
A.   a stereotype; discrimination
B.   a stereotype; prejudice
C.   racism; prejudice

D.   discrimination; racism

(21)   Answer B, Type FAC, Reference 397
Which of the following is false?
A.   Strong gender stereotypes continue to exist.
B.   Few women accept gender stereotypes.
C.   Gender stereotypes are generally stronger than racial stereotypes.
D.   Stereotypes are not prejudices.

(22)   Answer B, Type CON, Reference 397
"Women are more tactful than men" is an example of _____. "Women should not hold political office" is an example of _____.
A.   sex-role norm; a sexist attitude
B.   gender stereotype; a gender-role norm
C.   misogynist attitude; a gender stereotype
D.   sex-role norm; an institutional prejudice

(23)   Answer D, Type FAC, Reference 397
Porter, Geis, and Jennings showed subjects a picture of a group of graduate students working together on a project and asked subjects to guess which member contributed the most to the group. When the pictured group was mixed sex, the subjects chose
A.   a woman only if she was seated at the head of the table.
B.   a woman only if she appeared to be the oldest member of the group.
C.   a woman only if women in the group outnumbered the men.
D.   None of the above.

(24)   Answer C, Type FAC, Reference 398
_____ are very strong.
A.   Self-perceived differences between the sexes
B.   Actual behavioral differences between the sexes
C.   Stereotypes about gender-related differences
D.   All of the above.

(25)   Answer A, Type FAC, Reference 399
In 1988, _____ percent of Americans said they would vote for a qualified woman whom their party nominated for President.
A.   90
B.   70
C.   50
D.   30

(26)   Answer B, Type FAC, Reference 399
In reviewing the research on gender attitudes, Alice Eagly and her associates report that most people
A.   have gut-level negative emotions about women even though they describe them favorably.
B.   like "women" more than "men."
C.   express more admiration than affection for women.
D.   view men and women as equally understanding and helpful.

(27)   Answer A, Type FAC, Reference 400
Which statement best summarizes the findings to date on people's evaluations of work attributed either to men or to women authors?
A.   The author's gender does not significantly affect people's judgments of it.
B.   Both males and females tend to deprecate women's work.
C.   Males tend to deprecate women's work while females' judgments are not affected by an author's gender.
D.   Females but not males tend to deprecate women's work.

(28)   Answer A, Type FAC, Reference 400
In summarizing research findings on people's evaluations of women and men as leaders, professors, and so forth, Alice Eagly concludes that experiments have
A.   not demonstrated any overall tendency to devalue women's work.
B.   demonstrated a significant overall tendency to devalue women's work.
C.   demonstrated a tendency to devalue women's work as professors and men's work as schoolteachers.
D.   demonstrated a tendency to devalue women's work as psychologists and men's work as social workers.

(29)   Answer D, Type FAC, Reference 400
When Ian Ayres and his colleagues visited Chicago area car dealers and used a uniform strategy to negotiate the lowest price on a new car, dealers charged _____ the highest average price.
A.   White males
B.   White females
C.   Black males
D.   Black females

(30)   Answer B, Type FAC, Reference 400
Most women believe that sex discrimination
A.   has affected them personally.

226

B.   affects most working women.
C.   Both A and B.
D.   Neither A nor B.

(31)   Answer C, Type FAC, Reference 401
Research indicates that _____ of the world's unschooled children are girls.
A.   one-third
B.   one-half
C.   two-thirds
D.   90 percent

(32)   Answer D, Type FAC, Reference 400
In which of the following groups do individual members believe that their group
is discriminated against and at the same time deny suffering any personal
disadvantage?
A.   unemployed people
B.   African Americans
C.   out-of-the-closet lesbians
D.   All of the above.

(33)   Answer D, Type FAC, Reference 402
Which of the following does the text cite as a social source of prejudice?
A.   scapegoating
B.   authoritarianism
C.   just-world phenomenon
D.   unequal status

(34)   Answer B, Type FAC, Reference 402
The text indicates that, until recently, prejudice was greatest in regions where
slavery was practiced. This fact is clearly consistent with the principle that
_____ breeds prejudice.
A.   frustration
B.   unequal status
C.   conformity
D.   the media

(35)   Answer B, Type CON, Reference 403
Knowing that members of Group X in Transylvania have primary responsibility
for making the law is likely to lead people to conclude that members of Group X
A.   reflect the full variation of abilities, traits, and interests that are present in
the larger population.

227

B.   have traits that fit their legislative role.
C.   tend to have authoritarian personalities and are thus somewhat prejudiced.
D.   Ñone of the above.

(36)   Answer A, Type FAC, Reference 403
A consistent finding concerning Christianity is that, in comparison to non-members, church members show _____ than nonmembers.
A.   more racial prejudice
B.   less racial prejudice
C.   more sexism but less racism
D.   more conformity but less authoritarianism

(37)   Answer D, Type FAC, Reference 403
Which of the following could explain the correlation found between religion and racial prejudice?
A.   People with less education may be both more fundamentalist and more prejudiced.
B.   Prejudice may "cause" religion by leading people to create religious ideas that support their prejudices.
C.   Religion may cause prejudice by leading people to believe that everyone has free will, so minorities are to blame for their own victimization.
D.   All of the above.

(38)   Answer C, Type FAC, Reference 404
Which of the following is true?
A.   Faithful church attenders are more prejudiced than occasional attenders.
B.   Those who score highest on Gallup's "spiritual commitment" index are less accepting of a person of another race moving in next door.
C.   Those for whom religion is an end in itself express less prejudice than those for whom religion is more a means to an end.
D.   All of the above.

(39)   Answer C, Type FAC, Reference 404
Those for whom religion is a _____ exhibit little prejudice.
A.   matter of church membership
B.   means to other ends
C.   an open-ended quest
D.   matter of professing fundamentalist Christian beliefs

(40)   Answer B, Type FAC, Reference 404
Gordon Allport has concluded, "The role of _____ is paradoxical. It makes

228

prejudice and it unmakes prejudice."
A. power
B. religion
C. self-esteem
D. education

(41)   Answer D, Type FAC, Reference 404
Word, Zanna, and Cooper had White Princeton University men interview both White and Black job applicants. When the applicant was Black, the interviewers _____ than when the applicant was White.
A. ended the interview sooner
B. sat farther away from the applicant
C. made more speech errors
D. All of the above.

(42)   Answer D, Type DEF, Reference 405
Stereotype vulnerability refers to
A. the greater likelihood that minority groups will be negatively stereotyped.
B. the greater tendency for authoritarians to engage in negative stereotyping.
C. the tendency for stereotyping to lead to prejudice and discrimination.
D. a self-confirming apprehension that one's behavior will verify a negative stereotype.

(43)   Answer A, Type CON, Reference 405
Unfortunately, Mr. Smith, a high school speech teacher, communicates to his class that he thinks boys tend to be less anxious and thus make better speeches than girls do. As a result, some of the girls in his class become apprehensive in preparing and giving speeches in Mr. Smith's class. This provides an example of
A. stereotype vulnerability.
B. the just-world phenomenon.
C. the scapegoating effect.
D. Gause's law.

(44)   Answer B, Type CON, Reference 406
Betsy and Tina, both third-graders in the same classroom, are assigned by their teacher to different groups that will compete in a spelling bee. Betsy and Tina each believe that their own group is composed of the better spellers. The girls' beliefs best illustrate
A. the just-world phenomenon.
B. ingroup bias.
C. the fundamental attribution error.

D.   authoritarianism.

(45)   Answer A, Type FAC, Reference 406
Ingroup bias can be promoted
A.   by the mere experience of people's being formed into groups.
B.   only by the consistent lesson that other groups are inferior.
C.   only by the repeated experience that one's ingroup is superior.
D.   only by direct competition between ingroup and outgroups.

(46)   Answer C, Type DEF, Reference 407
The aspect of our self-concept that comes from our group memberships is called our
A.   social consciousness.
B.   multiple identity.
C.   social identity.
D.   group awareness.

(47)   Answer C, Type CON, Reference 407
Which of 14-year-old Kata's following statements clearly reflects an aspect of her social identity?
A.   "I am fun-loving."
B.   "I want to be a social worker."
C.   "I am Canadian."
D.   All of the above.

(48)   Answer A, Type FAC, Reference 408
While ingroup bias is the consequence of many forces, research indicates that it results primarily from perceiving that
A.   one's own group is good.
B.   one's major enemy is bad.
C.   all alternative outgroups are bad.
D.   one can accomplish more with the help of the group.

(49)   Answer B, Type FAC, Reference 409
If prejudice is a social norm, many people will follow the path of least resistance and conform to the fashion. Thus once established, prejudice is maintained largely by
A.   pressure.
B.   inertia.
C.   conscious effort.
D.   social engineering.

(50)   Answer B, Type FAC, Reference 409
Studies of Whites by Thomas Pettigrew in South Africa in the 1950s, when
apartheid ruled, revealed that those who _____ were also most prejudiced.
A.   had the most education
B.   conformed most to other social norms
C.   were the most disadvantaged
D.   had the greatest amount of social power

(51)   Answer C, Type CON, Reference 409
If prejudice is a social norm, most people will act prejudiced out of a need to
A.   rebel.
B.   assert their uniqueness.
C.   be liked and accepted.
D.   express themselves honestly.

(52)   Answer A, Type CON, Reference 409
Conformity is to _____ sources of prejudice as authoritarianism is to
_____ sources of prejudice.
A.   social; emotional
B.   emotional; cognitive
C.   cognitive; social
D.   social cognitive

(53)   Answer B, Type FAC, Reference 409
Children of _____ have less stereotyped views of men and women.
A.   authoritarian parents
B.   employed women
C.   devoutly religious parents
D.   bisexual men

(54)   Answer C, Type FAC, Reference 410
Usually, a culture's institutional supports for prejudice
A.   are obvious and easily identified but difficult to change.
B.   reflect the attitudes of a culture's leaders but not of its general population.
C.   simply reflect a culture's assumptions about life.
D.   reflect the strength of authoritarian tendencies in the general population.

(55)   Answer A, Type FAC, Reference 411
In examining photographs of people in magazines and newspapers, Dane Archer
and his colleagues found that, relative to the average female photo, the average

male photo is more likely to
A.   emphasize the face.
B.   emphasize the body.
C.   include the situational context
D.   display a standing posture.

(56)   Answer D, Type FAC, Reference 411
In research in Germany, Norbert Schwarz and Eva Kurz confirmed that people whose faces are prominent in photos seem
A.   more physically attractive.
B.   less powerful.
C.   younger.
D.   more intelligent and ambitious

(57)   Answer C, Type FAC, Reference 412
More lynchings of Blacks took place in the old South during years when cotton prices were low, suggesting that prejudice is explained by
A.   group-serving bias.
B.   the just-world hypothesis.
C.   displaced aggression.
D.   institutional supports.

(58)   Answer B, Type FAC, Reference 413
In a famous experiment by Miller and Bugelski, college-age men staying at a summer camp were asked to state their attitudes toward Japanese and Mexicans. Some did so before, and then after, being forced to complete tests and being deprived of a long-awaited free evening at a theater. Results most clearly supported
A.   realistic group conflict theory.
B.   the scapegoat theory of prejudice.
C.   the principle that unequal status breeds prejudice.
D.   the just-world hypothesis.

(59)   Answer D, Type DEF, Reference 413
Realistic group conflict theory suggests that prejudice arises
A.   whenever people try to live together.
B.   when a new group moves into an area.
C.   between groups who fail to communicate clearly with each other.
D.   when groups compete for scarce resources.

(60)   Answer B, Type DEF, Reference 413

According to Gause's Law, maximum _____ will exist between species that have identical needs.
A.   understanding
B.   competition
C.   communication
D.   attraction

(61)   Answer D, Type FAC, Reference 414
In one study at Northwestern University, members of _____ sororities were more disparaging of other sororities than were members of _____ sororities.
A.   academic honors; athletic
B.   athletic; academic honors
C.   higher-status; lower-status
D.   lower-status; higher-status

(62)   Answer C, Type FAC, Reference 414
In a study by Cialdini and Richardson, students who were told that their test scores on a creativity task were low subsequently gave lower ratings to _____ school.
A.   their own
B.   a prestigious
C.   a rival
D.   a fictitious

(63)   Answer A, Type CON, Reference 414
As part of an exercise in a life span psychology course, students are asked to think about their own mortality and the emotions they feel in reflecting on their eventual death. Research suggests that this exercise may, at least for the moment, lead them to
A.   experience greater ingroup favoritism and outgroup prejudice.
B.   feel lower self-esteem.
C.   express less conformity to social norms.
D.   feel greater social compassion.

(64)   Answer D, Type FAC, Reference 414
When Grube, Kleinhesselink, and Kearney had men view young women's videotaped job interviews, men with low self-acceptance disliked
A.   women with low self-esteem.
B.   dependent, traditional women.
C.   physically attractive women.

D.   strong, nontraditional women.

(65)   Answer D, Type FAC, Reference 415
Which of the following is a characteristic of the authoritarian personality?
A.   low tolerance for ambiguity
B.   low tolerance for weakness
C.   respect for ingroup authorities
D.   All of the above.

(66)   Answer B, Type DEF, Reference 415
A belief in the superiority of one's own ethnic and cultural group and a
corresponding disdain for all other groups make up the attitude known as
A.   conservatism.
B.   ethnocentrism.
C.   scapegoating.
D.   the just-world phenomenon.

(67)   Answer B, Type FAC, Reference 415
An important conclusion of research on the authoritarian personality is that
prejudices against different minorities
A.   are not founded in hostility.
B.   tend to coexist within an individual.
C.   have an institutional origin and are maintained by institutional supports.
D.   are a by-product of normal thinking processes.

(68)   Answer D, Type FAC, Reference 416
Research has indicated that those _____ tend to have authoritarian
attitudes.
A.   who become torturers
B.   who most strongly favored apartheid in South Africa
C.   Russians who oppose democratic reform
D.   All of the above.

(69)   Answer C, Type FAC, Reference 417
The newest perspective in social psychology on prejudice proposes that prejudices
develop and exist primarily as a result of
A.   frustrating economic forces.
B.   personality dynamics and emotional needs.
C.   by-products of normal thinking processes.
D.   social inequalities and institutional supports.

(70)   Answer A, Type FAC, Reference 417
Which of the following is <u>false</u> regarding the process of "categorization," that is, of organizing the world by clustering objects into groups?
A.   Categorization is a form of prejudice when it is applied to people.
B.   A benefit of categorization is that it can provide useful information with a minimum of effort.
C.   Experiments suggest that we spontaneously categorize people by race.
D.   All of the above are false.

(71)   Answer B, Type CON, Reference 418
Jeffrey, age 21, is a White male college senior who is majoring in history. Research on the categorization process suggests that Jeffrey is likely to think that most
A.   Whites tend to share the same basic values.
B.   math professors tend to have the same personality characteristics.
C.   men tend to have similar attitudes about sex.
D.   college seniors prefer the same kinds of leisure activities.

(72)   Answer C, Type FAC, Reference 418
Which of the following is <u>true</u> regarding the relationship between positive emotions and our thought processes?
A.   Positive emotions and more complex thinking naturally go together.
B.   Happy people seem to commit more effort to wrestling with differences.
C.   Feeling very good may prime feelings of superiority.
D.   Good moods necessarily reduce outgroup stereotyping.

(73)   Answer C, Type FAC, Reference 418
In general, the greater our familiarity with a social group, the more we see its
A.   members as similar.
B.   flaws rather than its strengths.
C.   diversity.
D.   strengths rather than its flaws.

(74)   Answer C, Type DEF, Reference 420
The own-race bias appears to be an automatic cognitive tendency
A.   that is usually related to the perceiver's racial attitudes.
B.   to see one's own race as attractive, and others less so.
C.   to have difficulty distinguishing different members of another racial group.
D.   to think that all members of one's own group "look alike."

(75)   Answer D, Type FAC, Reference 421

A Black in an otherwise White group, a man in an otherwise female group, or a woman in an otherwise male group seems
A.   less prominent than the others in the group.
B.   less responsible for what is happening in the group.
C.   to have both fewer good and fewer bad qualities than others in the group.
D.   None of the above.

(76)   Answer C, Type FAC, Reference 421
Kleck and Strenta had women who falsely believed they appeared disfigured by theatrical makeup interact with a female partner. Results indicated that women who thought they were disfigured
A.   interacted for a longer period of time with their partners.
B.   interacted for a shorter period of time with their partners.
C.   rated their partners as more tense, distant, and patronizing.
D.   rated their partners as warmer, more open, and friendlier.

(77)   Answer D, Type CON, Reference 422
Mildred learns that ten Danerians were arrested for nonviolent crimes such as shoplifting and that ten Transylvanians were arrested for violent crimes such as rape. Mildred's tendency to estimate that more crimes were committed by Transylvanians than by Danerians best illustrates the effect of
A.   group-serving bias.
B.   authoritarianism.
C.   the just-world phenomenon.
D.   distinctive cases.

(78)   Answer D, Type DEF, Reference 422
Because we are sensitive to distinctive events, the simultaneous occurrence of two such events is especially noticeable. Our attentiveness to unusual occurrences can create
A.   the group-serving bias.
B.   authoritarianism.
C.   the outgroup homogeneity effect.
D.   illusory correlations.

(79)   Answer A, Type CON, Reference 423
Although most suspects in cases of incest, child molestation, and sexual abuse are heterosexual males, the local newspaper omits the word "heterosexual" in any related headline. In contrast, whenever a self-described gay male is arrested for a crime, the headline proclaims "homosexual arrested" in the case. The resulting prejudice that gay males are more likely to commit violent crimes can in part be

236

blamed on
A.   illusory correlation.
B.   ingroup bias.
C.   outgroup homogeneity effects.
D.   group-serving bias.

(80)   Answer D, Type DEF, Reference 424
Explaining away outgroup members' positive behaviors and attributing negative behaviors to their dispositions is known as
A.   the scapegoat theory of prejudice.
B.   the just-world bias.
C.   Gause's Law.
D.   group-serving bias.

(81)   Answer B, Type CON, Reference 425
Jeremy's belief that earthquake victims are being punished by God for their own sins best illustrates
A.   Gause's law.
B.   the just-world phenomenon.
C.   ingroup bias.
D.   stereotype vulnerability.

(82)   Answer A, Type CON, Reference 425
The just-world phenomenon can lead people to
A.   think that the winners of a lottery actually deserved their good fortune.
B.   think that judges have greater sensitivity to the problem of injustice than most people in the general population.
C.   distrust those who are wealthy or well educated.
D.   overestimate differences within an outgroup and underestimate differences within an ingroup.

(83)   Answer A, Type FAC, Reference 427
William Ickes and his colleagues falsely forewarned subjects that they were about to interact with a partner who was either extremely friendly or unfriendly. All subjects acted friendly, whatever their expectations, and got a warm response from their partners. Results showed that subjects who expected their partners to be _____ tended to _____.
A.   unfriendly; interpret their partners' smiles as "forced"
B.   unfriendly; show greater trust and liking of them
C.   friendly; suspect hostilities lurking below the surface
D.   friendly; believe that their partners were merely role-playing

(84)   Answer D, Type FAC, Reference 429
Research on whether stereotypes bias our judgments of individuals indicates that
A.   we often evaluate individuals more positively than the groups they compose.
B.   we may have strong gender stereotypes yet ignore them when judging a particular individual.
C.   stereotypes sometimes bias our judgments of individuals by creating a contrast effect.
D.   All of the above.

(85)   Answer D, Type FAC, Reference 430
When Thomas Nelson and his colleagues had students estimate the heights of individually pictured men and women, they judged the individual men as taller
A.   except when the heights of men and women were actually equal.
B.   except when they were told that, in this sample, sex didn't predict height.
C.   except when they were offered cash rewards for accuracy.
D.   None of the above.

THE FOLLOWING ITEMS ALSO APPEAR IN THE STUDY GUIDE:

(86)   Answer C, Type DEF, Reference 390
Prejudice is a negative _____, while discrimination is a negative _____.
A.   belief; feeling
B.   generalization; practice
C.   attitude; behavior
D.   stereotype; practice

(87)   Answer D, Type CON, Reference 391
Stereotypes are to discrimination as _____ are to _____.
A.   categories; feeling
B.   attitudes; actions
C.   emotions; practice
D.   beliefs; behavior

(88)   Answer B, Type FAC, Reference 399
Most Americans agree with the statement
A.   "The activities of married women are best confined to the home and family."

B.   "There should be equal pay for women and men when they are doing the same job."
C.   "I would probably move if Black people came to live in great numbers in my neighborhood."
D.   The majority of Americans agree with all of the above.

(89)   Answer C, Type FAC, Reference 407
Charles Perdue and his colleagues found that a nonsense syllable such as "yof" seemed more pleasant
A.   if spoken by a female than by a male.
B.   to a low authoritarian than to a high authoritarian.
C.   if it had been paired with words like "we" or "us" than with words like "they" or "them."
D.   if spoken on Friday than on Monday.

(90)   Answer D, Type FAC, Reference 422
A 1990 Gallup poll found that the average American estimated that _____ percent of the U.S. population was Black.
A.   4
B.   8
C.   16
D.   32

(91)   Answer A, Type FAC, Reference 393
A survey of the racial attitudes of White Americans found that a _____ said they would be unhappy if their child married a Black person and a _____ said that they wouldn't want their child to attend an integrated school.
A.   majority; minority
B.   majority; majority
C.   minority; majority
D.   minority; minority

(92)   Answer A, Type FAC, Reference 423
In one study, students were told that various members of Group A or Group B did either something desirable or something undesirable. While many more statements described members of Group A than Group B, both groups were associated with nine desirable behaviors for every four undesirable behaviors. Results indicated
A.   that students perceived members of Group B more negatively.
B.   that students perceived members of Group A more negatively.

C.   no differences in the students' perceptions of the groups.

D.   that authoritarian students viewed Group A more negatively.

(93) Answer C, Type CON, Reference 391

Mr. Watson's belief that Blacks are lazy is an example of _____. His refusal to rent an apartment to a Black family is an example of _____.

A.   a stereotype; sexism

B.   discrimination; prejudice

C.   a stereotype; discrimination

D.   racism; prejudice

(94) Answer D, Type CON, Reference 392

Which of the following would be an example of "sexism" as the term is defined in the text?

A.   A manufacturing firm hires only men as accountants.

B.   Mr. Jones believes women lack intelligence and should not be allowed to hold political office; he votes only for males.

C.   A hospital refuses to hire males as nurses.

D.   All of the above.

(95) Answer D, Type CON, Reference 424

Which of the following would you <u>not</u> expect to be true of the authoritarian personality?

A.   Discriminating against American Indians

B.   Wanting to achieve high social status

C.   Being respectful of police

D.   Being opposed to capital punishment

(96) Answer A, Type CON, Reference 424

Which of the following would be an example of the group-serving bias?

A.   Veryl believes that women are unemployed because of discrimination but that men are unemployed because of low motivation.

B.   Sue believes that members of her own family are prejudiced but that her husband's family is tolerant

C.   Chuck believes that mistakes made by both men and women are due to low intelligence.

D.   Bill believes that groups outperform individuals in solving problems.

(97) Answer B, Type CON, Reference 425

The just-world phenomenon may lead us to believe that an unemployed person is

A.   a victim of discrimination.

B.   lazy.
C.   in need of sympathy.
D.   in need of a retraining program.

(98)   Answer C, Type CON, Reference 412
John has just failed a chemistry test. He goes back to his apartment and criticizes his roommate's choice of music. What term best describes John's behavior?
A.   institutionalized aggression
B.   just-world action
C.   displaced aggression
D.   authoritarian regression

(99)   Answer D, Type CON, Reference 392
Which of the following would be an example of racism as the term is defined in the text?
A.   Mr. Jones' refusal to rent his apartments to Chinese
B.   Mrs. Smith's prejudice toward Hispanics
C.   a government regulation that prevents inner-city residents from being recruited to serve as Army officers
D.   All of the above.

(100) Answer D, Type CON, Reference 425
The results of one social-psychological study indicated that observers who discovered that a fellow worker had received a large prize as the result of a random drawing subsequently concluded that he had in fact worked especially hard. This is an example of
A.   vivid, anecdotal information being more important than base-rate data.
B.   disguised hostility.
C.   outgroup bias.
D.   the just-world phenomenon.

CHAPTER TWELVE: AGGRESSION: HURTING OTHERS

<u>Multiple Choice</u>

(1)   Answer D, Type FAC, Reference 436
Across the world , spending for arms and armies approaches the amount of
_____ per day.
A. $3 million
B. $30 million
C. $300 million
D. $3 billion

(2)   Answer D, Type DEF, Reference 436
Aggression is any physical or verbal behavior that
A.   may result in physical or psychological damage.
B.   springs from anger or hostility.
C.   results in harm regardless of intent.
D.   is intended to hurt someone.

(3)   Answer B, Type CON, Reference 436
Which of the following would be an example of aggression as defined in the text?
A.   Sam accidentally slams the car door too quickly, and it hits Tim's knee.
B.   Luisa urges her classmates not to vote for Marcy for dormitory senator,
citing some rumors about Marcy's social life.
C.   Carla, a dentist, delivers a shot of novocaine before pulling her patient's
diseased tooth.
D.   Joe's eagerness and enthusiasm result in his being promoted to sales
manager in a very short time.

(4)   Answer C, Type CON, Reference 436
Which of the following would be considered aggression as the term is defined in
the text?
A.   A motorist accidentally hits a child who has run into the path of his car.
B.   An assertive salesperson manages to sell $200,000 worth of automobiles in
one month.
C.   A child attempts to hit her playmate with a rock but misses.
D.   All of the above.

(5)   Answer C, Type FAC, Reference 437
Animals exhibit _____ aggression, characterized by displays of rage, and
_____ aggression, as when a predator stalks its prey.

A. emotional; physical
B. physical; emotional
C. social; silent
D. silent; social

(6)   Answer B, Type FAC, Reference 437
_____ aggression in humans appears to parallel _____ aggression in animals.
A. Hostile; silent
B. Hostile; social
C. Instrumental; social
D. Social; silent

(7)   Answer C, Type CON, Reference 437
Of the following, which is the best example of instrumental aggression?
A. An angry football player tackles a quarterback after he has attempted a long pass.
B. A jealous wife finds her husband with another woman and shoots them both.
C. A group of mercenaries, hired to kill the dictator of a small country, arrange to poison him.
D. A man smashes his TV set after he cannot make it work.

(8)   Answer C, Type DEF, Reference 437
_____ aggression has a goal of _____.
A. Hostile; solving a problem for the aggressor
B. Instrumental; hurting the victim
C. Instrumental; achieving another end by hurting someone
D. Social aggression; defeating a competitor

(9)   Answer A, Type FAC, Reference 437
According to the text, most murders are acts of
A. hostile aggression.
B. instrumental aggression.
C. predatory violence.
D. silent aggression.

(10)   Answer A, Type FAC, Reference 437
In analyzing the causes of aggression, social psychologists have focused on three primary ideas. Which of the following is not one of them?
A. Aggression is a variable trait; some humans rarely behave aggressively, while others cannot control aggressive impulses.

B.   There is an inborn aggressive drive among human beings.
C.   Aggression is a natural response to frustration.
D.   Like other social behaviors, aggression is learned.

(11)   Answer B, Type DEF, Reference 437
Instinctive behavior is behavior that is
A.   survival-oriented and common to most members of a species.
B.   innate, unlearned, and shown by all members of a species.
C.   reflexive and automatic but easily overcome by learning.
D.   the way members of a species ought to behave.

(12)   Answer B, Type FAC, Reference 437
Sigmund Freud argued that aggression ultimately springs from
A.   an innate sexual drive.
B.   a primitive death urge.
C.   observation of aggressive adult models.
D.   blocking of goal-directed behavior.

(13)   Answer C, Type FAC, Reference 437
Who among the following argued that there is an inborn aggressive drive?
A.   Bandura
B.   Berkowitz
C.   Lorenz
D.   Dollard

(14)   Answer B, Type FAC, Reference 437
In contrast to Freud's view of aggression, Lorenz argued that
A.   aggression is innate.
B.   we have innate mechanisms for inhibiting aggression.
C.   aggression is biologically influenced but is not instinctive.
D.   aggression is socially learned.

(15)   Answer C, Type FAC, Reference 437
In contrast to Freud, Lorenz maintained that aggression is basically
A.   prosocial.
B.   self-destructive.
C.   adaptive.
D.   learned.

(16)   Answer B, Type FAC, Reference 439
Instinct theories of aggression would have the most difficulty accounting for

A.   silent and social aggression in animals.
B.   wide variations in aggressiveness from culture to culture.
C.   biochemical influences on aggression.
D.   unprovoked outbursts of aggression.

(17)   Answer D, Type FAC, Reference 439
Which of the following statements about the study of instincts is true?
A.   Instinct theories of behavior have been criticized as circular explanations.
B.   Instinct theories do not so much explain behavior as name or label it.
C.   By the early 1920s social scientists had proposed nearly 6000 instincts to account for human behavior.
D.   All of the above.

(18)   Answer B, Type FAC, Reference 440
The study of neural influences on aggression has indicated that
A.   neural systems facilitate aggression in animals but not in humans.
B.   electrical stimulation of the amygdala can lead to aggression in humans.
C.   aggression does seem to have its basis in an instinctive drive.
D.   one specific spot in the brain seems to control aggression in both animals and humans.

(19)   Answer D, Type FAC, Reference 440
Which of the following statements about aggression is true?
A.   Animals of many species can be bred for aggressiveness.
B.   A fearless, impulsive, temper-prone child is at risk for violent behavior in adolescence.
C.   Identical twins are more likely than fraternal twins to agree on whether they have violent tempers.
D.   All of the above.

(20)   Answer D, Type FAC, Reference 441
Research on alcohol and aggression has indicated that
A.   violent people are both more likely to drink and more likely to become aggressive when intoxicated.
B.   people who have been drinking commit about half of all violent crimes.
C.   in experiments, intoxicated people administer stronger shocks.
D.   All of the above.

(21)   Answer C, Type FAC, Reference 441
Research indicates that the murderer and/or the victim have been consuming alcohol in _____ percent of homicides.

A. 25
B. 40
C. 65
D. 85

(22) Answer B, Type FAC, Reference 441
Studies of hormonal influences on aggression indicate that
A. hormonal influences are as strong in humans as they are in lower animals.
B. after age 25, testosterone and rates of violent crime decrease together.
C. variations in testosterone seem to have no effect on behavior within the normal range of teen boys and adult men.
D. all of the above.

(23) Answer A, Type FAC, Reference 441
In their recent "statement on violence," scientists from a dozen nations have declared that "It is scientifically incorrect to say that war or any other violent behavior
A. is genetically programmed into our human nature."
B. is genetically or hormonally influenced."
C. is controllable through socialization or education."
D. has causes which can be identified through laboratory research."

(24) Answer A, Type CON, Reference 442
Jessie's car had a flat tire in the rain. After she managed to fix it, she arrived home late only to have a parking spot just in front of her apartment taken by a faster driver. Coming home, she kicks her pet cat who is waiting at the door. Jessie's behavior is perhaps most easily explained in terms of
A. frustration-aggression theory.
B. the weapons effect.
C. Parkinson's second law.
D. biochemical influences on aggression.

(25) Answer C, Type DEF, Reference 442
According to Yale researchers John Dollard and colleagues, frustration is anything that
A. leads to negative emotional arousal.
B. elicits feelings of helplessness and hopelessness.
C. blocks goal attainment.
D. causes deprivation.

(26) Answer D, Type DEF, Reference 442

Frustration grows when
A.   our motivation to achieve a goal is very strong.
B.   we expected gratification.
C.   we are completely blocked in attaining our goal.
D.   All of the above.

(27)   Answer A, Type DEF, Reference 442
The redirection of aggression to a target other than the source of frustration is referred to as
A.   displacement.
B.   substitution.
C.   instrumental aggression.
D.   projection.

(28)   Answer B, Type CON, Reference 442
After arguing with her boyfriend Peter over the telephone, Roberta smashes down the receiver and then throws the phone across the room. This behavior most clearly demonstrates
A.   the weapons effect.
B.   displacement.
C.   instrumental aggression.
D.   Parkinson's second law.

(29)   Answer C, Type CON, Reference 443
Frustration-aggression theory is to _____ as social learning theory is to
_____.
A.   Freud; Berkowitz
B.   Berkowitz; Lorenz
C.   Dollard; Bandura
D.   Lorenz; Dollard

(30)   Answer A, Type FAC, Reference 443
In a revision of frustration-aggression theory, Berkowitz maintained that frustration most directly produces
A.   anger.
B.   aggression.
C.   relative deprivation.
D.   accentuation.

(31)   Answer A, Type FAC, Reference 443
In a revision of frustration-aggression theory, Berkowitz emphasized the

248

importance of
A.   aggressive cues, such as weapons.
B.   the role of biochemical influences, such as alcohol.
C.   relative deprivation and the adaptation level phenomenon.
D.   catharsis as a reducer of frustration.

(32)   Answer D, Type FAC, Reference 443
According to revised frustration-aggression theory, we are especially ready to
aggress when the one who has frustrated us
A.   has acted out of frustration.
B.   profits from his or her actions.
C.   is a stranger rather than an acquaintance.
D.   could have chosen to act otherwise.

(33)   Answer C, Type FAC, Reference 443
Research suggests that the sight of a weapon can
A.   elicit frustration.
B.   sensitize one to the danger of violence.
C.   amplify aggression.
D.   produce catharsis.

(34)   Answer C, Type FAC, Reference 443
Handguns in homes are far more likely to kill _____ than _____.
A.   property criminals; violent criminals
B.   innocent strangers; guilty ones
C.   household members; intruders
D.   casual acquaintances; household members

(35)   Answer B, Type FAC, Reference 443
Although Seattle, Washington, and Vancouver, British Columbia, share similar
populations, climates, economies, and rates of criminal activity, Vancouver has a
much lower overall murder rate because
A.   it has more space per person.
B.   it carefully restricts handgun ownership.
C.   it punishes violent crime more quickly and surely.
D.   its police force is twice as large as Seattle's.

(36)   Answer D, Type FAC, Reference 444
After the Detroit riots of the late 1960s, the National Advisory Commission on
Civil Disorders concluded that when there occurs a "revolution of _____,"
frustrations can escalate even while conditions improve.

A.   poverty
B.   abstinence
C.   helplessness
D.   rising expectations

(37)   Answer B, Type FAC, Reference 444
An important conclusion of research on the sources of social and civil unrest is
that frustration arises from
A.   a mismatch between achievements and rewards.
B.   the gap between expectations and attainments.
C.   deprivation of elements essential to survival.
D.   learned helplessness and hopelessness.

(38)   Answer D, Type FAC, Reference 445
The top-rated objective among entering collegians in 1993 was
A.   raising a family.
B.   helping others in difficulty.
C.   finding fulfilling work.
D.   being very well off financially.

(39)   Answer C, Type FAC, Reference 445
In 1957, 35 percent of Americans surveyed reported themselves "very happy"; in
1993, after years of improving affluence, _____ declared themselves to be "very
happy."
A.   twice as many
B.   51 percent
C.   32 percent
D.   only 12 percent

(40)   Answer D, Type DEF, Reference 446
According to the _____, feelings of success, failure, satisfaction, and
dissatisfaction are relative to prior achievements.
A.   relative attainment hypothesis
B.   achievement motivation syndrome
C.   social prestige principle
D.   adaptation-level phenomenon

(41)   Answer A, Type CON, Reference 446
Donna has been short of money and worried about her job security. Yesterday
she was surprised to find she was being promoted and given a 10 percent raise.
The adaptation-level phenomenon suggests that she will

A.   soon be financially worried again.
B.   have much better self-esteem from now on.
C.   behave much less aggressively from now on.
D.   be a much more ambitious, achievement-oriented worker now that she sees that her past behavior has paid off.

(42)   Answer D, Type FAC, Reference 446
In a study of the experiences of lottery winners, Brickman and his colleagues found that
A.   over time, their self-reported overall happiness increased.
B.   the moment of winning the lottery was not much of an emotional high.
C.   over time, ordinary activities like reading and eating a good breakfast became more pleasurable for them.
D.   None of the above.

(43)   Answer B, Type DEF, Reference 446
The perception that one is less well off than others to whom one compares oneself is referred to as
A.   the adaptation level phenomenon.
B.   relative deprivation.
C.   Parkinson's second law.
D.   the unjust-world principle.

(44)   Answer B, Type CON, Reference 446
Arvid didn't work very hard on his last class essay assignment, so he was relieved at first to find he'd gotten a C on it. But when he learned that most of his classmates had gotten B's and A's, he felt unhappy and angry about his grade. Arvid's experience is best explained in terms of
A.   the adaptation-level phenomenon.
B.   the relative deprivation principle.
C.   displacement.
D.   Parkinson's second law.

(45)   Answer B, Type FAC, Reference 447
Hennigan and colleagues suggest that the larceny theft rate in U.S. cities jumped after television was first introduced because the thieves
A.   observed too much crime on television.
B.   felt deprived relative to wealthy television characters and those portrayed in advertisements.
C.   became more removed from the socializing influence of home and school.
D.   wanted but could not afford the luxury of a television set.

(46) Answer C, Type FAC, Reference 448
Marshall Dermer and colleagues had university women view depictions of deprived or tragic lives, and afterward the women expressed feelings of
A.   depression.
B.   frustration.
C.   satisfaction with their own lives.
D.   anger.

(47) Answer A, Type FAC, Reference 448
Crocker and Gallo found that subjects felt less depressed and more satisfied with life after five times completing the sentence:
A.   "I'm glad I'm not a _____."
B.   "I wish I were a _____."
C.   "I'm sorry I never _____."
D.   "My saddest moment was _____."

(48) Answer C, Type FAC, Reference 448
People who are facing a severe personal threat often search for a silver lining by
A.   analyzing the cloud.
B.   comparing upward.
C.   comparing downward.
D.   displacing aggression onto a scapegoat.

(49) Answer C, Type CON, Reference 448
Jeremy instigates more and more fights with younger children on the school playground because it gains him the attention and respect of his friends. This most clearly suggests that his aggression is
A.   the result of frustration.
B.   instinctive.
C.   a learned response.
D.   the result of displacement.

(50) Answer B, Type FAC, Reference 449
Terrorism is a form of aggression fueled by "the oxygen of _____," suggests former Prime Minister Margaret Thatcher.
A.   modeling
B.   publicity
C.   competition
D.   frustration

(51) Answer D, Type FAC, Reference 449

According to Albert Bandura, an important influence on one's tendency to be aggressive is

A.   hormonal factors.
B.   how much anger or frustration has built up inside.
C.   one's hereditary predisposition to be aggressive.
D.   observations of others' behavior.

(52) Answer B, Type FAC, Reference 450

In a famous experiment by Albert Bandura and colleagues, children watched an adult attack a Bobo doll with a mallet. They were then shown some attractive toys they were forbidden to play with. When they were taken to another room, they

A.   began fighting with each other.
B.   attacked a Bobo doll.
C.   verbally attacked the adult experimenter.
D.   chose to watch a violent rather than a nonviolent film.

(53) Answer B, Type FAC, Reference 450

Research on the role of family influences on aggression indicates that

A.   most abused children become abusive parents.
B.   higher rates of violence occur where father care is minimal.
C.   an only child tends to be more aggressive in social situations outside the family.
D.   All of the above.

(54) Answer D, Type CON, Reference 450

Research with children suggests that observing aggressive behavior can

A.   lower their inhibitions against aggression.
B.   teach them ways to be aggressive.
C.   lead them directly to aggressive imitation.
D.   All of the above.

(55) Answer A, Type FAC, Reference 451

Richard Nisbett suggests that the higher rates of violence in southern towns settled by Scotts-Irish herders can be understood in terms of

A.   a tradition that emphasizes "manly honor" and the aggressive protection of one's flock.
B.   the frequent absence of fathers from the family unit.
C.   social isolation and its accompanying alienation and frustration.
D.   a history of physical deprivation accompanied by feelings of helplessness

and hopelessness.

(56) Answer A, Type FAC, Reference 451
According to social learning theory, aggression is most likely when we
_____ and _____.
A.   are aroused; it seems safe and rewarding to aggress
B.   feel hopeless; alternative strategies to achieve important goals have failed
C.   are deprived; see others profiting from aggression
D.   suffer a loss of self-esteem; want to impress others

(57) Answer B, Type FAC, Reference 452
Which of the following is true about the findings of Azrin and colleagues in their
research on the pain-attack response in rats?
A.   The rats attacked each other only after they had been painfully shocked for
several minutes.
B.   The greater the shock (and pain), the more violent the attack.
C.   The shocked rats only attacked members of their own species.
D.   None of the above.

(58) Answer A, Type FAC, Reference 453
In view of research on the pain-attack response, Leonard Berkowitz now believes
that _____ is the basic trigger of hostile aggression.
A.   aversive stimulation
B.   physiological sensitivity
C.   frustration
D.   rage

(59) Answer D, Type FAC, Reference 453
Which of the following environmental irritants has been associated with
aggression?
A.   cigarette smoke
B.   offensive odors
C.   air pollution
D.   All of the above.

(60) Answer B, Type FAC, Reference 454
In an experiment by William Griffitt, students who answered questionnaires
while they were _____ reported feeling more tired and aggressive and expressed
more hostility toward a stranger than did subjects in a control group.
A.   distracted by loud noise
B.   in an uncomfortably hot room

C. being closely observed
D. eating popcorn and peanuts

(61) Answer B, Type FAC, Reference 454
During the 1986 to 1988 major league baseball seasons, the number of batters hit
by a pitch was greater for games played
A. between teams with losing records.
B. when the temperature was in the 90s.
C. in the most crowded and congested cities.
D. in the first half of the season.

(62) Answer D, Type CON, Reference 455
In most studies of attack aggression, competing subjects get to choose how much
shock to give the loser after they beat him or her in one round of a contest.
Which of the following axioms seems to guide the behavior of subjects who have
received escalating shocks from a programmed opponent?
A. "Turn the other cheek."
B. "The word is mightier than the sword."
C. "A soft answer turneth away wrath."
D. "An eye for an eye."

(63) Answer C, Type DEF, Reference 455
Crowding is defined
A. as too many people in one place.
B. as too little space for a person to feel a sense of control.
C. as a feeling of not enough space per person.
D. in terms of an objective assessment of density.

(64) Answer C, Type FAC, Reference 456
In Schachter and Singer's classic study, subjects injected with adrenaline were
exposed to either an angry or a euphoric confederate. Subjects who expected the
injection to make them feel _____ became _____ when placed with the angry
confederate.
A. aroused; angry
B. aroused; euphoric
C. no side effects; angry
D. no side effects; euphoric

(65) Answer A, Type FAC, Reference 456
The results of the Schachter and Singer experiment in which subjects were
injected with adrenaline prior to waiting with either a hostile or euphoric person

support the idea that

A.   bodily arousal feeds one emotion or another depending on how we interpret the arousal.

B.   distinct physiological differences exist among the emotions.

C.   frustration is largely a function of our prior experience and of whom we compare ourselves with.

D.   every emotion triggers an opposing emotion.

(66)   Answer C, Type FAC, Reference 457

Dolf Zillmann and colleagues found that people who have just pumped an exercise bike or watched a film of a rock concert find it easy to

A.   identify the true source of their arousal.

B.   reduce their arousal by fantasizing aggression.

C.   misattribute their arousal to a provocation.

D.   ignore being insulted by a stranger.

(67)   Answer A, Type FAC, Reference 458

Malamuth and Check reported that men who watched two movies depicting a man sexually overcoming a woman were subsequently

A.   more accepting of violence against women.

B.   more likely to believe that rape was a serious crime.

C.   more likely to underestimate the frequency of rape in society.

D.   less likely to believe that women enjoy aggressive sexual treatment.

(68)   Answer B, Type FAC, Reference 459

John Court reports that as pornographic materials have become more widely available, the rate of reported rapes has generally been found to

A.   decrease.

B.   increase.

C.   remain the same.

D.   increase in the short run but decrease in the long run.

(69)   Answer B, Type FAC, Reference 460

Edward Donnerstein showed university men either a neutral, an erotic, or a rape film before the men, in a different setting, taught a subject nonsense syllables by administering punishment for wrong answers. Results showed that the men who had watched the rape film

A.   gave stronger shocks to male subjects but not to female subjects.

B.   gave stronger shocks to female subjects but not to male subjects.

C.   gave stronger shocks to both male and female subjects.

D.   gave weaker shocks to females subjects but not to males subjects.

(70)   Answer B, Type FAC, Reference 460
Check and Malamuth reported that students who read erotic rape stories and were then debriefed about the study's true purpose were
A.   more accepting of the "women enjoy rape" myth than other subjects.
B.   less accepting of the "women enjoy rape" myth than other subjects.
C.   more likely to overestimate the occurrence of rape in society than other subjects.
D.   more likely to underestimate the occurrence of rape in society than other subjects.

(71)   Answer D, Type FAC, Reference 461
Which of the following statements about rape is <u>true</u>?
A.   Most stranger rapes and nearly all acquaintance rapes go unreported to police.
B.   In surveys of students and working women, researchers have found that over one-quarter of women reported an experience that meets the legal definition of rape or attempted rape.
C.   About one-third of college males admit there is the possibility that they would rape a woman if they thought no one would know and they would not be punished.
D.   All of the above.

(72)   Answer A, Type FAC, Reference 462
Researchers studying the rate of violent crime in the United States <u>disagree</u> on
A.   whether women's vulnerability to rape is increasing.
B.   whether the homicide rate has increased since 1960.
C.   whether most violent crime is committed by males under 30.
D.   All of the above.

(73)   Answer B, Type CON, Reference 464
"Everyone has some feelings of anger or aggression sometime. Watching violence on a TV show gives us a harmless outlet for such feelings, so we feel better and don't have to hurt anyone in the process." This statement is most clearly consistent with the _____ hypothesis.
A.   sensitizing
B.   catharsis
C.   frustration-aggression
D.   social learning

(74)   Answer C, Type FAC, Reference 462

As an alternative to strict censorship of pornography portraying sexual violence, many psychologists favor
A.   federal registration of all those producing and distributing pornographic materials.
B.   a heavy tax on the sale and distribution of pornographic materials.
C.   media awareness training designed to promote critical viewing skills.
D.   more adequate control of who is allowed to purchase pornographic materials.

(75)   Answer C, Type FAC, Reference 466
Research on the relationship between television and behavior indicates that
A.   aggressiveness at age 8 predicts violence viewing at age 19.
B.   the correlation between TV viewing and violence seems to be due to the third variable of lower intelligence that predisposes some children both to prefer aggressive programs and to act aggressively.
C.   murder rates increase when and where television comes.
D.   viewing violence seems to have had little, if any, effect on prison convicts.

(76)   Answer B, Type FAC, Reference 467
Research has concluded that the correlation between viewing violent TV and behaving aggressively is due to the fact that
A.   aggressive children are the kind who prefer violent TV.
B.   viewing violence contributes to later violent behavior.
C.   viewing violent TV programs and developing aggressive behavior are both the results of large family size.
D.   both TV viewing preferences and aggressive behavior are caused by a third factor that is still unknown.

(77)   Answer C, Type FAC, Reference 467
The conclusion of the Surgeon General and researchers on the relationship between violence in television and real-life aggressive behavior is best stated as:
A.   Television is a primary cause of social violence.
B.   Television is not correlated with social violence.
C.   Television is a controllable cause of social violence.
D.   Television violence and social aggression are correlated but are not causally linked.

(78)   Answer A, Type FAC, Reference 468
Researchers have concluded that television violence affects social behavior in all but which of the following ways?
A.   Viewing violence produces a catharsis or release of aggressive energy.

B.   Viewing violence produces arousal in viewers.
C.   Viewing violence produces disinhibition in viewers.
D.   Media portrayals of violence evoke imitation.

(79)   Answer D, Type CON, Reference 470
Fourteen-year-old Kevin frequently watches violent television programs. This is most likely to lead him to
A.   experience more distress at the sight of teens fighting on the streets.
B.   underestimate the actual frequency of violent crimes in the world.
C.   become more interested in resolving the conflict between two of his personal friends.
D.   become more fearful of being criminally assaulted.

(80)   Answer A, Type FAC, Reference 470
Surveys of both adolescents and adults indicate that heavy viewers of television violence are more likely to
A.   exaggerate the frequency of violence in the world.
B.   experience distress at seeing children fighting in their own neighborhood.
C.   support laws restricting handgun ownership.
D.   support the censorship of violent television programming.

(81)   Answer D, Type FAC, Reference 471
According to the text, groups can amplify aggressive reactions through the processes of
A.   groupthink and minority influence.
B.   social loafing and social facilitation.
C.   crowding and conservative shift.
D.   diffusion of responsibility and polarization.

(82)   Answer A, Type FAC, Reference 473
It is the near consensus among social psychologists today that the catharsis hypothesis of aggressive expression, as Freud, Lorenz, and their followers supposed,
A.   has not been confirmed.
B.   works with aggressive action but not with aggressive fantasy.
C.   works for women but not for men.
D.   is well supported in most conditions and circumstances.

(83)   Answer B, Type FAC, Reference 474
Research with children and teenagers suggests that the least effective way to reduce aggression is to

259

A. model nonaggressive behavior.
B. physically punish aggression.
C. ignore aggressive behavior.
D. reward nonaggressive behavior.

(84) Answer C, Type CON, Reference 474
Which of the following would be the best advice to give parents who are concerned about the frequent aggressive outbursts of their 8-year-old daughter?
A. "Encourage your daughter to express her anger by attacking an old piece of furniture specifically set aside for that purpose."
B. "Spank your daughter for temper tantrums as well as for fighting with her brother."
C. "Make a point of rewarding and praising your daughter whenever she is socially cooperative and helpful."
D. "Encourage your daughter to view the devastating consequences of violence portrayed on television."

(85) Answer D, Type FAC, Reference 474
Goldstein and Glick's aggression-replacement program has reduced rearrest rates of juvenile offenders and gang members by
A. teaching the youths and their parents better communication skills.
B. training them to control anger.
C. raising their level of moral reasoning.
D. All of the above.

THE FOLLOWING ITEMS ALSO APPEAR IN THE STUDY GUIDE:

(86) Answer D, Type FAC, Reference 437
The murders committed by mobster hit men provide an example of
A. emotional aggression.
B. silent aggression.
C. how catharsis can reduce aggression.
D. instrumental aggression.

(87) Answer C, Type FAC, Reference 437
Which of the following is false?
A. Animals' social aggression and silent aggression seem to involve separate brain regions.
B. Worldwide spending for arms and armies approaches $3 billion per day.
C. Data from 110 nations indicates that enforcing the death penalty can result in fewer homicides.

D.   Hostile aggression springs from emotions such as anger.

(88)   Answer D, Type FAC, Reference 441
Which of the following has research identified as a biological influence upon aggression?
A.   testosterone
B.   heredity
C.   alcohol
D.   All of the above.

(89)   Answer A, Type FAC, Reference 444
To know whether people are frustrated, we need to know their
A.   expectations and their attainments.
B.   level of deprivation and their power.
C.   wants and their intelligence.
D.   needs and their age.

(90)   Answer D, Type FAC, Reference 446
The fact that affluent people often feel as frustrated as those who have less can be understood in terms of
A.   the catharsis hypothesis.
B.   the weapons effect.
C.   displacement.
D.   the adaptation-level phenomenon.

(91)   Answer D, Type DEF, Reference 451
Emotional arousal plus anticipated consequences provides the formula for aggression according to
A.   ethological theory.
B.   catharsis theory.
C.   frustration-aggression theory.
D.   social learning theory.

(92)   Answer A, Type FAC, Reference 452
Which of the following is false?
A.   Pain heightens aggressiveness in animals but not in humans.
B.   Being insulted by another is especially conducive to aggression.
C.   In laboratory experiments heat triggers retaliative actions.
D.   According to social learning theory, aggression is most likely when we are aroused and it seems safe and rewarding to aggress.

(93)   Answer A, Type FAC, Reference 455
Living three to a room in a college dorm seems to
A.   diminish one's sense of control.
B.   lead to the establishment of stronger friendships.
C.   lead to more hostile but less instrumental aggression.
D.   improve grades because students are more likely to study in the library.

(94)   Answer D, Type FAC, Reference 470
According to the author of the text, television's most influential effect may be that it
A.   desensitizes people to violence around them.
B.   is the major cause of social violence.
C.   presents an unreal picture of the world.
D.   replaces other activities that people might engage in.

(95)   Answer A, Type CON, Reference 436
Which of the following would be an example of aggression as defined in the text?
A.   A wife deliberately belittles her husband in front of friends after he burns the pot roast.
B.   A golfer accidentally hits another player with a golf ball.
C.   A nurse gives a penicillin shot to a child.
D.   A salesman tops his previous record by selling 50 cars in one month.

(96)   Answer B, Type CON, Reference 442
A person kicking a cat after losing a game of checkers is an example of
A.   regression.
B.   displacement.
C.   relative deprivation.
D.   the weapons effect.

(97)   Answer B, Type CON, Reference 446
A 65-degree day seems warm in February but cold in July. This is best explained in terms of
A.   relative deprivation
B.   the adaptation-level phenomenon
C.   displacement.
D.   Parkinson's second law.

(98)   Answer A, Type CON, Reference 446
John has just received a 5 percent increase in salary. However, after learning that his coworkers have all received 10 percent increases, John becomes angry with

his employer. We can understand John's feelings in terms of
A.   relative deprivation.
B.   the adaptation-level phenomenon.
C.   Parkinson's second law.
D.   the hydraulic model of aggression.

(99)   Answer C, Type CON, Reference 472
As part of therapy, a clinical psychologist encourages her patients to install a
punching bag in their homes to release hostility. The therapist apparently
believes in
A.   social learning theory.
B.   Parkinson's second law.
C.   the catharsis hypothesis.
D.   the adaptation-level phenomenon.

(100) Answer C, Type CON, Reference 437
Which of the following is the best example of instrumental aggression?
 A.   An angry football player tackles a quarterback after he has completed a
long pass.
B.   A jealous wife finds her husband with another woman and shoots both of
them.
C.   A group of former soldiers kill the dictator of a small country for
$10,000.
D.   A man smashes his television set after he finds it does not work.

CHAPTER THIRTEEN: ATTRACTION AND INTIMACY

Multiple Choice

(1)   Answer C, Type DEF, Reference 478
A motivation to bond with others in relationships that provide ongoing, positive interactions is the definition for
A.   association anxiety.
B.   the need for attachment.
C.   the need to belong.
D.   affiliative predisposition.

(2)   Answer B, Type FAC, Reference 479
When Warr and Payne asked a representative sample of British adults what, if anything, had emotionally strained them the day before, their most frequent answer was
A.   relationships at work.
B.   family.
C.   friend or neighbors.
D.   work.

(3)   Answer C, Type FAC, Reference 479
When Warr and Payne asked a representative sample of British adults what, if anything, had prompted yesterday's times of pleasure, their most frequent answer was.
A.   friendship.
B.   work.
C.   family.
D.   hobbies or leisure activities.

(4)   Answer A, Type FAC, Reference 479
A Finnish study of 96,000 widowed people found that
A.   their risk of death doubled in the week following their partner's death.
B.   a majority switched employers in the six months following their partner's death.
C.   a majority said that work rather than relationships brought greatest meaning to their lives.
D.   a sizeable minority said that it would have been better "never to have loved than to have loved and lost."

(5)   Answer D, Type FAC, Reference 479

When Pennebaker and O'Heeron contacted the surviving spouses of suicide or car accident victims, they found that, compared to those who expressed their grief openly, those who bore their grief alone
A. experienced less anxiety and depression.
B. scored higher in self-efficacy.
C. were more likely to have been firstborns.
D. had more health problems.

(6)   Answer C, Type FAC, Reference 480
In one experiment, volunteers who wrote about personal traumas in a dairy
A. were subsequently more likely to seek out a psychotherapist.
B. were subsequently more likely to seek out friendships and dating partners.
C. had fewer health problems during the next six months.
D. experienced more stress and depression.

(7)   Answer B, Type FAC, Reference 480
Among 800 alumni of Hobart and William Smith Colleges surveyed by Wesley Perkins, those who preferred a high income, occupational status, and prestige to having very close friends and a close marriage were more likely to describe themselves as fairly or very
A. busy.
B. unhappy.
C. sophisticated.
D. focused.

(8)   Answer A, Type FAC, Reference 481
When asked what makes their lives meaningful or happy, most people mention _____ before anything else.
A. satisfying relationships
B. their health
C. their work
D. money

(9)   Answer B, Type FAC, Reference 482
Research on proximity and social attraction generally supports the view that
A. familiarity breeds contempt.
B. familiarity leads to liking.
C. proximity leads to affection and animosity with equal frequency.
D. distance makes the heart grow fonder.

(10)   Answer C, Type DEF, Reference 482

Functional distance refers to
A.   the natural geographic route between two locations.
B.   the distance between residences "as the crow flies."
C.   how often people's paths cross.
D.   the direction and route of travel one undertakes when deliberately seeking out a given person.

(11)   Answer C, Type CON, Reference 482
If you are new in the office and want to make new friends, your best bet is to get a desk
A.   that is smaller than that of anyone else.
B.   in the quietest corner of the office.
C.   near the coffeepot.
D.   next to the air conditioner.

(12)   Answer A, Type CON, Reference 483
Research suggests that randomly assigned college roommates
A.   will most likely become friends.
B.   will likely be unhappy about the assignment and come to dislike each other.
C.   are as likely to become enemies as they are to become friends.
D.   will show initial attraction that fades over time.

(13)   Answer A, Type CON, Reference 483
Penny has just arrived as a new student on campus and does not know anyone.
All else being equal, is she most likely to become friends with Joni who lives next door, with Crissy who lives two doors down, with Beth who lives three doors down, or with Helda who lives in the room directly above?
A.   Joni
B.   Crissy
C.   Beth
D.   Helda

(14)   Answer B, Type FAC, Reference 483
Darley and Berscheid gave university women ambiguous information about two other women. Asked how much they liked each other, the subjects reported feeling more attracted to the person whom they
A.   expected they would probably not meet.
B.   expected they would eventually meet.
C.   had read about first.
D.   had read about second.

(15)   Answer C, Type FAC, Reference 483
The text suggests that our tendency to like people with whom we need to have continuing interactions even though we may not have chosen them
A.   shortcircuits critical thinking.
B.   leads to inefficient use of time.
C.   is adaptive.
D.   demonstrates how the need to belong becomes dysfunctional.

(16)   Answer A, Type DEF, Reference 483
The tendency for novel stimuli to be liked more after repeated exposure to them is referred to as
A.   the mere exposure effect.
B.   the novelty phenomenon.
C.   display liking.
D.   proactive stimulation.

(17)   Answer D, Type FAC, Reference 483
Robert Zajonc found that the mere exposure effect works with which of the following stimuli?
A.   nonsense syllables
B.   people's faces
C.   musical selections
D.   All of the above.

(18)   Answer A, Type FAC, Reference 484
The mere exposure effect will be stronger
A.   when people perceive stimuli without awareness.
B.   if the repetitions are incessant rather than distributed over time.
C.   if one's initial reactions to the stimulus are negative.
D.   for animate than for inanimate objects.

(19)   Answer C, Type FAC, Reference 484
In experiments by Robert Zajonc and his coworkers, subjects were exposed to brief novel passages of music while they focused their attention on other tasks. Results indicated that mere exposure leads to liking
A.   only when the exposed stimulus is task-related.
B.   only when people are consciously attending to the exposed stimulus.
C.   even when people are unaware of what they have been exposed to.
D.   unless background stimuli create a distraction and interfere with the processing of the task.

(20) Answer B, Type FAC, Reference 485
On the basis of his research on the mere exposure effect, Robert Zajonc argues
that our emotions are often more _____ than our thinking.
A.   sophisticated
B.   instantaneous and primitive
C.   slowly aroused
D.   complex

(21) Answer C, Type FAC, Reference 485
When Mita, Dermer, and Knight showed women and their close friends
photographs of the women and asked them to state their preferences among them,
they found that the subjects themselves liked the _____ photographs best.
A.   black-and-white
B.   color
C.   mirror-image
D.   true-image

(22) Answer A, Type FAC, Reference 485
In political election campaigns, the mere exposure effect works best when
A.   people don't have strong feelings about the candidate.
B.   the candidate is relatively well known.
C.   the candidate is female.
D.   the issues in the campaign are emotionally charged.

(23) Answer B, Type CON, Reference 485
A political campaign booklet seems to be applying the _____ when it
says, "Repetition breeds familiarity and familiarity breeds trust."
A.   the matching phenomenon
B.   mere exposure effect
C.   equity principle
D.   disclosure reciprocity effect

(24) Answer A, Type FAC, Reference 486
A young woman's physical attractiveness is a moderately good predictor of
A.   how frequently she dates.
B.   her ultimate educational level.
C.   her marital happiness.
D.   All of the above.

(25) Answer B, Type FAC, Reference 486
Researchers provide men and women students with various pieces of information

about someone of the other sex, including a picture of the person or a brief introduction, and later ask them how interested they are in dating the subject. Results show that

A.   women are as influenced by a man's looks as men are by a woman's.

B.   men are somewhat more influenced by a woman's looks than women are by a man's.

C.   women are somewhat more influenced by a man's looks than men are by a woman's.

D.   men are influenced by a woman's looks, while women are not influenced at all by a man's looks.

(26)   Answer C, Type FAC, Reference 487

Elaine Hatfield and her coworkers matched University of Minnesota freshmen for a Welcome Week computer dance. When the students were asked to evaluate their dates, what determined whether they liked each other?

A.   similarity of values

B.   similarity of academic competence

C.   physical attractiveness.

D.   common family background

(27)   Answer B, Type DEF, Reference 487

Researchers have found that people tend to pair off with partners who are about as attractive as themselves. This is known as

A.   physical equity.

B.   the matching phenomenon.

C.   the reciprocity effect.

D.   the resignation effect.

(28)   Answer A, Type FAC, Reference 487

When Gregory White studied some UCLA dating couples, he found that those who were most similar in physical attractiveness were most likely, nine months later, to have

A.   fallen more deeply in love with each other.

B.   broken up.

C.   less passionate but more companionate relationships.

D.   ingratiating but inequitable relationships.

(29)   Answer B, Type FAC, Reference 487

When people describe themselves in personal ads seeking partners of the other sex, women often offer _____ and seek _____.

A.   companionship; attractiveness

B.   attractiveness; status
C.   status; companionship
D.   commitment; excitement

(30)   Answer A, Type FAC, Reference 488
Clifford and Hatfield showed fifth-grade teachers identical information about a
boy or girl, with the photograph attached of an attractive or unattractive child.
The teachers judged _____ as being _____.
A.   attractive children; more honest and concerned about others
B.   unattractive children; more independent and assertive
C.   attractive children; more likely to do well in school
D.   unattractive children; less popular but probably harder workers and better
students

(31)   Answer A, Type FAC, Reference 488
Which of the following best expresses the meaning of the physical attractiveness
stereotype?
A.   What is beautiful is also good.
B.   What is beautiful is also unpredictable.
C.   What is beautiful is also superficial.
D.   What is beautiful is also untouchable.

(32)   Answer B, Type FAC, Reference 488
Kalick had Harvard students indicate their impressions of eight women, judging
from photos taken before or after cosmetic surgery, and found that
A.   presurgery women were judged to be more genuine, honest, and appealing.
B.   postsurgery women would judged to be kinder and more likable.
C.   presurgery women were judged to be more intelligent and competent.
D.   postsurgery women were judged to be more independent and insensitive.

(33) Answer B, Type FAC, Reference 489
Which of the following is not true of physically attractive people?
A.   They have more prestigious jobs.
B.   They are more academically capable.
C.   They make more money.
D.   They describe themselves as happier.

(34)   Answer A, Type FAC, Reference 489
The text suggests that small average differences between attractive and
unattractive people in areas like self-confidence and social skills are probably the
result of

271

A.   self-fulfilling prophecies.
B.   personality traits that are genetically linked with physical appearance.
C.   psychological reactance to social expectations.
D.   social and economic differences in family background.

(35)   Answer D, Type FAC, Reference 490
People judge women as more attractive is they have features that suggest
A.   maturity.
B.   sociability.
C.   assertiveness.
D.   nondominance.

(36)   Answer C, Type FAC, Reference 490
The evolutionary view of physical attractiveness is supported by research
showing that men in many cultures worldwide prefer female characteristics that
signify
A.   high energy.
B.   sociability.
C.   reproductive capacity.
D.   maturity and dominance.

(37)   Answer D, Type FAC, Reference 492
Research indicates that we perceive people as more attractive
A.   if they are portrayed as warm, helpful, and considerate.
B.   if we discover they are similar to us.
C.   as we grow to like them.
D.   All of the above.

(38)   Answer A, Type FAC, Reference 492
Commenting on the relationship between love and perceived attractiveness, Miller
and Simpson note, "The grass may be greener on the other side, but happy
gardeners are
A.   less likely to notice."
B.   not interested in grass."
C.   always flitting from flower to flower."
D.   the most critical gardeners of all."

(39)   Answer A, Type CON, Reference 493
At a party, Ellie meets Rob and Blake and talks with each of them. She talks to
Rob only briefly, but they agree on all three topics. She talks longer with Blake,
and they agree on six of nine topics. Research suggests that Ellie will probably

A.   like Rob better.
B.   like Blake better.
C.   like Rob and Blake equally.
D.   like a stranger she merely anticipates meeting more than either Rob or
Blake.

(40)   Answer B, Type FAC, Reference 493
In a classic study, Newcomb found that among students who lived together in a
boardinghouse for many weeks, the ones who were most likely to have formed
close friendships were those who
A.   were most similar in level of physical attractiveness.
B.   had the highest initial agreement on attitudes.
C.   had opposite but complementary personality characteristics.
D.   came from the same region or state.

(41)   Answer D, Type CON, Reference 493
Which of the following proverbs finds greatest support in the research on social
attraction?
A.   "Familiarity breeds contempt."
B.   "Absence makes the heart grow fonder."
C.   "You can't tell a book by its cover."
D.   "Birds of a feather flock together."

(42)   Answer D, Type FAC, Reference 493
When Sprecher and Duck put 83 student couples together on a blind get-
acquainted date, the 16 who saw each other again were especially likely to
A.   see themselves as having different but complementary personality needs.
B.   have engaged debate over some important issue on their first date.
C.   have lived in a multicultural setting as children.
D.   see themselves as similar to one another.

(43)   Answer C, Type FAC, Reference 495
Research shows that it is _____ persons who most prefer the company of happy
people.
A.   pessimistic
B.   depressed
C.   nondepressed
D.   anxious

(44)   Answer C, Type DEF, Reference 496
According to the _____ hypothesis, people are attracted to those whose needs are

different in ways that complete each other.
A.   accentuation
B.   matching
C.   complementarity
D.   reciprocity

(45)   Answer A, Type CON, Reference 496
Which of the following proverbs is clearly not supported by the research findings?
A.   "Opposites attract."
B.   "Familiarity breeds fondness."
C.   "Out of sight, out of mind."
D.   "Even virtue is fairer in a fair body."

(46)   Answer D, Type FAC, Reference 496
According to researcher David Buss, the tendency for opposites to mate or marry
A.   has only been documented among teenage couples.
B.   has increased in the United States since 1960.
C.   is just as powerful as the similarity-attraction connection.
D.   has never been reliably demonstrated.

(47)   Answer D, Type FAC, Reference 497
Berscheid and colleagues asked students how much they liked people who had evaluated them. They found that students liked a rater who had said eight positive things about them _____ compared to another rater who had said seven positive things and one negative thing about them.
A.   much less
B.   slightly less
C.   about the same
D.   more

(48)   Answer D, Type DEF, Reference 498
_____ includes strategies, such as flattery, by which people seek to gain another's favor.
A.   Social elicitation
B.   Self-disclosure
C.   Social penetration
D.   Ingratiation

(49)   Answer A, Type FAC, Reference 498
Seligman, Fazio, and Zanna asked dating couples to list reasons why they went

out with their partners. Those who had been asked to list extrinsic reasons later expressed _____ compared to those who were made aware of intrinsic reasons.
A. less love for their partners
B. greater similarity to their partners
C. more love for their partners
D. lower self-esteem

(50) Answer B, Type FAC, Reference 498
Hatfield gave university women evaluations, affirming the self-esteem of some and wounding others with negative evaluations. Each subject was then asked to evaluate a man who had earlier asked her for a date. Women whose evaluations had been _____ expressed _____ the man.
A. positive; more liking of
B. negative; more liking of
C. positive; more hostility toward
D. negative; more hostility toward

(51) Answer A, Type FAC, Reference 499
Aronson and Linder allowed women to overhear another woman's evaluations of them. Some sequences of comments were consistent, while others changed over time. Subjects then reported greatest _____ for evaluators whose comments about them _____.
A. liking; went from negative to positive
B. respect; were slightly negative but consistent over time
C. liking; were consistently positive
D. respect; went from positive to slightly negative

(52) Answer D, Type FAC, Reference 499
According to Elliot Aronson, "as a relationship ripens toward greater intimacy, what becomes increasingly important is
A. the absence of conflict."
B. consistent praise."
C. autonomy."
D. authenticity."

(53) Answer B, Type FAC, Reference 500
Most attraction researchers have studied
A. friends or acquaintances in brief interactions.
B. brief encounters between strangers.
C. nonsexual friends or partners in long-term relationships.
D. romantic or marital partners in committed relationships.

(54)   Answer A, Type FAC, Reference 500
Psychologist Robert Sternberg views love as a triangle whose three sides include all but which of the following?
A.   attachment
B.   passion
C.   commitment
D.   intimacy

(55)   Answer D, Type CON, Reference 500
Eros is to _____ as storge is to _____.
A.   game playing; passion
B.   passion; game playing
C.   friendship; game playing
D.   passion; friendship

(56)   Answer B, Type DEF, Reference 501
Which of the following is one of the three components assessed by Zick Rubin's Love Scale?
A.   respect
B.   caring
C.   commitment
D.   friendship

(57)   Answer A, Type FAC, Reference 501
Which of the following statements from Rubin's Love Scale best illustrates attachment?
A.   "If I were lonely, my first thought would be to seek X out."
B.   "If X were feeling bad, my first duty would be to cheer him/her up."
C.   "I feel that I can confide in X about virtually everything."
D.   None of the above.

(58)   Answer C, Type DEF, Reference 501
Hatfield defines _____ as a state of intense longing for union with another.
A.   attraction anxiety
B.   attachment
C.   passionate love
D.   intimate attraction

(59)   Answer D, Type DEF, Reference 502
The two-factor theory of emotion indicates that passionate love can be increased

by
A.   mere exposure.
B.   the matching phenomenon.
C.   secure attachment.
D.   physical arousal.

(60)   Answer B, Type FAC, Reference 502
Dutton and Aron had interviewers approach men crossing bridges in a scenic
state park, ask them to complete questionnaires, and give them their phone
numbers in case the men wanted to call them. Results showed that subjects were
most likely to call the interviewer if they had been interviewed by a
A.   woman on a low, secure bridge.
B.   woman on a high, wobbly bridge.
C.   man on a low, secure bridge.
D.   man on a high, wobbly bridge.

(61)   Answer C, Type FAC, Reference 503
By the mid 1980s, almost 9 in 10 young adults surveyed indicated that _____ is
essential for marriage.
A.   economic security
B.   attitude similarity
C.   love
D.   sexual compatibility

(62)   Answer D, Type FAC, Reference 504
Snyder and Simpson report that, compared to low self-monitors, high self-
monitors are more
A.   affected by a prospective date's physical appearance.
B.   willing to end a relationship in favor of a new partner.
C.   sexually promiscuous.
D.   All of the above.

(63)   Answer C, Type FAC, Reference 505
In comparison to women, men fall in love more _____ and out of love
more _____.
A.   readily; readily
B.   slowly; slowly
C.   readily; slowly.
D.   slowly; readily

(64)   Answer A, Type DEF, Reference 505

277

The affection we feel for those with whom our lives are deeply intertwined is called
A.   companionate love.
B.   filial affection.
C.   secure attachment.
D.   committed friendship.

(65)   Answer A, Type FAC, Reference 505
According to the text, the course of romantic love often follows the pattern of
A.   addictions to alcohol and drugs.
B.   the sleep cycle.
C.   cult indoctrination.
D.   the general adaptation syndrome.

(66)   Answer B, Type FAC, Reference 507
A study of 50 couples in India found that after five years of marriage those in love-based marriages reported _____ feelings of love and those in arranged marriages showed _____ feelings of love.
A.   stable; decreasing
B.   decreasing; increased
C.   increased; stable
D.   stable; increased

(67)   Answer C, Type CON, Reference 509
Ten-month-old Brian enters an unfamiliar laboratory playroom with his mother. When she leaves, he shows no distress. When she returns, he is also emotionless. Brian demonstrates the characteristics of _____ attachment.
A.   secure
B.   insecure
C.   avoidant
D.   ambivalent

(68)   Answer C, Type FAC, Reference 510
Which adult attachment style is marked by individuals having difficulty trusting others and thus becoming possessive and jealous?
A.   avoidant
B.   apathetic
C.   anxious-ambivalent
D.   overbearing

(69)   Answer A, Type FAC, Reference 510

Married men are _____ single men; married women are
_____ single women.
A.   happier than; happier than
B.   not as happy as; not as happy as
C.   happier than; not as happy as
D.   not as happy as; not as happy as

(70)   Answer B, Type DEF, Reference 511
The fact that we like those people whom we associate with good feelings is most
clearly consistent with the _____ theory of attraction.
A.   cognitive dissonance
B.   reward
C.   two-factor
D.   James-Lange

(71)   Answer D, Type FAC, Reference 512
In research at the University of Warsaw, Lewicki asked students to choose which
of two photographs looked friendlier and found that their choices were almost
always influenced by whether or not the photographs
A.   were of men or women.
B.   looked like their own friends.
C.   were in color or black-and-white.
D.   reminded them of friendly or unfriendly experimenters.

(72)   Answer D, Type FAC, Reference 513
In a study of reward theory, Maslow and Mintz found that subjects who _____
gave _____ ratings to photographs of other people.
A.   scored high on loneliness; higher
B.   were in love; lower
C.   were depressed; higher
D.   sat in a shabby, dirty room; lower

(73)   Answer B, Type FAC, Reference 513
Which theory provides the best explanation for the effects that proximity,
similarity, and attractiveness have on liking?
A.   two-factor theory
B.   reward theory
C.   disclosure theory
D.   attachment theory

(74)   Answer C, Type FAC, Reference 514

According to Hatfield, Walster, and Berscheid, equity exists in a relationship when the benefits both partners get out of it
A.   are equal.
B.   meet both partners' needs.
C.   are proportional to what they put into it.
D.   grow as the relationship endures.

(75)   Answer A, Type CON, Reference 514
Melanie believes that her boyfriend enjoys far more benefits from their relationship than she does, even though she invests more time, effort, and resources in their friendship. Clearly Melanie believes that her relationship with her boyfriend lacks
A.   equity.
B.   attachment.
C.   disclosure reciprocity.
D.   loyalty.

(76)   Answer B, Type CON, Reference 514
Margaret and Leah have invested in a small business venture together. Their initial capital investment totaled $15,000, with Margaret putting up $10,000 and Leah supplying $5,000. In their first year they net $21,000 profit. Which of the following distributions of their profits is equitable?
A.   It depends on Margaret and Leah's respective needs.
B.   Margaret gets $14,000 and Leah gets $7,000.
C.   Margaret and Leah each get $10,500.
D.   An equitable distribution is not possible because they invested different amounts to begin with.

(77)   Answer A, Type FAC, Reference 514
People who are in love or friends who have been roommates for some time tend to maintain equity by
A.   exchanging a variety of benefits without keeping track of who owes whom.
B.   exchanging favor for favor, keeping a mental account of who owes what to whom.
C.   not exchanging favors unless they can be returned in kind.
D.   not exchanging favors or resources at all.

(78)   Answer C, Type FAC, Reference 514
According to the text, one clue that an acquaintance is becoming a friend is
A.   his or her willingness to return a favor.
B.   his or her request for a favor in the first place.

C.   that he or she shares when sharing is not expected.
D.   that he or she keeps a running mental track of who owes what to whom.

(79)   Answer C, Type FAC, Reference 514
In studies at the University of Maryland, Clark, and Mills found that tit-for-tat exchanges _____ people's liking for each other when _____.
A.   boosted; their relationship was relatively formal
B.   diminished; they sought true friendship
C.   Both A and B.
D.   None of the above.

(80)   Answer B, Type DEF, Reference 516
The tendency for one person's intimacy of self-disclosure to match that of a conversational partner is referred to as
A.   the matching phenomenon.
B.   disclosure reciprocity.
C.   reciprocal exchange.
D.   mutual self-revelation.

(81)   Answer A, Type FAC, Reference 516
According to humanistic theorist Carl Rogers, growth-promoting listeners have the qualities of
A.   genuineness, acceptance, and empathy.
B.   honesty, critical judgment and compassion.
C.   sympathy, shared attitudes, and expertise.
D.   social competence, emotional expressiveness, and intuitive judgment.

(82)   Answer C, Type FAC, Reference 518
Slightly more than _____ of American marriages now end in divorce.
A.   one-quarter
B.   one-third
C.   one-half
D.   two-thirds

(83)   Answer D, Type FAC, Reference 519
Divorce risk appears to be lower for people who
A.   are religiously committed.
B.   grew up in stable, two-parent families.
C.   dated for a long time before marriage.
D.   All of the above.

(84)   Answer C, Type FAC, Reference 520
According to Caryl Rusbult and her colleagues, which of the following is not one of the alternative responses to exiting a dissatisfying relationship?
A.   voicing concern
B.   loyalty
C.   aggression
D.   neglect

(85)   Answer B, Type FAC, Reference 520
John Gottman's observation of 2000 couples led him to conclude that healthy marriages are marked by
A.   an absence of conflict.
B.   an ability to reconcile differences and to overbalance criticism with affection.
C.   success in maintaining the passion of initial romance.
D.   both parties having fulfilling work as well as friends and relatives who provide social support.

THE FOLLOWING ITEMS ALSO APPEAR IN THE STUDY GUIDE:

(86)   Answer A, Type FAC, Reference 479
Compared with college women who have experienced nonsexual traumas, sexually abused women reported more health problems especially if
A.   they had kept their secret to themselves.
B.   the abuser was a relative.
C.   they were high in self-monitoring.
D.   they were planning to marry in the next year.

(87)   Answer A, Type FAC, Reference 483
Which of the following principles is supported by the research on social attraction?
A.   Familiarity breeds fondness.
B.   Familiarity breeds contempt.
C.   Beauty times brains equals a constant.
D.   What is beautiful is frivolous.

(88)   Answer C, Type FAC, Reference 487
Based on research presented in the text, if you go out on a blind date you would be most influenced by your date's
A.   open-mindedness.
B.   sense of humor.

C.   physical attractiveness.
D.   sincerity.

(89)   Answer B, Type FAC, Reference 510
In terms of adult attachment styles, _____ individuals seem to be possessive and jealous, while _____ individuals fear closeness and are thus less invested in relationships.
A.   secure; insecure
B.   anxious-ambivalent; avoidant
C.   avoidant; anxious-ambivalent
D.   insecure; apathetic

(90)   Answer D, Type FAC, Reference 519
People seem to have a lower risk of divorce if they
A.   are well educated.
B.   live in a small town or on a farm.
C.   did not cohabit before marriage.
D.   All of the above.

(91)   Answer C, Type FAC, Reference 514
Which of the following is true?
A.   Companionate love typically leads to romantic love.
B.   Self-disclosure reduces feelings of romantic love.
C.   Companionate love is more likely to endure when both partners feel it to be equitable.
D.   All of the above.

(92)   Answer A, Type CON, Reference 514
An employee who feels underpaid may demand an increase in wages or exert less effort at his or her task. This behavior is an
A.   attempt to restore equity.
B.   attempt to achieve complementarity.
C.   example of the matching phenomenon.
D.   example of the overexposure effect.

(93)   Answer A, Type CON, Reference 482
Tom, who tends to be extraverted, has just moved into the dormitory at Federal College. He is most likely to make friends with
A.   Bill, his next-door neighbor.
B.   John, a chemistry major who lives across campus.
C.   Michael, an introvert who lives on the next floor.

D.   Stuart, a student who lives off campus and who loves dogs.

(94)   Answer D, Type CON, Reference 487
Mary, who is attractive, very intelligent, and high in social status, marries Tom, who is also attractive, very intelligent, and high in social status. Their relationship is best understood as an example of
A.   the ingratiation effect.
B.   complementarity.
C.   the mere-exposure effect.
D.   the matching phenomenon.

(95)   Answer A, Type CON, Reference 483
Some years ago, a mysterious student enveloped in a big, black bag began attending a speech class at a state university. While the teacher knew "Black Bag's" identity, the other students did not. As the semester progressed, the students' attitude toward Black Bag changed from hostility to curiosity to friendship. What may best explain the students' change in attitude?
A.   Exposure breeds liking.
B.   Stress produces affiliation.
C.   Boredom breeds a liking for the novel.
D.   Similarity attracts.

(96)   Answer D, Type CON, Reference 496
Mary, a talkative, extraverted young woman, is strongly attracted to Ronald, a quiet, introverted, middle-aged man. Mary's attraction to Ronald would be best explained by
A.   exchange theory.
B.   the matching phenomenon.
C.   the equity principle.
D.   the complementarity hypothesis.

(97)   Answer B, Type CON, Reference 498
You overhear a casual acquaintance express approval of you in the coffee shop. You are most likely to think well of that acquaintance if
A.   you had learned an hour earlier that you had received an average grade on a history test.
B.   you had learned an hour earlier that you had failed a chemistry test.
C.   the acquaintance is unattractive.
D.   the acquaintance is engaged to be married.

(98)   Answer A, Type CON, Reference 504

Joe, a college sophomore, has dated several women for short periods of time. His dating preferences are strongly influenced by physical appearance and he quickly ends a relationship in favor of a new partner. Joe is probably
A. high in self-monitoring.
B. low in self-monitoring.
C. low in authoritarianism.
D. high in authoritarianism.

(99) Answer A, Type CON, Reference 516
Bill and Sara's relationship becomes progressively more intimate as each engages in a bit more self-revelation in response to the other's self-disclosure. Their relationship is marked by the _____ effect.
A. disclosure reciprocity
B. mutual disinhibition
C. reciprocal disinhibition
D. reciprocal intimacy

(100) Answer D, Type CON, Reference 483
A stranger rides the same bus you do to school every day. According to the mere exposure effect, as the days pass you will come to view the stranger
A. merely as another student.
B. more unfavorably.
C. more critically.
D. more favorably.

CHAPTER FOURTEEN: ALTRUISM: HELPING OTHERS

<u>Multiple Choice</u>

(1)   Answer D, Type DEF, Reference 527
Altruism is a motive to increase _____ without conscious regard for
_____.
A.   another's immediate happiness; the long-term consequences it has for that
person.
B.   another's resources; how he or she will ultimately use them.
C.   social harmony; individuals' needs
D.   another's welfare; one's self-interests

(2)   Answer B, Type FAC, Reference 527
According to the text, _____ provides the classic illustration of altruism.
A.   the parable of the Prodigal Son
B.   the parable of the Good Samaritan
C.   the Kitty Genovese case
D.   the Sylvia Likens case

(3)   Answer B, Type FAC, Reference 527
Human interactions are guided by a sort of social economics. This statement
reflects the perspective of _____ theory.
A.   social comparison
B.   social exchange
C.   network investment
D.   cultural value

(4)   Answer C, Type FAC, Reference 527
According to social exchange theory, we use a _____ strategy in deciding
when and whether to help others.
A.   social comparison
B.   compensatory
C.   minimax
D.   marginal utility

(5)   Answer A, Type DEF, Reference 527
According to social exchange theory, our willingness to help others is guided by
A.   the calculation of rewards and costs.
B.   the norm of social responsibility.
C.   the principle of justice.

D.   genetic relatedness.

(6)   Answer D, Type FAC, Reference 528
The idea that our careful calculation of the benefits and the costs of donating
blood determines whether we will participate in a blood drive is most clearly
consistent with
A.   social norms theory.
B.   evolutionary psychology.
C.   self-monitoring theory.
D.   social exchange theory.

(7)   Answer D, Type FAC, Reference 528
Social exchange theorists argue that we are most likely to help someone
A.   who is dependent on us.
B.   who is less attractive than we are.
C.   who deserves to be helped.
D.   whose approval is important to us.

(8)   Answer C, Type CON, Reference 528
The executives of a major corporation contribute to charitable causes only when
they are certain their gift will be well publicized, improve their public image,
and ultimately translate into increased profits. The corporation's charitable acts
are more easily explained in terms of
A.   evolutionary psychology.
B.   Latane and Darley's decision tree.
C.   social exchange theory.
D.   the moral exclusion principle.

(9)   Answer A, Type FAC, Reference 528
Researcher Dennis Krebs found that Harvard University men whose physiological
responses revealed the most distress in response to another's distress
A.   gave the most help to the person.
B.   become self-focused and gave little help to the person.
C.   were more likely to rationalize the other's distress as deserved.
D.   tended to be majoring in the humanities rather than in the natural sciences.

(10)   Answer B, Type FAC, Reference 529
In analyzing why people volunteer, as when befriending AIDS patients, Mark
Snyder identified all of the following motivations <u>except</u> to
A.   reduce guilt or escape personal problems.
B.   convert those helped to a particular religious belief system.

C.   act on humanitarian values and concerns for others.
D.   be part of a group and gain approval.

(11)   Answer C, Type FAC, Reference 529
A major weakness of social exchange theory is that it
A.   is impossible to test experimentally.
B.   fails to account for the reciprocal exchange of favors.
C.   easily degenerates into explaining-by-naming.
D.   ignores the role of internal self-rewards in motivating altruism.

(12)   Answer B, Type DEF, Reference 529
The doctrine of psychological egoism maintains that
A.   self-esteem is a more important motive than social approval.
B.   self-interest motivates all behavior.
C.   our self-concept is determined by others' evaluation of us.
D.   the healthy personality has a strong ego.

(13)   Answer D, Type CON, Reference 529
Altruism is to _____ as egoism is to _____.
A.   Gouldner; Batson
B.   self-awareness; self-monitoring
C.   evolutionary theory; social norms theory
D.   another's welfare; one's own welfare

(14)   Answer B, Type FAC, Reference 529
A cost-benefit analysis of helping behavior suggests that the passive bystanders
who observed the screaming switchboard operator being dragged off the street by
a rapist were probably
A.   engaged in just-world rationalizing.
B.   paralyzed by their awareness of the potential dangers of intervening.
C.   apathetic and unconcerned about the victim's fate.
D.   misinterpreting what was actually happening.

(15)   Answer C, Type FAC, Reference 530
Psychologist Daniel Batson maintains that _____ motivates true
altruism.
A.   the justice principle
B.   the social responsibility norm
C.   empathy
D.   anxiety

(16) Answer A, Type FAC, Reference 531
In 1983, people watched on television as an Australian bushfire wiped out hundreds of homes near Melbourne. Afterward, researcher Paul Amato studied donations of money and goods, and found that those who felt _____ gave the least to the victims.
A.   angry
B.   distressed
C.   empathic
D.   worried

(17) Answer B, Type FAC, Reference 531
Batson and his colleagues had university women watch another woman suffer a series of painful shocks. Some subjects were led to feel empathy for her and were then asked if they would trade places, taking her remaining shocks. The results indicated that
A.   most subjects agreed to help but only if they knew they would otherwise continue to see her suffer.
B.   most subjects agreed to help even if they knew that their part in the experiment was complete and that they would no longer have to see her suffer.
C.   most subjects downplayed the victim's suffering or convinced themselves that she deserved to be shocked.
D.   most subjects refused to trade places but expressed sympathy and sought compensation for the victim from the experimenters.

(18) Answer A, Type FAC, Reference 532
Schaller and Cialdini told subjects who felt sad over a suffering victim that their sadness was going to be relieved by listening to a comedy tape. Under these conditions, subjects who felt empathy for the victim
A.   were not especially helpful.
B.   became distressed at the attempt to turn their attention away from victim.
C.   were even more likely to offer aid to the victim.
D.   asked the experimenters to include the victim in the mood-boosting experience.

(19) Answer D, Type FAC, Reference 532
Which of the following is consistent with research findings?
A.   Empathy produces helping only when people believe the other will receive the needed help.
B.   People whose empathy is aroused will help even when they believe no one will know about their helping.
C.   People will sometimes persist in wanting to help a suffering person even

290

when they believe their distressed mood has been temporarily frozen by a "mood-fixing" drug.
D.   All of the above.

(20)   Answer C, Type FAC, Reference 533
Researchers studying helping behaviors
A.   agree that some acts are truly altruistic and are performed only to increase another's welfare.
B.   agree that all helpful acts are either obviously or subtly egoistic.
C.   debate whether some acts are truly altruistic and performed simply to increase another's welfare.
D.   agree that all helpful acts are unconsciously motivated by gene survival.

(21)   Answer B, Type FAC, Reference 533
Robert Cialdini and his colleagues question whether research can show that empathy-based helping is a source of genuine altruism because
A.   neither empathy nor altruism can be adequately defined.
B.   no experiment rules out all possible egoistic explanations for helpfulness.
C.   personal survival overrides all other human motives.
D.   psychological egoism has been convincingly demonstrated in all other forms of social behavior.

(22)   Answer A, Type CON, Reference 534
If you find a lost wallet, you ought to return it to its owner or turn it in to the proper authorities. Such a prescription for appropriate behavior is an example of a
A.   norm.
B.   templet
C.   moral schema.
D.   natural law.

(23)   Answer A, Type FAC, Reference 534
Two social norms that can motivate altruism are
A.   reciprocity and social responsibility.
B.   kin selection and moral inclusion.
C.   social exchange and reciprocity.
D.   social responsibility and kin selection.

(24)   Answer C, Type FAC, Reference 534
Sociologist Alvin Gouldner has contended that the norm of reciprocity
A.   is the ultimate basis for feelings of empathy.

B.   is stronger in females than in males.
C.   is as universal as the incest taboo.
D.   has little application in close relationships such as marriage.

(25)   Answer C, Type CON, Reference 534
After Mr. Walters's neighbor helped him paint his house, Mr. Walters felt
obligated to offer to help the neighbor remodel his kitchen. Mr. Walters's sense
of obligation most likely resulted from the
A.   door-in-the-face phenomenon.
B.   overjustification effect.
C.   reciprocity norm.
D.   equal status norm.

(26)   Answer C, Type FAC, Reference 534
The reciprocity norm applies most strongly to interactions with
A.   superiors.
B.   inferiors.
C.   equals.
D.   relatives.

(27)   Answer A, Type DEF, Reference 535
The belief that people should help those who need help, regardless of possible
future exchanges, has been labeled the
A.   social responsibility norm.
B.   moral inclusion norm
C.   foot-in-the-door effect.
D.   code of cultural dues.

(28)   Answer D Type FAC, Reference 535
_____ societies seem to support the social responsibility norm more
strongly than _____ societies.
A.   North American; European
B.   European; North American
C.   Individualist; collectivist
D.   Collectivist; individualist

(29)   Answer B, Type FAC, Reference 535
According to the text, the social responsibility norm gets selectively applied
according to the following principle:
A.   Give but require repayment with interest.
B.   Give people what they deserve.

C. Give away only what you will never use.
D. Do unto others as they have done unto you.

(30) Answer B, Type FAC, Reference 535
If victims seem to have created their own problems by laziness or lack of foresight, we are less willing to offer help. Responses are thus closely tied to
A. the overjustification effect.
B. attributions.
C. self-concept.
D. empathy.

(31) Answer B, Type FAC, Reference 535
When people need our help, we are most likely to provide assistance if we attribute their need to
A. a lack of motivation.
B. circumstances beyond their control.
C. poor planning or foresight.
D. their mood or disposition.

(32) Answer C, Type CON, Reference 535
A classmate of Bianca's wants to borrow Bianca's notes to study for an upcoming exam. Research suggests that Bianca is most likely to agree if the woman says she needs the notes because she
A. takes inadequate notes.
B. doesn't like this class as well as her other courses.
C. has been absent due to illness.
D. has not been able to concentrate in class.

(33) Answer A, Type DEF, Reference 536
Evolutionary psychology contends that the essence of life is
A. gene survival.
B. self-actualization.
C. holistic health.
D. the discovery of meaning.

(34) Answer A, Type FAC, Reference 537
Evolutionary theory predicts that we are most likely to engage in altruism
A. in the form of kin selection or reciprocity.
B. based on empathy or the social responsibility norm.
C. in the form of kin selection or based on the justice principle.
D. based on reciprocity or the social responsibility norm.

293

(35)   Answer C, Type DEF, Reference 537
The idea that evolution has selected altruism toward one's close relatives to enhance the survival of mutually shared genes is referred to as
A.   evolutionary kinship.
B.   altruistic selection.
C.   kin selection.
D.   self-serving helpfulness.

(36)   Answer A, Type FAC, Reference 537
Which theory specifically predicts that we will be more altruistic toward our relatives than toward close friends?
A.   evolutionary psychology
B.   social norms theory
C.   social exchange theory
D.   self-presentation theory

(37)   Answer B, Type CON, Reference 537
Evolutionary psychology is to _____ as social exchange theory is to _____.
A.   reciprocity; empathy
B.   kin selection; rewards and costs
C.   social responsibility norm; the reciprocity norm
D.   empathy; rewards and costs

(38)   Answer A, Type CON, Reference 537
Evolutionary psychologists would have greatest difficulty explaining why
A.   Jill agrees to donate bone marrow to save the life of a stranger.
B.   Milly agrees to drive her neighbor to the doctor.
C.   Simon donates a kidney to save the life of his son.
D.   Rick helps his best friend paint his house.

(39)   Answer C, Type FAC, Reference 537
Reciprocity of help works best in
A.   individualistic cultures.
B.   industrialized cities.
C.   small, isolated groups.
D.   middle-sized towns.

(40)   Answer A, Type FAC, Reference 537
People who live in _____ are least likely to relay a phone message, mail lost

letters, cooperate with survey interviewers, do small favors, or help a lost child.
A.   big cities
B.   small towns
C.   rural environments
D.   apartments

(41)   Answer B, Type FAC, Reference 537
According to Donald Campbell, the reason that humans sometimes demonstrate nonreciprocal altruism toward strangers is that
A.   unique circumstances have created a genetic predisposition to be selfless in rare individuals.
B.   human societies have evolved ethical rules such as "Love your neighbor."
C.   improved communication has made the world smaller and thus everyone is our kin.
D.   helpers misperceive strangers as either close kin or capable of reciprocity.

(42)   Answer D, Type FAC, Reference 538
According to your text, the _____ theory of altruism proposes two types of prosocial behavior: a tit-for-tat reciprocal exchange and a more unconditional helpfulness.
A.   social norms
B.   social exchange
C.   evolutionary
D.   All of the above.

(43)   Answer D, Type FAC, Reference 538
According to your text, which theory of altruism is vulnerable to charges of being speculative and after the fact?
A.   social norms
B.   social exchange
C.   evolutionary
D.   All of the above.

(44)   Answer C, Type FAC, Reference 539
In observing people's responses to staged emergencies, John Darley and Bibb Latané found that _____ greatly decreased intervention.
A.   social alienation
B.   a lack of empathy
C.   the presence of other bystanders
D.   self-concern

(45)   Answer A, Type FAC, Reference 540
By 1980, about four dozen studies of bystander nonintervention involving nearly 6000 people showed that bystanders were most likely to offer help if they were
A.   alone.
B.   female.
C.   self-forgetful.
D.   part of a group.

(46)   Answer C, Type FAC, Reference 540
Darley and Latané describe a sequence of decisions a bystander must make before he or she will intervene in an emergency. Which of the following is <u>not</u> one of the specific steps?
A.   noticing the incident
B.   interpreting the incident as an emergency
C.   assessing the victim's level of need
D.   assuming personal responsibility for intervening

(47)   Answer C, Type FAC, Reference 540
The presence of many others at the scene of an emergency increases the probability that any individual bystander will
A.   notice the emergency.
B.   overestimate the degree of the victim's injury.
C.   fail to interpret the incident as an emergency.
D.   assume personal responsibility for helping the victim.

(48)   Answer B, Type FAC, Reference 540
Latané and Darley had university students complete questionnaires in a small room, and then had smoke pour into the room from a wall vent. Students who were working _____ tended to notice the smoke in _____.
A.   in groups; less than five seconds
B.   alone; less than five seconds.
C.   on a challenging task; about 20 seconds
D.   on a rote task; less than five seconds

(49)   Answer B, Type FAC, Reference 540
The fact that a bystander may be less likely to interpret an incident as an emergency when other unresponsive bystanders are present provides an example of
A.   normative influence.
B.   informational influence.
C.   diffusion of responsibility.

296

D.   social loafing.

(50)   Answer A, Type FAC, Reference 541
After Latané and Darley's smoke-filled room experiment, subjects were asked
what they thought caused the smoke. Subjects who had been working in groups
offered a variety of explanations--but not one mentioned
A.   fire.
B.   a leak in the air conditioning.
C.   chemistry labs in the building.
D.   truth gas.

(51)   Answer A, Type DEF, Reference 541
The bystander effect refers to the tendency for people to be less likely to provide
help when
A.   there are other bystanders.
B.   they are frustrated.
C.   the victim is responsible for his or her predicament.
D.   helping is costly.

(52)   Answer D, Type FAC, Reference 541
Latané and Rodin staged a "lady in distress" experiment, in which subjects
overheard a woman in an adjoining room fall and injure herself. Results showed
that _____ of the subjects who were _____ responded by entering the room to
offer assistance.
A.   none; in pairs
B.   20 percent; alone
C.   70 percent; in pairs
D.   70 percent; alone

(53)   Answer B, Type FAC, Reference 542
In staging physical fights between a man and a woman, Shotland and Straw found
that bystanders intervened only 19 percent of the time when she shouted,
A.   "Get away from me, I don't know you!"
B.   "Get away from me, I don't know why I ever married you!"
C.   "Get away from me, I have a gun!"
D.   "Get away from me, you're drunk!"

(54)   Answer B, Type FAC, Reference 543
Darley and Latané set up an experiment in which subjects listening over
headphones heard another subject suffering a seizure and crying for help. Of
subjects who believed there were _____ other witnesses, _____ sought to help the

victim.
A. no; none
B. no; 85 percent
C. no; 31 percent
D. four; 85 percent

(55)   Answer A, Type FAC, Reference 543
When the experimenter in Darley and Latané's "seizure" experiment went in to check on the subjects who had not responded to the emergency, she found that most of them were
A. very upset and concerned about the victim.
B. too distracted by the experimental task to have noticed the crisis.
C. apathetic and detached.
D. unsympathetically blaming the victim.

(56)   Answer C, Type FAC, Reference 543
When Irving Piliavin and his colleagues staged an emergency--a staggering, collapsing man--on 103 subway trips, they found that the victim was promptly offered assistance almost every time, even when he appeared to be drunk rather than disabled. Further research seems to confirm that bystander helpfulness was due to
A. subway passengers' fear of street crime.
B. the sophistication and experience of the observers in offering first aid.
C. the fact that the situation was unambiguous.
D. the fact that subway riders were not in very large groups.

(57)   Answer A, Type FAC, Reference 544
When Robert Levine and his colleagues approached people in 36 cities and asked for change, dropped an unnoticed pen, or simulated a blind person needing help at a corner, they found that
A. the bigger and more densely populated the city, the less likely people were willing to help.
B. the more modern and spacious the city, the less likely people were willing to help.
C. the higher the crime rate, the more likely people were willing to help.
D. the more integrated and racially mixed the city, the more likely people were willing to help.

(58)   Answer B, Type FAC, Reference 545
The research on bystander intervention in emergencies indicates that the presence of other bystanders inhibits helping if the emergency is _____ and the

other bystanders are strangers who _____.
A.   serious; are in an unfamiliar setting
B.   ambiguous; cannot easily read one another's reactions
C.   minor; are members of diverse ethnic or racial groups
D.   serious; can readily escape the environment

(59)   Answer B, Type FAC, Reference 545
In the experimental studies of bystander nonintervention, researchers have
A.   always first obtained the subjects's informed consent.
B.   been careful to debrief their laboratory subjects.
C.   subsequently found that most research participants believe the laboratory
experiments have little, if any, application to everyday life.
D.   All of the above.

(60)   Answer C, Type FAC, Reference 545
Research evidence indicates that prosocial models
A.   presented on television have virtually no effect on children.
B.   promote altruism in children but not in adults..
C.   promote altruism in the observers.
D.   in the long run decrease helping because observers seem to believe that aid
is less necessary.

(61)   Answer A, Type FAC, Reference 546
Research indicates that exposure to models who say one thing but do another
leads children to
A.   say what the model says and do what the model does.
B.   ignore the model.
C.   say nothing but simply act as the model acts.
D.   say what the model says and bring their behavior in line with their own
pronouncements.

(62)   Answer D, Type FAC, Reference 546
In an enactment of the Good Samaritan situation, Darley and Batson studied the
helpfulness of Princeton seminarians in order to assess whether helping behavior
is influenced by
A.   religious education.
B.   age differences.
C.   gender differences.
D.   time pressures.

(63)   Answer C, Type FAC, Reference 546

Darley and Batson had Princeton seminary students think about a talk they were about to have recorded in an adjacent building. Subjects who had been _____ were most likely to stop and offer aid to a "victim" they encountered enroute to the recording studio.

A.   asked to talk about career opportunities
B.   asked to talk about the Good Samaritan parable
C.   given extra time to reach the studio
D.   told they were already late in departing for the studio

(64)   Answer C, Type FAC, Reference 547
Experiments have induced guilt by having people deliver shock, lie, cheat, or destroy property. Such studies show that people who feel guilty
A.   typically displace their frustration by justifying others' suffering.
B.   are more likely to help an undeserving person than an innocent victim.
C.   will do whatever they can to expunge the guilt and restore their self-esteem.
D.   tend to be distracted and thus are less likely to notice others' need for help.

(65)   Answer B, Type FAC, Reference 547
In a study by McMillen and Austin, subjects were induced to feel guilty by denying that they had been tipped off by an accomplice about how to answer test questions. After the test, the experimenter asked subjects if they had any spare time to volunteer. Results showed that
A.   guilty subjects wanted to leave immediately.
B.   guilty subjects volunteered significantly more time than nonguilty subjects did.
C.   nonguilty subjects volunteered significantly more time than guilty subjects did.
D.   guilty subjects agreed to stay but distraction over their guilt feelings kept them from performing the task adequately.

(66)   Answer B, Type FAC, Reference 548
A negative mood is more likely to boost helping in _____ than in _____.
A.   children; adults
B.   adults; children
C.   men; women
D.   women; men

(67)   Answer D, Type FAC, Reference 548
Cialdini, Kenrick, and Baumann surmise that, in comparison to children, adults are

A.   less likely to be motivated by empathy.
B.   less sensitive to the reciprocity norm.
C.   more likely to find altruism to be costly.
D.   more likely to find altruism to be self-gratifying.

(68)   Answer D, Type CON, Reference 549
Of the following people in a negative mood, who is most likely to respond
positively to a request for help?
A.   John, a 50-year-old, who is depressed over losing his job as an accountant.
B.   Sally, a 30-year-old, who is in profound grief over the sudden death of her
newborn daughter.
C.   Greta, a 20-year-old, who is angry over her husband's infidelity.
D.   Lois, a 40-year-old, who feels guilty over the fact that she lied on a job
application.

(69)   Answer D, Type FAC, Reference 550
Thompson, Cowan, and Rosenhan had Stanford University students experience
grief by imagining the death of a close friend. When asked if they would help a
graduate student with her work,
A.   female students were more likely to help than were male students.
B.   male students were more likely to help than were female students.
C.   students whose grief was self-focused were more likely to help than were
students whose grief was other-focused.
D.   students whose grief was other-focused were more likely to help than were
students whose grief was self-focused.

(70)   Answer A, Type FAC, Reference 550
Few findings have been more consistent than the fact that _____ people are
helpful people.
A.   happy
B.   well-rested
C.   well-educated
D.   easy-going

(71)   Answer B, Type CON, Reference 550
Who of the following is most likely to respond favorably to an unexpected
request for a charitable donation to a local hospital?
A.   Melvin's older sister, who is hurrying to get to her scheduled appointment
with the family doctor.
B.   Melvin's mother, who just received a very favorable job evaluation from
her employer.

C.   Melvin's younger brother, who is depressed over receiving a D on a physics exam.

D.   Melvin's father, who is distraught over the newspaper boy's trampling of his flower bed.

(72)   Answer B, Type FAC, Reference 552
Preliminary indications of research on personality traits are that those high in _____ are most likely to be concerned and helpful.
A.   femininity, assertiveness, and dominance
B.   emotionality, empathy, and self-efficacy
C.   masculinity, sympathy, and nurturance
D.   sensitivity, compassion, and introversion

(73)   Answer C, Type FAC, Reference 552
Compared to low self-monitoring people, high self-monitoring people are especially helpful <u>if</u> they think that
A.   no one is watching them.
B.   helping will be effective.
C.   helpfulness will be socially rewarded.
D.   no one else is likely to help.

(74)   Answer B, Type FAC, Reference 552
According to the text, the interaction of person and situation is clearly seen in the relationship of _____ to helping behavior.
A.   educational background
B.   gender
C.   social class
D.   age

(75)   Answer C, Type FAC, Reference 553
Most altruism studies explore spontaneous acts of helping. Researchers who have explored planned or sustained helping report that, when people make intentional choices about long-term altruism, _____ predicts altruism.
A.   age
B.   gender
C.   religiosity
D.   intelligence

(76)   Answer A, Type FAC, Reference 555
Which of the following statements about the relationship between gender and helping is true?

302

A.   Male helpers are more likely to help female victims than male victims.
B.   Female helpers are more likely to help female victims than male victims.
C.   Men and women are equally likely to seek help.
D.   All of the above.

(77)   Answer B, Type FAC, Reference 556
Confederates who were dressed either conservatively or in counterculture garb approached either "straight" or "hip" Purdue students and asked for change to make a phone call. Results of this experiment confirmed a _____ bias in helping.
A.   familiarity
B.   similarity
C.   credibility
D.   complementarity

(78)   Answer C, Type FAC, Reference 556
What seems to be the critical factor in determining whether or not Whites show a racial bias in helping?
A.   Whites's level of education
B.   geographical location
C.   whether the norms for appropriate behavior are well defined or ambiguous.
D.   gender of the victim, that is, Whites discriminating only against Black males.

(79)   Answer D, Type FAC, Reference 557
We can increase people's helpfulness by
A.   reducing the ambiguity of the situation.
B.   extending personal invitations to friends to offer help.
C.   having bystanders identify themselves.
D.   All of the above.

(80)   Answer A, Type FAC, Reference 559
Bystanders increase their helpfulness as they become more
A.   self-aware.
B.   depressed.
C.   anxious.
D.   self-accepting.

(81)   Answer D, Type CON, Reference 559
A charitable organization telephones to ask Mary to contribute $100 to send delinquent youth to a summer camp. After she refuses, the solicitor asks if she

would be willing to give just $10. Relieved by this smaller request and wanting to feel better about herself, Mary agrees. Mary has fallen victim to the _____ technique.
A.   foot-in-the-door
B.   face-in-the-mirror
C.   overjustification
D.   door-in-the-face

(82)   Answer D, Type CON, Reference 561
In times of war, people often dehumanize and even torture their enemies. This provides an example of what the text refers to as
A.   kin exclusion.
B.   moral irrationality
C.   the overjustification effect.
D.   moral exclusion.

(83)   Answer B, Type FAC, Reference 561
European Christians who risked their lives to rescue Jews during the Nazi era and civil rights activists of the 1950s report that
A.   they came from families who themselves had been victims of some form of social injustice.
B.   they had warm, close relationships with parents who were committed to humanitarian causes.
C.   their efforts were in part a reaction to having been raised in a troubled family environment in which parents and children were in frequent conflict.
D.   they were firstborn or only children whose parents had taught them courage and independence.

(84)   Answer C, Type FAC, Reference 562
What principle or concept suggests that rewarding people for their helpfulness may, in the long run, undermine their self-motivated altruism?
A.   the door-in-the-face principle
B.   moral exclusion
C.   the overjustification effect
D.   the insufficient justification effect

(85)   Answer B, Type FAC, Reference 563
Findings suggest that students who have learned about the research on the bystander effect are subsequently more
A.   likely to suspect that victims in emergency situations may be part of a social psychological experiment.

B.   likely to offer help to victims in emergency situations.
C.   sensitive to the ethical dilemmas faced by psychologists working with human subjects.
D.   likely to actively support the passage of Good Samaritan laws.

THE FOLLOWING ITEMS ALSO APPEAR IN THE STUDY GUIDE:

(86)   Answer D, Type FAC, Reference 554
Research indicates that, compared to those who never attend church or synagogue, weekly attenders
A.   are more responsive to minor emergencies.
B.   are more morally exclusive.
C.   are more susceptible to the door-in-the-face technique.
D.   give a higher percentage of their income to charity.

(87)   Answer A, Type DEF, Reference 535
The social-responsibility norm is an expectation that people will
A.   help those dependent on them.
B.   help those who have helped them.
C.   assume responsibility for helping their parents.
D.   assume responsibility for correcting past mistakes.

(88)   Answer C, Type FAC, Reference 537
Since we are born selfish, evolutionary psychologists propose that we attempt to
A.   develop a drug that will encourage altruism.
B.   develop an "altruistic gene."
C.   teach altruism.
D.   live only in small, isolated communities.

(89)   Answer A, Type FAC, Reference 539
Latane and Darley attempted to explain people's failure to intervene in cases like that of Kitty Genovese in terms of
A.   a situational influence.
B.   a personality trait.
C.   a mood factor.
D.   selfish genes.

(90)   Answer C, Type FAC, Reference 540
Which of the following is not one of the steps in Darley and Latane's decision tree?
A.   noticing the incident

B.   interpreting the incident as an emergency
C.   weighing the costs and benefits of helping
D.   assuming responsibility for intervening

(91)   Answer B, Type FAC, Reference 547
According to the text, people in a hurry may be less willing to help because
A.   they have weighed the costs of helping and have decided they are too high.
B.   they never fully grasp the situation as one requiring their assistance.
C.   they tend to be selfish and primarily concerned with meeting their own needs.
D.   they tend to be in a negative mood state and therefore are less likely to help.

(92)   Answer D, Type FAC, Reference 533
Researchers who have investigated the relationship between empathy and altruism
A.   agree that empathy leads to genuine altruism.
B.   agree that empathy leads to helping that is egoistically motivated.
C.   agree that empathy leads to pure altruism in females but not in males.
D.   debate whether empathy leads to pure altruism.

(93)   Answer C, Type FAC, Reference 547
Which of the following negative moods is most likely to motivate altruism?
A.   depression
B.   anger
C.   guilt
D.   grief

(94)   Answer D, Type FAC, Reference 552
What does research indicate regarding the role of gender difference in predicting helping?
A.   Gender is unrelated to helping.
B.   Males are more helpful than females.
C.   Females are more helpful than males.
D.   Gender difference interacts with the situation.

(95)   Answer A, Type CON, Reference 540
You trip over a fallen branch and sprain your ankle. According to research on the bystander effect, a stranger who sees your plight will be most likely to offer aid if there are _____ others present.
A.   no
B.   two

C. four
D. ten

(96) Answer B, Type CON, Reference 546
Who of the following is least likely to help an injured pedestrian?
A.   Peter, who has just found $10 in a grocery store.
B.   Anita, who is five minutes late for a committee meeting.
C.   Carol, who has just lost a $1 in a poker game.
D.   Ralph, who is five minutes early for work.

(97) Answer C, Type CON, Reference 559
Your roommate asks you to loan her $25 to buy her boyfriend a birthday
present, and you refuse. She then asks for $3 to purchase a new notebook. You
loan her the $3. Your roommate has successfully used the
A.   overjustification effect.
B.   insufficient justification effect.
C.   door-in-the-face technique.
D.   foot-in-the-door technique.

(98) Answer D, Type CON, Reference 537
From an evolutionary perspective it would be most difficult to explain why
A.   John paid his son's hospital bill.
B.   Phyllis helps her mother clean the house.
C.   William helps his next-door neighbor paint his house.
D.   Ruth risked her life to save a stranger from being murdered.

(99) Answer A, Type CON, Reference 561
Which of the following techniques should elementary schoolteachers use if they
hope to promote enduring altruistic tendencies in students?
A.   Show them films of heroes who risked their own welfare to help others.
B.   Offer a new bicycle to the boy or girl who is most helpful to other students
in a two-week period.
C.   Severely reprimand and punish any overt aggression.
D.   All of the above will be effective in promoting lasting altruism.

(100) Answer B, Type CON, Reference 534
The statement, "There is no duty more indispensable than that of returning a
kindness," reflects the _____ norm.
A.   restitution.
B.   reciprocity.
C.   social-responsibility.

D.   equity.

CHAPTER FIFTEEN: CONFLICT AND PEACEMAKING

Multiple Choice

(1)   Answer A, Type FAC, Reference 568
According to the text, almost every nation claims concern for _____ and arms itself _____.
A.   peace; in self-defense
B.   its citizens; to improve its standard of living
C.   its own survival; to prevent internal chaos
D.   justice; to correct oppression

(2)   Answer B, Type FAC, Reference 568
The occurrence of conflict in any relationship
A.   is usually a sign of lack of motivation.
B.   can stimulate improved relations.
C.   is a necessary evil of human interaction.
D.   necessarily signifies an incompatibility of goals.

(3)   Answer A, Type DEF, Reference 568
Conflict is defined as
A.   perceived incompatibility of actions or goals.
B.   dissatisfaction with relationship outcomes.
C.   hostility that results from frustrating interaction.
D.   competition for mutually exclusive goals.

(4)   Answer C, Type FAC, Reference 569
Which of the following is not one of the ingredients of conflict explored in the chapter on Conflict and Peacemaking?
A.   competition
B.   social dilemmas
C.   instinctive hostility
D.   misperception

(5)   Answer D, Type FAC, Reference 569
According to the text, problems such as overpopulation, natural resource depletion, and the greenhouse effect arise as people
A.   give expression to their natural aggressive drive.
B.   seek the welfare of others but at the expense of the physical environment.
C.   give expression to their needs for mastery and control over their environment.

D.   pursue their self-interest to their collective detriment.

(6)   Answer D, Type FAC, Reference 569
Pursuing one's self-interest to the collective detriment of one's community or society--resulting in problems like pollution, the greenhouse effect, overpopulation, and natural resource depletion--is the central pattern in
A.   mirror-image perception.
B.   the jigsaw problem.
C.   perceived injustice.
D.   a social dilemma.

(7)   Answer A, Type FAC, Reference 569
In the Prisoner's Dilemma, if both prisoners confess, each will _____; if neither confesses, each will _____.
A.   get a moderate sentence; get a light sentence
B.   get a severe sentence; get a light sentence
C.   get a severe sentence; go free
D.   get a moderate sentence; get a severe sentence

(8)   Answer A, Type FAC, Reference 569
In the playing the laboratory version of Prisoner's Dilemma, you would personally obtain the best payoff on any given trial if you _____ and the other person _____ .
A.   defect; cooperates
B.   defect; defects
C.   cooperate; defects
D.   cooperate; cooperates

(9)   Answer B, Type FAC, Reference 570
The cold war between the United States and the U.S.S.R. after 1945 was characterized by the military policy of _____, with the appropriate acronym of MAD.
A.   Military Attack Deployment
B.   Mutually Assured Destruction
C.   Martial Accumulation Detente
D.   Managerial Arbitration Defense

(10)   Answer C, Type CON, Reference 571
Garret Hardin is to _____ as Charles Osgood is to _____ .
A.   Prisoner's Dilemma; superordinate goals
B.   bargaining; mediation

C.   tragedy of the commons; GRIT
D.   mirror-image perceptions; GRIT

(11) Answer C, Type DEF, Reference 571
In the tragedy of the commons, the "commons" refer to
A.   disputed border territory.
B.   stolen goods or winnings.
C.   any jointly used, finite resource.
D.   private property that repeatedly changes ownership.

(12) Answer D, Type FAC, Reference 571
In real life, which of the following parallels the tragedy of the commons?
A.   pollution of rivers and streams
B.   littering in public places
C.   use and overuse of natural resources
D.   All of the above.

(13) Answer B, Type DEF, Reference 572
In Garret Hardin's original metaphor for the tragedy of the commons, the "tragedy" literally turns out to be
A.   an empty street.
B.   a grassless mud field.
C.   a waste-covered landfill.
D.   a poisoned well or harbor.

(14) Answer C, Type CON, Reference 572
Despite official government warning of a severe water shortage, most citizens fail to conserve in the belief that their personal water consumption will have little effect on the community's total water supply. The eventual depletion of the community's water resources provides an example of
A.   mirror-image perceptions.
B.   individualistic calamity.
C.   the tragedy of the commons.
D.   rational disaster.

(15) Answer A, Type FAC, Reference 572
Julian Edney's Nuts Game best illustrates the dynamics of
A.   the Commons Dilemma.
B.   the Prisoner's Dilemma.
C.   final-offer arbitration.
D.   inequitable relationships.

(16)   Answer D, Type FAC, Reference 572
In Julian Edney's Nuts Game, each player seated beside a bowl of nuts wants to accumulate as many nuts as possible, and every 10 seconds the bowl's total is doubled. Most of Edney's groups
A.   wait until the bowl's contents have multiplied many times and then divide this larger sum equally among themselves.
B.   wait until the bowl's contents have multiplied many times and then compete for the lion's share of the nuts.
C.   go through about two replenishment periods before emptying the bowl.
D.   empty the bowl before even the first 10-second replenishment.

(17)   Answer B, Type FAC, Reference 573
Kaori Sato gave Japanese students opportunities to harvest trees in a simulated forest for money. When the students shared equally the costs of planting the forest, the result was that
A.   most of the trees were left to grow too tall for harvesting because the students bickered about the criterion to be used in sharing profits.
B.   most of the trees were harvested before they had grown to the most profitable size.
C.   none of the trees were harvested because the collectivist students did not want to be the first to ask for his or her share.
D.   students made maximum profit not only for themselves individually but for the group.

(18)   Answer C, Type FAC, Reference 573
In both the Prisoner's Dilemma and the Commons Dilemma, people are tempted to explain their own behavior _____ and others' behavior _____.
A.   situationally; situationally
B.   dispositionally; dispositionally
C.   situationally; dispositionally
D.   dispositionally; situationally

(19)   Answer A, Type FAC, Reference 573
Which of the following is not a feature of the Prisoner's Dilemma and Commons Dilemma?
A.   One party's wins necessarily equals the other party's losses.
B.   Participants tend to commit the fundamental attribution error.
C.   Participants' motives change in the course of the entrapment.
D.   Both are non-zero-sum games.

(20) Answer D, Type DEF, Reference 573
Games in which outcomes need not sum to zero are called _____ games.
A. nonintegral
B. qualitative
C. coalition
D. non-zero-sum

(21) Answer B, Type FAC, Reference 574
According to theorist Garrett Hardin, _____ in a commons brings ruin to all.
A. regulation
B. freedom
C. unrest
D. competition

(22) Answer A, Type FAC, Reference 574
Which of the following is specifically cited in the text as a method for resolving social dilemmas?
A. regulations
B. equal-status contact
C. the jigsaw technique
D. catharsis

(23) Answer A, Type FAC, Reference 574
Which of the following is cited in the text as a method for resolving social dilemmas?
A. Keep the group small.
B. Deregulate participants' behavior.
C. Prevent changes in the payoff matrix.
D. All of the above.

(24) Answer D, Type FAC, Reference 574
Which of the following is not cited in the text as a method for resolving social dilemmas?
A. Keep the group small.
B. Appeal to participants' altruistic norms.
C. Keep lines of communication open.
D. Equip all participants with the same capacity to retaliate.

(25) Answer A, Type FAC, Reference 574
The smaller the commons, the more

A.   responsibility each person feels for it.
B.   intense the conflict among individual members.
C.   apathetic people are about its preservation.
D.   the more likely communication will take the form of intimidation and deception.

(26)   Answer C, Type FAC, Reference 575
When people are in a social trap together, communication
A.   most often degenerates into threats and name calling.
B.   has no effect.
C.   enables groups to cooperate more.
D.   promotes cooperation in Prisoner's Dilemma but not in the Commons Dilemma.

(27)   Answer A, Type FAC, Reference 576
Which of the following is cited in the text as an example of changing payoffs to resolve social dilemmas?
A.   allowing carpoolers to drive in the faster, freeway lane
B.   requiring carpool cars and vans to park in special, larger parking lots farther away from the office building
C.   lowering the price of gasoline well below $1 per gallon
D.   All of the above.

(28)   Answer D, Type FAC, Reference 577
According to research, it seems that just knowing about the dire consequences of noncooperation in a social dilemma
A.   is sufficient to convince people to behave cooperatively.
B.   leads to greater mistrust of others.
C.   tends to foster greater self-interest and competition.
D.   has little real effect on people's behavior.

(29)   Answer A, Type FAC, Reference 577
Robyn Dawes and colleagues gave people a short sermon about group benefits, exploitation, and ethics prior to having them play a dilemma game. Results showed that
A.   the appeal worked.
B.   the appeal had little effect on players' behavior.
C.   players developed reactance and became more competitive.
D.   females became less competitive and males become more competitive.

(30)   Answer A, Type FAC, Reference 577

Jeffrey Scott Mio and colleagues found that after reading about the commons dilemma, theater patrons
A.   littered less.
B.   demanded reserved seats.
C.   were more likely to assist a handicapped person find a seat.
D.   spent more for theater refreshments.

(31)   Answer B, Type FAC, Reference 578
Muzafer Sherif's famous study of group relations in boys' camps was undertaken to examine the power of _____ to evoke intergroup hostility.
A.   social dilemmas
B.   competition
C.   racial prejudice
D.   status differences

(32)   Answer D, Type FAC, Reference 579
Despite the fact that, as Sherif noted, the behavior of the boys in the warring camps seemed "wicked, disturbed, and vicious," what actually triggered their evil behavior was
A.   their leaders' modeling of aggression.
B.   their delinquent backgrounds.
C.   their ethnic identities.
D.   an evil situation.

(33)   Answer A, Type DEF, Reference 579
Equity exists when
A.   rewards are distributed in proportion to individuals' contributions.
B.   partners share equally in the rewards of collective effort.
C.   rewards are distributed in relation to individuals' needs or deservingness.
D.   group members decide among themselves how rewards are to be distributed.

(34)   Answer B, Type CON, Reference 579
Before they married, Melinda and Michael, who are both employed full time and collect the same pay, agreed to share equally in routine household tasks such as cleaning and grocery shopping. In reality, Melinda is now doing about 80 percent of the household work. This situation is an example of
A.   an integrative disaster.
B.   an inequitable relationship.
C.   a social dilemma.
D.   a zero-sum relationship.

(35)   Answer C, Type FAC, Reference 579
When parties in a relationship disagree about the relevant criteria for the relationship's input, researchers have found that the _____ usually prevails.
A.   most vocal
B.   most authoritarian
C.   one with the most social power
D.   one with the most education

(36)   Answer D, Type DEF, Reference 579
What does your text refer to as the "golden rule" of social justice?
A.   "Equity for strangers, equality for friends."
B.   "An eye for an eye, a tooth for a tooth."
C.   "Care most for those in greatest need."
D.   "Whoever has the gold makes the rules."

(37)   Answer D, Type FAC, Reference 580
Research indicates that the more competent and worthy people feel, the more likely they are to
A.   devalue their inputs to a relationship.
B.   feel that a given outcome from a relationship is sufficient.
C.   tolerate exploitation from others without any retaliation.
D.   feel underbenefitted in a relationship and inclined to retaliate.

(38)   Answer B, Type FAC, Reference 580
Compared to Americans, people socialized in China and India are more likely to favor _____ as the basis for justice when rewards are distributed to those within their groups.
A.   equity
B.   equality
C.   achievement
D.   whatever the group leader pronounces

(39)   Answer A, Type CON, Reference 580
Individualistic cultures are to _____ as collectivistic cultures are to
_____.
A.   equity; equality
B.   need; equality
C.   achievement; aptitude
D.   equality; need

(40)   Answer B, Type FAC, Reference 580
Compared to the United States, pay in Japan is more often based on _____ and less often on _____.
A.   productivity; seniority
B.   seniority; productivity
C.   education; achievement
D.   achievement; education

(41)   Answer B, Type FAC, Reference 581
All the following except _____ are cited in the text as possible seeds of misperception as a major cause of conflict.
A.   the self-serving bias
B.   the naturalistic fallacy
C.   groupthink
D.   the fundamental attribution error

(42)   Answer C, Type FAC, Reference 582
According to psychologist Urie Bronfenbrenner, the misperceptions of those who are in conflict with each other, such as two nations who regard each other with suspicion and hostility, are
A.   nonreciprocal.
B.   unilateral.
C.   mutual.
D.   inequitable.

(43)   Answer A, Type FAC, Reference 582
Urie Bronfenbrenner notes that, during the cold war years, the Russians' view of Americans was _____ the Americans' view of the Russians.
A.   a mirror image of
B.   more optimistic than
C.   much more distorted than
D.   much more accurate than

(44)   Answer D, Type FAC , Reference 583
Studies of political statements reveal that during the cold war years people in both the United States and the Soviet Union held which of the following attitudes?
A.   They preferred mutual disarmament to all other outcomes
B.   They wanted above all not to disarm while the other side armed
C.   They perceived the other side as preferring to achieve military superiority
D.   All of the above.

(45) Answer A, Type DEF , Reference 583
The reciprocal views that parties in conflict often hold of one another are referred to as
A.   mirror-image perceptions.
B.   stereotypic reciprocation.
C.   complementary images.
D.   reciprocal illusions.

(46) Answer C, Type CON, Reference 583
The Republic of Fredonia believes its long-time enemy, the kingdom of Franistan, is aggressive, greedy, and impulsive. On the other hand, Franistan believes Fredonia is hostile, selfish, and unpredictable. This is an example of
A.   an inequitable relationship.
B.   a zero-sum relationship.
C.   mirror-image perceptions.
D.   the tragedy of the commons.

(47) Answer A, Type FAC, Reference 583
In times of tension, as during an international crisis,
A.   views of the opposing side become more simplistic.
B.   political statements acknowledge that each country's motives are complex.
C.   judgments about action are prolonged and postponed by time-consuming reevaluations.
D.   All of the above.

(48) Answer B, Type FAC, Reference 584
When two sides have clashing perceptions, at least one of them is misperceiving the other, and when that is the case, according to Urie Bronfenbrenner, "It is characteristic of such images that they are _____."
A.   self-defeating
B.   self-confirming
C.   self-handicapping
D.   self-monitoring

(49) Answer D, Type FAC , Reference 585
Destructive mirror-image perceptions operate in conflicts between
A.   countries.
B.   small groups.
C.   individuals.
D.   All of the above.

(50)   Answer A, Type FAC, Reference 585
In a study by executives who were asked to describe a recent conflict, Thomas and Pondy found that 12 percent described the opposing party as _____ and 74 percent perceived themselves as _____.
A.   cooperative; cooperative
B.   intelligent; intelligent
C.   cooperative; competitive
D.   rational; competent

(51)   Answer C, Type CON , Reference 585
The management of a large manufacturing company believes that recent worker unrest at its plant is the result of a few union leaders who are manipulating and intimidating employees who are basically loyal to the company and content with existing working conditions. The management's view is likely an example of
A.   mirror-image perception
B.   a superordinate attributional error
C.   an evil leader-good people illusion
D.   a self-fulfilling misperception.

(52)   Answer C, Type FAC, Reference 585
The text suggests that the attitudes of the United States and other nations toward Iraq provide a good example of how perceptions
A.   are founded in deep-seated ethnic and religious differences.
B.   are more stable and resistant to change than other attitudes.
C.   shift quickly as conflicts wax and wane.
D.   become more complex as conflict intensifies.

(53)   Answer B, Type FAC, Reference 587
Which of the following is not one of the four C's of peacemaking identified in the text?
A.   contact
B.   correction
C.   conciliation
D.   communication

(54)   Answer A, Type FAC, Reference 587
According to the text, the fact that the desegregation of public housing units in New York City seemed to reduce racial prejudice suggests that _____ sometimes reduces conflict.
A.   contact
B.   conciliation

319

C.   mediation
D.   a superordinate goal

(55)   Answer B, Type FAC, Reference 588
In 1986 social psychologist Walter Stephan reviewed studies of the effects of school desegregation and concluded that
A.   school desegregation is the only real success story in efforts to change racial attitudes in the United States.
B.   school desegregation has not particularly affected racial attitudes in the United States.
C.   the effect of school desegregation has been consistently positive but gradual.
D.   such programs have caused significant deterioration in race relations nationwide.

(56)   Answer A, Type FAC, Reference 588
Surveys of nearly 4000 Europeans reveal that an important factor determining whether attitudes toward a minority group will become more favorable is whether
A.   one has a friend who is a member of that minority group.
B.   the minority group tends to be submissive.
C.   the minority group has a history of significant accomplishment.
D.   the language of the minority group can be easily mastered.

(57)   Answer C, Type FAC, Reference 588
For Blacks, the most noticeable consequence of desegregated schooling has been
A.   very short-term improvement of interracial relations.
B.   reduced likelihood of attending primarily White colleges.
C.   increased likelihood of living and working in integrated settings.
D.   a more favorable self-image.

(58)   Answer B, Type FAC, Reference 588
Which of the following is true, based on researchers' observations at dozens of desegregated schools?
A.   Race is a more decisive factor than sex in determining socializing patterns.
B.   Whites disproportionately associate with other Whites and Blacks with Blacks.
C.   Cross-race associations and friendships are about as numerous as within-race interactions.
D.   Desegregation promotes more favorable racial attitudes in older children than it does in younger children.

(59)   Answer B, Type FAC, Reference 589
In order for contact between opposing racial groups to reduce conflict, the contact must
A.   occur in a zero-sum context.
B.   be structured to confer equal status on both races.
C.   temporarily award superior status to the minority group.
D.   be mediated by a third party.

(60)   Answer C, Type CON, Reference 589
Sondra is a Black ninth-grade student whose family has just moved into a new school district. Her last school was academically inferior, but her new school is a predominantly White middle-class neighborhood school. Chances are that Sondra will
A.   achieve and be quickly accepted in this vastly improved environment.
B.   achieve some improvement but likely at the expense of holding back several of her White classmates.
C.   be perceived by both her classmates and herself as having lower academic status.
D.   will not do very well in class but will be readily accepted by the White, middle-class students.

(61)   Answer C, Type FAC, Reference 589
In the typical school classroom, desegregated or not, students' behavior can best be described as
A.   apprehensive and inhibited.
B.   diverse but equal.
C.   competitive and unequal.
D.   interdependent and cohesive.

(62)   Answer D, Type FAC, Reference 590
John Lanzetta put four-man groups of Naval ROTC cadets to work on problem solving tasks and then informed some of the groups that they were incorrect, unproductive, and stupid. He observed that the group members who were under duress
A.   were more hostile toward each other.
B.   showed much improved performance on subsequent tasks.
C.   downplayed the significance of the problem-solving tasks.
D.   developed a more cohesive spirit.

(63)   Answer A, Type FAC, Reference 590

Just being reminded of the existence or presence of _____ heightens people's responsiveness to their own group.
A. an outgroup
B. danger in the world
C. evaluators or superiors
D. interpersonal differences

(64) Answer C, Type FAC, Reference 590
Muzafer Sherif's boys' camp experiments provided ample evidence of the _____ effect of a common enemy on conflicting groups.
A. divisive
B. prejudicial
C. unifying
D. reactance

(65) Answer D, Type FAC, Reference 590
Times of interracial strife are likely to become times of heightened _____ within groups.
A. conflict
B. self-deprecation
C. dissonance
D. pride

(66) Answer C, Type FAC, Reference 590
Conflict between groups tends to promote _____ within groups.
A. instability
B. quiet reflection
C. unity
D. debate

(67) Answer D, Type FAC, Reference 590
As portrayed in Orwell's novel 1984, leaders have been known to _____ as a technique for building group cohesiveness.
A. use arbitration
B. use equal-status contact
C. correct injustice
D. create a threatening external enemy

(68) Answer B, Type FAC, Reference 591
In Muzafer Sherif's studies of the boys' camps, the breakdown in the camp's water supply and the proposed rental of a costly movie were examples of the use

of _____ to promote intergroup cooperation.
A.	contact
B.	superordinate goals
C.	bargaining
D.	conciliation

(69)	Answer B, Type CON, Reference 591
Generalizing from Sherif's study of conflict resolution between two groups of boy campers, one way for the United States and China to improve their relationship would be to:
A.	restrict their exchange of communications.
B.	work together on a program to solve the problem of world hunger.
C.	arrange highly publicized table-tennis tournaments between the two countries.
D.	have social scientists from each country debate the relative merits of individualism versus collectivism.

(70)	Answer C, Type CON, Reference 591
After their town was ravaged by a disastrous tornado, two rival community groups set aside their differences and worked together on repairing the damage. This cooperation best illustrates the importance of
A.	mediation.
B.	the GRIT strategy.
C.	superordinate goals.
D.	the jigsaw technique.

(71)	Answer C, Type FAC, Reference 591
Blake and Mouton studied executives' behavior in several series of experiments that paralleled Sherif's boys' camp paradigm and concluded that
A.	superordinate goals do not reduce conflict among Type A personalities.
B.	cooperative strategies fail to reduce conflicts between groups of adults with competitive histories.
C.	adult reactions parallel those of Sherif's subjects.
D.	adults maintain competitive attitudes, hold grudges longer, and are less willing to cooperate than children.

(72)	Answer B, Type FAC, Reference 592
In experiments with University of Virginia students, Stephen Worchel and his associates found that _____ boosts groups' attraction for one another.
A.	any effort to cooperate, whether successful or not,
B.	a successful cooperative experience

C.   cooperation on physical but not on mental tasks
D.   cooperation among females but not among males

(73)   Answer B, Type FAC, Reference 593
Elliot Aronson's jigsaw technique involved having elementary school children
A.   study in small, racially mixed teams and then compete with other teams in a class tournament.
B.   form academically and racially diverse groups with each member of the group becoming an expert in one area.
C.   role-play being members of another race for two-week periods.
D.   take turns telling each other about their family backgrounds in small-group discussions.

(74)   Answer D, Type FAC, Reference 593
Elliot Aronson reports that students in jigsaw classrooms
A.   grow to like each other better.
B.   develop greater self-esteem than children in traditional classrooms.
C.   grow to like school better than children in traditional classrooms.
D.   All of the above.

(75)   Answer A, Type FAC, Reference 594
By emphasizing the contribution Jackie Robinson might make to the Brooklyn Dodgers' winning the 1947 pennant, Branch Rickey used _____ to reduce racial prejudice and conflict among team members.
A.   a superordinate goal
B.   an integrative agreement
C.   arbitration
D.   the GRIT strategy

(76)   Answer D, Type FAC, Reference 595
According to race-relations expert John McConahay, the most effective known practice for improving race relations in desegregated schools is
A.   community-supported athletic programs.
B.   after-school leisure classes.
C.   support groups composed of parents from different races
D.   cooperative learning.

(77)   Answer D, Type DEF, Reference 595
_____ occurs when conflicted parties submit their disagreement to someone who will study the issues and impose a settlement.
A.   Bargaining

B.   Amelioration
C.   Mediation
D.   Arbitration

(78)   Answer C, Type FAC, Reference 596
A mediator seeks to achieve a mutually beneficial resolution by having the parties
adopt a _____ orientation.
A.   carefree
B.   win-lose
C.   win-win
D.   submissive

(79)   Answer B, Type FAC, Reference 596
Compared to _____, in which each party sacrifices something important, _____
are more enduring and lead to better ongoing relationships.
A.   integrative agreements; compromises
B.   compromises; integrative agreements
C.   integrative agreements; arbitrated settlements
D.   arbitrated settlements; competitions

(80)   Answer B, Type FAC, Reference 597
According to conflict researchers, you are more likely to divulge your needs and
concerns if your relationship with your partner includes
A.   mediation.
B.   trust.
C.   passion.
D.   the threat of withdrawal.

(81)   Answer B, Type FAC, Reference 599
A mediator may try to improve relationship communication by having conflicting
parties restrict their arguments to statements of
A.   the opposing side's underlying motives.
B.   how they feel or think in response to the other's actions.
C.   personal analysis of the probable causes of the conflict.
D.   proposed solutions or conditions for reconciliation.

(82)   Answer D, Type DEF, Reference 600
If mediation fails or conflict is so intractable that a mutually satisfactory
resolution is unattainable, the parties in conflict may turn to _____ by having the
mediator or another third party impose a settlement.
A.   compromise

B.   the GRIT strategy
C.   conciliation
D.   arbitration

(83)   Answer B, Type FAC, Reference 601
Charles Osgood's GRIT strategy is an alternative that best fits into the _____ category of the "four C's of peacemaking."
A.   contact
B.   conciliation
C.   communication
D.   cooperation

(84)   Answer A, Type FAC, Reference 602
Which of the following is not one of the steps in Charles Osgood's GRIT strategy?
A.   Build up first-strike capability to negotiate from a position of strength.
B.   Announce your conciliatory intent.
C.   Carry out several verifiable conciliatory acts.
D.   Maintain retaliatory capability.

(85)   Answer C, Type FAC, Reference 602
Conflict expert Morton Deutsch captures the spirit of GRIT in advising negotiators to be
A.   strong-willed and sober.
B.   poker-faced and stoic.
C.   firm, fair, and friendly.
D.   soft, smiling, and sympathetic.

THE FOLLOWING ITEMS ALSO APPEAR IN THE STUDY GUIDE:

(86)   Answer A, Type FAC, Reference 568
Which of the following is true of conflict?
A.   Without conflict, people seldom face and resolve their problems.
B.   Conflict always involves a real incompatibility of goals.
C.   Social psychologists have studied interpersonal but not international conflict.
D.   Social psychologists have not been able to study conflict in a laboratory setting.

(87)   Answer D, Type FAC, Reference 572
Edney's Nuts Game

A.   is a non-zero-sum game played between two persons.
B.   demonstrates how mirror-image perceptions can increase conflict.
C.   demonstrates how conciliation reduces conflict.
D.   illustrates the tragedy of the commons.

(88)   Answer B, Type FAC, Reference 576
Research on laboratory dilemmas reveals that cooperation is facilitated
A.   if one person is 100 percent cooperative.
B.   if the opponents can communicate with one another.
C.   if the game is changed into a zero-sum game.
D.   All of the above.

(89)   Answer B, Type FAC, Reference 595
Bargaining tough is likely to backfire
A.   when the conflict is over a pie of fixed size.
B.   when the conflict is over a pie that can shrink.
C.   when females bargain tough with males.
D.   in virtually every situation.

(90)   Answer D, Type FAC, Reference 603
The Kennedy experiment was an application of_____ to
international tension reduction.
A.   equal status contact
B.   the jigsaw technique
C.   arbitration
D.   the GRIT model

(91)   Answer A, Type CON, Reference 569
Two gas station owners in Roseville cut their gas prices in order to capture a
portion of their competitor's business. However, neither gained any of the
other's customers and in the long run both operated at a loss. This outcome best
illustrates the dynamics of
A.   a social dilemma.
B.   he GRIT strategy .
C.   an inequitable relationship.
D.   mirror-image perceptions.

(92)   Answer A, Type CON, Reference 579
Rodney and Ralph are twin brothers who each contributed $75 to purchase a new
bicycle. Rodney rides it 75 percent of the time. This would be an example of
A.   an inequitable relationship.

B.   the tragedy of the commons.
C.   a zero-sum relationship.
D.   mirror-image perceptions.

(93)   Answer B, Type CON, Reference 582
John believes he is hardworking but his wife, Rachel, is lazy. Rachel believes she is hardworking but John is lazy. This is an example of
A.   an inequitable relationship.
B.   mirror-image perception.
C.   a superordinate goal.
D.   a social trap.

(94)   Answer C, Type CON, Reference 590
Which of the following best illustrates a superordinate goal?
A.   A college student who has been failing English gets an "A" on a paper.
B.   A woman beats her husband at tennis.
C.   Apartment dwellers install a television antenna they can all use.
D.   An obese person loses 20 pounds in two weeks.

(95)   Answer C, Type CON, Reference 589
According to the text, contact between two conflicting racial groups can often improve relationships and correct misperceptions. Which kind of contact is, however, least likely to have that effect?
A.   placing Black and White athletes on the same baseball team.
B.   having Black and White employees work together in small groups in an industrial plant
C.   placing White policemen on duty in predominantly Black residential neighborhoods
D.   having Blacks and Whites move into the same apartment building

(96)   Answer C, Type CON, Reference 591
Sherif's studies of conflict in summer camp should lead one to suggest which of the following to a couple having marital difficulties?
A.   play poker, keeping a cumulative score
B.   encounter each other: express your true feelings
C.   work together on something
D.   take separate vacations

(97)   Answer B, Type CON, Reference 600
Factory workers want a pay rate of $15 per hour and management offers $12 per hour. After weeks of conflict they agree to have a third party set the pay scale.

After hearing both sides the third party sets the rate at $14. This is an example of resolving conflict through

A. bargaining.
B. arbitration.
C. mediation.
D. conciliation.

(98) Answer D, Type CON, Reference 603
The GRIT model could be applied to the reduction of conflict between

A. individuals.
B. groups.
C. nations.
D. All of the above.

(99) Answer D, Type CON, Reference 598
To fight constructively, psychologists Ian Gotlib and Catherine Colby recommend that you

A. apologize prematurely.
B. tell the other party how they are feeling.
C. bring in unrelated issues.
D. divulge your positive and negative feelings.

(100) Answer D, Type CON, Reference 596
Kevin and Joel, two teenage brothers, are fighting over the evening newspaper. Knowing Kevin only wants the sports section and Joel only wants the latest stock quotations, their mother takes the paper and gives each boy the section containing the news of interest. In this case the mother arrived at a(n)

A. mutual compromise.
B. cooperative settlement.
C. enlightened consensus.
D. integrative agreement.